NEW PROBLEMS IN MEDICAL ETHICS

Third Series

Edited in English

BY

DOM PETER FLOOD

O.S.B., B.A., M.D., M.Ch., J.C.L.
Barrister-at-Law

Translated from the French "Cahiers Laënnec"

BY

MALACHY GERARD CARROLL

MCMLVI
THE NEWMAN PRESS
WESTMINSTER, MARYLAND

Nihil Obstat:
    Hubertus Richards, S.T.D., L.S.S.
       Censor deputatus
Imprimatur:
    E. Morrogh Bernard
      Vic. Gen.
    Westmonasterii, die 27a Januarii, 1955

First published in the U.S.A. by
THE NEWMAN PRESS
Westminster, Maryland.

Made in Great Britain at the Pitman Press, Bath

EDITOR'S NOTE

IN 1934 *Père Riquet, then chaplain to the medical students and doctors in Paris decided to launch a review of medical deontology called, the "Cahiers Laënnec," which would describe the problems and "cases of conscience" that arise in medical practice and expound their solution on the basis of Catholic moral principles. This venture was crowned with immediate success and continued until interrupted by World War II. After the war, the review was revived by Père Riquet's successor, Père Larère, S.J., and at the request of the "Mouvement international des Intellectuels Catholique de Pax Romana," the "Cahiers Laënnec" became the official review of the Medical Secretariat. It would be unjust not to mention the older "Conference Laënnec" founded in 1875 by the Jesuit Fathers in Paris with similar objectives which, after the First World War, was to inspire the formation of the well-known body called "les Amis de Laënnec."*

It is our intention in presenting this translation to English speaking readers, clerical and medical, to demonstrate what has been done by these efforts to enunciate the rule of Christian principles in the practice of our colleagues in France, whose difficulties so nearly approach our own although their approach to them from the scientific angle may not always be the same as ours. Each contributor has presented the problem under examination from his own standpoint and though we do not always find ourselves in agreement with the views expressed, nevertheless their expression has been necessary to a clear understanding of the difficulty as it appears to them and as it requires solution according to the moral principles applicable to the case.—EDITOR.

CONTENTS

FIRST STUDY

CASTRATION
By Rev. M. Riquet, S. J.

EDITOR'S FOREWORD

THIS little work from the pen of Fr. Riquet, S.J., so faithfully translated by Mr. Carroll, will do much to furnish the correct answer to those who have sometimes to reply, on behalf of the Church, to the charge that she permitted "euphonic castration" in the interest of the famous Sistine Choir. In addition to his historical survey Fr. Riquet has given a clear exposition of the teaching of the Church on the morality of therapeutic castration which is still employed in certain cases of cancer in both sexes.

It is well to remember that castration is never practised as a penalty in criminal law nor, indeed, as a preventive measure, "artificial sterilization" being employed for this purpose; but this raises questions which are not relevant to the end Fr. Riquet has in view in his book, and we shall content ourselves with adding that the principles which he enunciates apply in determining the morality of irradiating both ovaries with a view to procuring permanent sterility.

It is hoped that this translation will prove helpful to those students of medico-moral problems who prefer to do their reading in the vernacular.

CASTRATION

AN HISTORICAL AND MORAL STUDY

CASTRATION and sterilization refer to operations which are distinct as to method, but not as to principal effect, since both aim at sterilizing the patient. Formerly, over a long period of time, castration was the only known method of depriving the individual, male or female, of the power to reproduce the species. The same result is reached to-day by methods which allow the essential organs of generation to remain, and do not entail the same privations as castration does.

It does not follow that castration is no longer practised; it is still the only known remedy for certain serious diseases localized in the sexual organs of the man or of the woman. Some psychiatrists recommend it as an effective remedy for certain sexual anomalies. Again, it is known to have been used, here and there, as the surest method of eugenic sterilization.

It is, therefore, not inopportune to attempt a complete study of the problems which arise from the practice of castration whether with a medical, eugenic or penal aim in view.

Moreover, the practice of castration in antiquity and throughout history has occasioned the formulation by philosophers, psychologists, and especially by the Catholic Church, of certain moral rulings on this matter and of reflections which are not without a present context, but which it is necessary to present here in their authentic form, free from the legends and questionable stories which abound in the books usually cited on this subject.

We shall give, therefore—

1. A history of castration drawn from exact and checked sources.

2. An exposition of the attitude of Catholic Christianity to this practice, and in particular to singers, male sopranos (euphonic castration).

3. A study of the psycho-physical effects of castration.

4. A synthesis of moral rules in this matter.

THE HISTORY OF CASTRATION

THE word *castration* is not a recent coinage. It is derived from Sancrit *ssastram* (knife) and *ssasati* (to cut), and it designates an operation which consists essentially in suppressing the generative organs, the *testicles* in the man, the *ovaries* in the woman.

The vocabulary suggests that different methods were successively adopted. *Castration, emasculation, ovariotomy, oophorectomy* consist in cutting testicles or ovaries. Furthermore, they are crushed (Θλάω or Θλιβω), whence the name *thlasiae* or *thlibiae* given by the Greeks and the Romans to individuals deprived of their testicles. The Latin translation of the Bible speaks of him who is an eunuch, either from having been *crushed* or from having been *cut*: *"Non intrabit eunuchus, attritis vel amputatis testiculis absciso veretro, ecclesiam Domini"* (Deut. xxiii. 1).

In every case, *castrated, eunuch* or *spado, thlasiae* or *thlibiae* designate equally an individual deprived of testicles. An old Latin-French lexicon of the thirteenth century has: *"Castratus—Excoullié."*

At what epoch did this practice arise?

The most ancient documents which witness to the custom of castration (*c.* 2000 B.C.) suggest that it was originally a penal or vindictive mutilation. Criminals and the conquered enemy were castrated, because the deprivation of virility seemed the heaviest and most humiliating torture that could be inflicted on a man. The castrated, the eunuch is but a half-man, because, according to the ancients, he has lost not only the power to reproduce his kind, but also the energy, the vigour which is the prerogative of men.

Nothing suggests so well the drastic import of castration as does the cult paid in primitive religions to the virile organ, the *phallus* of the Greeks and the Romans, the *lingam* of the Hindu. It is the sacred symbol of all the superiority which virility implies. To be deprived of it is the supreme loss for a man, and hence the punishment inflicted on the criminal and the conquered.

Moreover, the castration performed on male animals, horses, bulls, rams, with the object of making them more apt for work, more tractable and gentle, was soon extended, with the same object of domesticating them, to the slaves. It had the added advantage, often, of eliminating the concern which naturally arose with the practice of entrusting to male slaves the custody of the women in the harem or the gynecium.

Destined to service, the faithful, intelligent and devoted eunuch would become the confidant of his master, his counsellor often, the representative and first minister of princes. It would happen, also, that his artificially prolonged youth, his bearing, and his womanish figure made him a much-sought accomplice in unnatural vice. Eunuchism and pederasty mutually attract and strengthen each other. Asia, Greece and Rome are sad illustrations of this.

It is only later on that one finds castration motivated by ascetic and mystical considerations.

As regards medical or therapeutic castration, the School of Cos was already practising it in the fifth century before Christ, and the School had doubtless no monopoly in this matter. The therapeutic indications for this operation have varied, but it seems evident that both doctors and moralists have always agreed on the perfect legitimacy of an intervention which sacrificed a part of an individual in the interests of the whole.

Chinese

Under the Emperors Yao (2357–2258 B.C.) and Choen (2258–2205 B.C.), castration, *Kong*, is one of the *Five Punishments* provided by the Penal Code. At the end of the nineteenth century, this punishment was still inflicted on a murderer's sons less than sixteen years old. These eunuchs were exclusively reserved to the Imperial Palaces, and the Emperor Ho-ti (in A.D. 111) decreed that eunuchs only could remain in the palace after sunset. (Dr. Matignon: "Les Eunuques du Palais Impérial de Pekin," *Arch. Cliniques de Bordeaux*, mai 1896).

On the other hand, the private practice of castration is severely forbidden and punished. This attitude is natural in a country where respect for the family and for paternity takes on the proportions of a religion. (G. Boulais: *Manuel du Code chinois*, Shanghai, 1924.)

Hindus

The *Mahâbhârata* (III cl. 46) informs us that castration was both known and practised in Vedic India from quite an early date, and that the eunuch was there held in contempt.

"The dregs of humanity are the Mlechchhas (the non-Aryans); the dregs of the Mlechchhas are the dealers in oil; the dregs of the dealers are the eunuchs." (*Mahâbhârata* VIII, 45, 25.)

The eunuch, "the man with the long-hair," is neither man nor woman; he cannot inherit; he is excluded from the sacrifice to the spirits of the dead, and the food prepared for him cannot be eaten by a

Brahmin. The dancing professionals are recruited from their number, and also the accomplices in unnatural vice. (*Encycl. of Religion and Ethics*: "Eunuch.")

Egyptians

Eunuchs are already numerous in the reign of Dynasty XX (1202–1102 B.C.). This is easily verified by studying, on the bas-reliefs of Karnak and Thebes, the numbers of castrations inflicted on prisoners after the victory of the Pharaonic Ramses II (*fl.* 1271 B.C.) over the Khati, or of the Pharaonic Minephtah (*fl.* 1210 B.C.) over the Lybians. The number of "phallus cut" is counted in thousands.

The Book of Genesis also furnishes evidence of the presence of eunuchs in the court of the Pharaos. (Gen. xl. 1; xxxvii. 36; xxxiv. 1–7). The fact that the eunuch Putiphar was married does not necessarily exclude his having been castrated (Lesètre). (Cf. Rawlinson: *History of Ancient Egypt*, London, 1881, ch. XXII.)

In recent centuries, Egypt, the Sudan and Abyssinia have still furnished the majority of their eunuchs to the Turkish harems. Despite the agreement of August 17th, 1877, between England and Egypt, which forbade the making of eunuchs in that country, Zambaco-Pasha could still find them there about 1910.

Assyrians and Babylonians

According to Ammiamus Marcellinus (XIV, VI, 17), it was the legendary Semiramis who, "first of all," could have introduced the custom of castrating infants. In any case, eunuchs are a commonplace pretty early in Assyrian and Persian history. The Book of Esther (i. 10–15; vi. 2; vii. 9) shows them surrounding the prince, guarding the gynecium, watching the palace entrances; Herodotus (VIII, 104 *seq.*), in speaking of Hermotimus, eunuch of Xerxes, informs us that, in the fifth century B.C., "the eunuchs were valued by the barbarians at a higher price than the rest of the slaves, because of the entire confidence they inspired." We also know from the same history that the hero Panionius of Chios, "having made eunuchs of young boys endowed with beauty, sold them at Sardus and Ephesus and acquired great sums thereby."

Hebrews

Deuteronomy (xxiii. 1) and Leviticus (xxii. 24) stigmatizes castration of both man and animal: "He that is wounded in the stones, or hath his privy member cut off, shall not enter into the congregation of the Lord."

This respect for the generative organs of life appears also in that severe prescription of Deuteronomy, which orders that the hand of a wife shall be cut off, who, to defend her husband in a struggle, seizes his adversary "by his secret parts." (Deut. xxv. 11–12.)

Nevertheless, the history of Israel mentions more than one eunuch in the service of its kings (2 Kings ix. 31), and Josephus shows Herod surrounded by elegant eunuchs serving his table or watching by his bed (Ant. Jud., XVI, VIII, 1).

Roman Empire

The first eunuchs of Rome were undoubtedly prisoners of war, but the number of eunuchs multiplied as slavery increased. The right of master over slave is absolute: *servile caput nullam lex habet* (a servile head has no rights) says the Roman jurist; everything is permitted with slaves *"in quas stuprum non committitur"* (Dig., XXV, VII, 1). Consequently, the slave was castrated with the same ease and for the same reasons as a domestic animal.

The perversion of Roman manners in the time of Nero and Helio-gabalus makes the eunuch the accomplice in the worst excesses. The castration of young and beautiful boys was calculated to preserve that charm which caused them to be chosen in preference to women by pervert masters. *"Exoletos suos ut ad longiorem patientiam impudicitiae sint, amputant."* (Seneca, *Exc. Controv.*, X, 4.)

Eunuchs were not less prized by Roman matrons who used them, says St. Jerome, *"in longam securamque libidinem."* (Adv. Jov., P.L., XXIII, 277.) Juvenal (Satyr., VI, 366 *sq.*) says clearly that security was not the sole reason for this preference:

> Sunt quas eunuchi imbelles ac mollia semper
> Oscula delectent, et desperatio barbae
> Et quod abortivo non est opus.

To those who were castrated in thousands for purposes of pleasure, we must add those whom the mystic fury of the priests of Cybele inspired to renew in themselves the mutilation of Attis.

They became very numerous when Claudius had officially admitted the full practice of their bloody rites.

These excesses were, of course, vigorously stigmatized by the satirists: Plautus, Horace, Juvenal, Martial, Lucian, and by the Christian apologists from Justin to St. Augustine. But it was not till the end of the first century of the Christian era that the imperial authority began to suppress these abuses.

Indeed, the prohibition of castration in Roman law comes only with Domitian (+ 96) (Suet. Domit., 7) and Nerva (+ 98) (Dion Cassius, LXVII, 3). Hadrian (117–138) sentences to the punishments of the *Lex Cornelia* the person who performs castration, the doctor and even the person castrated: "*Nemo enim liberum servumve invitum sinentemve castrare debet, neve quis se sponte castrandum praebere debet.*" (Dig., XLVIII, 8, 4.) The penalties provided by the *Lex Cornelia* ranged from confiscation of property to the death sentence. "*Medico quidem, qui exciderit, capitale erit, item ipsi qui se sponte excidendum praebuit.*"

Constantine (+ 337) (Cod. Just., IV, 42, 1) inflicted the death penalty on the person who performed a castration, confiscated the mutilated slave and even the house where the crime was committed, if it was established that the owner had known of it and connived at it. "*Si quis . . . eunuchos fecerit, capite puniatur: mancipio tali nec non etiam loco, ubi hoc commissum fuerit domino sciente et dissimulante, confiscando.*" The emperor Leo (Cod. Just., IV, 42, 2) forbade the sale of eunuchs of Roman citizenship, "*poena gravissima statuenda,*" but he allowed the sale of those of the barbarians who had been made eunuchs outside the boundaries of the Empire.

Finally, Junstinian (Novel. 142) inflicted the punishment of retaliation on anybody who dared to castrate any person whomsoever, freeman or slave: "*hoc idem patiantur quod fecerunt*"; at the very least, the culprit suffered confiscation of his property and exile. All the eunuch slaves who underwent castration for health reasons, were given the right to liberty. "*Si tamen propter morbum contingat ut servus castretur, illum quoque jubemus libertate potiri.*" (Rein: *Das Criminalrecht der Romer*, Leipzig, 1844, pp. 422–424.)

We shall point out later how the energetic attitude of the Christian Bishops and of the Councils, in the first centuries of Christianity, would strengthen the effectiveness of imperial laws for eliminating this degrading practice from the civilized world.

In fact, it did not survive through the Middle Ages except under Moslem rule and in certain mystic sects.

Islam

Mahomet forbade the practice of castration whether of self or of another. "Whoever castrates himself or others cannot be my disciple, because in Islam no other castration should be found but that by fasting." (*Mishkât almasâbîh*, tr. A. N. Matthews. Calcutta, 1809, 1, 151.)

But though the Mohammedan was forbidden to castrate anyone, he loved to confide the care of his harem to eunuchs. Among his slaves, the eunuchs enjoyed all the privileges and were bought at a very high price. That is the reason why the slave-merchants of the Sudan would have all the children castrated who were destined for the markets of Cairo and Constantinople.

"The Ethiopian eunuchs were made chiefly in Darfour and Kodorfan, whence they were sent to Tripoli. For Abyssinia, the centre of this infamous traffic was in Geillas.

In 1868, Kalil Aga, chief eunuch of the mother of the Khédive of Egypt, Ismaël Pasha, founded an establishment for the making of eunuchs at Massaouah, on the Red Sea. A doctor operated there. His methods, which were more scientific than those of the slave dealer, spared at least from suffering those unfortunate children condemned to this sad fate. He reduced the mortality to 50 per cent." (Gilles Roy: *Abdul-Hamid*, Paris, 1936, pp. 114–115.)

Besides being guardians of the harems, the eunuchs were also made custodians of the mosques, both of Mecca and Medina. As men who enjoyed the confidence of princes, the eunuchs were respected and even venerated by the people, who addressed them as *Aga* (Sir) and sometimes kissed their hands, as Burckhardt saw done at Mecca. (*Travels in Nubia*: London, 1822, and *Travels in Arabia*: London, 1829, I, 288–291.)

The great Statesmen of Islam were recruited from the eunuchs. *Kafur-al-Ikhsidi* was a castrated negro who, in the tenth century, reigned over all Egypt and Syria. Public prayers were offered up for him as far as Mecca. (*Encyl. of Religion and Ethics*: Hastings, V, "Eunuch.")

The Skoptzy of Russia and Rumania

It was in 1772, in the vicinity of Orjol, in the districts of Belev and Alexin (Russia), that the first Skoptzy (*skopets*—eunuch) are found. They were then about fifty people who had followed the example of Andrei Ivanov Blochin, a merchant of Brâsovo in the district of Sevsk. This man joined the sect of the Khitsty, and having announced that he was incapable of observing their rule of absolute continence, he took the initiative by castrating himself. He invoked, of course, the text in St. Matthew (xix. 12).

Andrei Ivanov, now known as Kondrati Sselivanov, claimed to be the Christ the Son of God, and at the same time the Emperor Peter III, "born in Holstein, by the operation of the Holy Spirit, of the Empress Elizabeth Petrowna, an immaculate virgin." Of course, history relates that Peter III was assassinated by his wife, Catherine II, in the palace of Ropscha; but according to the Skoptzy, it was a guard who was assassinated instead of the emperor, who continued his life under the name of Kondrati Sselivanov, to preach everywhere the necessity of Baptism by fire, that is to say, emasculation by the red-hot iron. In spite of the legend he had forged, Sselivanov was twice exiled to Siberia, and finally shut up as a madman in the claustral prison of Susdal. He died there in 1832. By that time, there were eight to ten thousand Skoptzy who had submitted to castration with the hot iron. Among these were rich merchants and money-changers, as well as officers and peasants. Since they had few or no children, their money found its way into the coffers of the sect, with the result that the doctrine was propagated in all Russia and even into Rumania, under the more or less benevolent surveillance of the police. (*Ency. Ethics and Religion*, V, "Russian Sects," XI, 339–342.)

The Skoptzy performed a double mutilation on men: the first (the little seal) suppressed only the testicles, "the keys of hell"; the second (the imperial seal), besides the testicles and the scrotum, amputated also the penis which they called "the key of the abyss." With the women Skoptzy, the mutilation comprised the amputation of all or part of the breasts, the resection of the labiae and the clitoris; it did not extend to the ovaries.

The conduct of the "White Doves" was far from lax. Already, Pelikan recognized their qualities: murderers, robbers, rogues were rare among them; they loved work and they fulfilled with zeal and punctuality their public and domestic duties; they led a regular and well-ordered life. They drank no wine nor alcoholic drink, and they did not smoke. They led a chaste life, and performed extremely rigorous fasts. They were vegetarians, but they ate fish. Their social conduct, apart from all that concerned the castration itself, was in conformity with their dogmas.

They were, however, audacious proselytizers. They would try, we are told, to spread the practice of castration by every means in their power, because the Kingdom of God was to come when the Skoptzy had reached the apocalyptic number of 144,000. Besides quotations from the Bible (Matthew xix. 12; Luke xxiii. 9; Mark ix. 43; Isaias xvi. 3, etc.), the following were some of the means they resorted to: money loans to the needy, with the undertaking to submit to castration in the event of failure to re-pay; the purchase of children, under cover of hirings or apprentising; alms to prisoners, etc.

Between 1910 and 1926, the anthropologist, Eugène Pittard, studied minutely the morphological effects of castration on some hundred of the Rumanian Skoptzy. He remarks that the number of the sectaries seems to have increased since the war. In any case, since the disappearance of the eunuchs of Turkey and Pekin, they form the sole ethnic group in which the practice of castration survives as a general custom. (Cf. E. Pittard, *La Castration chez l'Homme. Recherches sur les Skoptzy*, Paris, 1943; and the classic on this matter by Dr. Pelikan: *Gerichtliche medicinische untersuchungen über das Skopzenthum in Russland*, Giessen, 1876.)

THE CHURCH AND CASTRATION

Has the Church condemned castration? Has she favoured it as answering to ascetic needs, or has she complaisantly tolerated it at a time when the castrated male sopranos were the glory of the Sistine choirs? Finally, is it true that she excludes from the priesthood all eunuchs, irrespective of the motive for castration?

These are questions to which we shall give answers based on precise and strictly authentic sources.

*　*　*

The Church began her civilizing mission at the precise moment—the reign of Nero—when the depravity which the increase in the number of eunuchs manifested and fostered, had reached a pitch of exasperation. Vigorous texts of the apostles, the apologists and the Fathers, clearly mark the opposition of Christianity to the reigning vices, to unnatural conduct.

Written in 150, a century after the Epistle of St. Paul to the Romans, the *Apology of Justin* furnishes an indisputable proof that, faced with pagan manners, the reaction of a Greek turned Christian was not less healthy or less clear than the reaction of the Jew and pharisee that was the early St. Paul. The *Apology* speaks trenchantly "of those girls and boys who are reared like a herd of cows, goats or sheep, solely for infamous uses." It denounces the scandal of "claims, tributes and taxes which princes were imposing on and gathering from the sordid traffic in women, hermaphrodites and disreputable persons." It inveighs against "those who mutilate themselves publicly, when celebrating the mysteries of the mother of the gods (Cybele)" (1 Apol. xxix).

On the other hand, the Christians respect themselves, and respect the woman and the child. If they marry, it is with the intention of having children, and they do not abandon them (*ibid.*).

However, in the world the early Christians found, castration was so much a matter of course that it was inevitable some should be tempted to do, in the name of virtue, that which so many others were doing for purposes of vice. One cannot but admire, therefore, the sure-footed judgment which, from the beginning, considered as metaphorical the words of Christ: "There are some who have made

12

themselves eunuchs for the Kingdom of Heaven" (Matthew xix. 12).

St. Epiphanius (315–403), in his dictionary of heresies, tells us of a dissident Christian sect, the *Valetians*, which, taking the words of Christ literally, made castration an indispensable condition of salvation. The members of the sect were all *castigati*. (Hoer, LVIII; P.G., XLVI, 1009–1016.)

But, if they ever existed, these Valesians had so little influence in the young Church that no other author makes the least reference to them.

On the other hand, the scandal occasioned by certain castrations of known Christians shows clearly that the Christian conscience deprecated such an act, even when inspired by a desire for chastity.

It sufficed, however, to consider the well-known immorality of the eunuchs of their day, to be convinced that castration was no guarantee of virtue.

Zealous neophytes forgot this, sometimes. Their action always met with the reprobation of Christian communities, with the opposition of Bishops . . . and of magistrates.

The case of Origen is classic in this matter. Eusebius relates (H.E., VI, 8) how the young Origen, brilliant catechist of the Church of Alexandria, interpreted "in a most simple and childish manner" the words of Our Lord about those who "have made themselves eunuchs." Doubtless, too, he wished to deal drastically with suspicions and calumnies which might be aroused through his success with an audience that was partly one of women. He castrated himself.

The reaction of the Church of Alexandria against him was severe. Bishop Demetrius refused to ordain him, and forbade him to preach in the Church. Origen had the good fortune to find a more accommodating bishop of Caesarea in Palestine, who, assisted by his colleague of Jerusalem, ordained him in 228.

Origen himself, however, had recognized his error, and, in his commentary on St. Matthew (xix. 12), he reproves those who interpret the words in question literally. Furthermore, he admits the serious physiological inconveniences which were for him the consequences of his rash action: "headaches, dizziness, an unstable imagination engendering fantastic dreams." He concludes: "One castration only is permitted, that which achieves spiritually the chastity of the soul" (P.G., XIII, 1257).

The case of Leontius, in the fourth century, is also cited. He was a Phrygian by birth and a cleric of the Church of Antioch. Living with an *agape* woman, called Eustolia, and not wishing to be separated from her, he mutilated himself. His bishop, Eustathe, deposed him, but the Emperor Constans pigheadedly appointed him Bishop of Antioch.

St. Athanasius and his contemporaries protested vigorously, and their campaign influenced the decision taken in this matter by the Council of Nicea, in 325.

The first canon of Nicea says, in effect—

"If a sick person has been, in the course of his cure, mutilated by doctors, or if a person has been castrated by the barbarians, let him remain among the clergy; but if a man in good health castrates himself, he is to be excluded from the clergy, and, in future, whoever acts in this way is not to be ordained. But as it is clear that this measure is adopted only towards those who have acted intentionally or who have been willing to mutilate themselves, those who have been made eunuchs by the barbarians or by their master ought, in conformity with the Canon, to be accepted in the clerical state if they are found to be otherwise worthy." (Cf. Hefele-Leclerq: *Histoire des Conciles*, I, 528–532.)

This text of 325 fixed definitely the attitude of the Church to castration. The later councils, the papal decisions inserted in the *Decree of Gratian* or in the *Decretals of Gregory IX*, are merely a repetition of or a very close comment on the rules of Nicea.

They recognized the perfect legitimacy of castration performed by a doctor to save or to heal a patient. Neither such, nor those who were made eunuchs against their wishes, by violence, are excluded from the priesthood.

Far from being an excuse, the care for their chastity which inspires some to self-castration is the reason why they are expressly excluded. The Council of Arles, in 452, is explicit: "*Canon 7: Hi qui se, carnali vitio repugnare nescientes, abscindunt, ad clerum pervenire non possunt.*" And St. Martin of Braga (*c.* 575), in his Canon 21, says with equal clarity: "If anyone deceives himself that it is not by the discipline of religion and by abstinence, but solely by the mutilation of the body fashioned by God, that he can suppress the concupiscence of the flesh, and accordingly castrates himself, we forbid such a one to be received into any clerical office whatsoever."

This emphasis is understandable. There is sovereign need of inculcating, for these Christians, that chastity is essentially an attitude of soul, a will to purity, not a mutilation of the body.

The Fathers were at one with the Councils in their teaching. St. John Chrysostom, in his *Homilies on St. Matthew*, expresses vigorously the doctrine of all the Bishops of his time—

"When Christ said: '*They have made themselves eunuchs,*' He did not speak of the amputation of a member, far from it indeed; He meant the suppression of lascivious thoughts. Whoever amputates the member, mutilates himself. He comes under the malediction of which

St. Paul speaks: '*Let them be driven forth, those that trouble you.*' And this is just. Such a man, in effect, behaves like a murderer, he furnishes a pretext to those who malign the creative work of God, he opens the door to Manicheans, he breaks the law just the same as the pagan does who castrates himself. These amputations were originally of diabolical inspiration, the work of Satan. To practise them is to slander the work of God; it is to soil the living being; it is to refer all, not to the deliberation of the will, but to the instinct of the members, and many avail of it to sin without fear, declaring themselves to be without responsibility in this matter.

"For all these reasons, I exhort you to avoid such iniquity. Moreover, you must know that the libido is not weakened by this procedure, but becomes more ardent, because it has other sources in us; it simmers elsewhere. It is in the head, according to some, in the loins, according to others, that this raging passion is born. I say that it has no other origin except a lascivious soul and licence in thoughts. If the soul has the virtue of temperance, no damage can come to it from physical emotions." (In Matth., Homil. LXII (63); P.G., LVIII, 599 *sq.*).

We find in this vigorous text a summary of the Church's doctrine on this question. The Canon of Nicea envisages directly clerics and aspirants to the priesthood only; here, we find castration condemned purely and simply as a grave offence against Him who "made them male and female." Moreover, it does not ensure purity of soul; on the contrary, indeed.

Was the exclusion from the clerical state, pronounced by the Council of Nicea, the only sanction inflicted on the self-eunuch? The *Canons*, called *Apostolic*, which reflect exactly the discipline and the doctrine universally current in the Church at the beginning of the fifth century, add a penalty for the laity to the Nicean rule specially concerning the clergy: "Canon 24 (23): The layman who mutilates himself shall be deprived of the Communion for three years, because he acts as an enemy to his own life."

This severity, both for laity and clergy who were guilty of mutilating themselves—or of having themselves mutilated—will be that of the whole Christian Middle Ages.

It shows itself in the decisions of Councils, of Bishops and of Popes, gathered in the canonical collections, in the Decree of Gratian in the eleventh century, and in the *Decretals* from Gregory IX to Gregory XIII.

Hincman of Rheims and the Council of Tribur in the ninth century, Leo IX and Yves de Chartres in the eleventh, Clement III and Innocent III to Innocent XIII, all hold strictly to the rule of Nicea. The priest who mutilates himself finds that he is excluded from the ministry of the altar, and the cleric from the priesthood; he, on the contrary, who has been castrated against his will or for medical reasons, preserves his right to exercise the priestly ministry, and even, if he is deemed worthy, to be promoted to the episcopacy: *"in Episcopum promoveri."* (C. 35, X, *De corpore vitiatis*; Cf. Thomassin: *Ancienne et Nouvelle discipline de l'Eglise*, II, 1.1, ch. LXXXII.)

In short, unwilling or medically necessary castration has never been an obstacle to the priesthood or the episcopacy. Only *culpable* mutilation is such an obstacle.

For the laity, moreover, the severity of the Church was reinforced by Roman law. We have seen that, from the days of Constantine, Roman law was ruthless towards these kinds of mutilation. The Visigoth and Carolingian laws were equally severe on mutilators.

Thanks to the two-fold action of the Church and the civil power, eunuchs disappeared in the Christian West. Castration was no longer admissible except under two forms, both in conformity with Nicea: therapeutic castration performed by a doctor on a sick person; and penal castration, ordered by the laws then in force, and performed by the hangman. Some theologians, of the seventeenth and eighteenth centuries, attempted to justify *euphonic castration* in the interests of *bel canto*, but, as we shall see, without success. As to castration inspired by a false mysticism, it survives to-day only in the *Skoptzy* sect of Russia and Rumania (see above). It was only under the reign of Islam that the practices and perversions of pagan Rome and the Orient continued through the Middle Ages.

The castrated singers

At the age of puberty, between the age of thirteen and seventeen, the boy's voice drops an octave or an octave and a half, and takes on the deep male tone. This "breaking" of the voice, as it is called, is due to a transformation of the cartilages of the larynx and of the glottis which, in the man, increases in the proportion of 5 to 10; in the woman, 5 to 7 only.

Castration performed before puberty lessens the development of the larynx and the glottis, and preserves a child's contralto or alto voice in the grown man. Aristotle (*Gener. Anim.*, V. 6–12) noted this fact and explained it in his own way.

At a time when eunuchs were flourishing in Rome and in Byzantium, the idea arose of using their characteristic voice in choral singing. In the fourth century, we find even in Byzantium a choir of eunuchs in the imperial Chapel. Sozomene (Hist. Eccles., VIII, 8) gives us the name of the choir's leader: the eunuch Brison.

The severe laws of Constantine and Justinian, as also the decree of Nicea, put an end to this custom.

However, in the twelfth century, we learn from the illustrious Theodore Balsamon, in his commentaries on the Council of Trulles, that in his day (c. 1180) certain choirs were composed exclusively of eunuchs, but he adds that such was not the case formerly (P.G.). About the same time (in 1137), an eunuch of Byzantium came to Smolensk with two other eunuchs, to found a choir and a choral school.

In the West, where plain chant was the rule in churches and where polyphonic was for a long time overlooked or excluded, the question of eunuchs did not arise clearly before the end of the fifteenth century. At that period, the introduction into church services of contrapuntal and polyphonic choral singing posed a problem: who would sing the soprano and the alto parts? They could not be given to women, since church discipline excluded women from any choral function. There were, of course, the boys—but scarcely had they been taught to read the musical score, then very complicated, when their voices broke and all the effort came to nothing.

An attempt was made to preserve them by teaching the youths to sing in a head-voice or falsetto: *soprani falsetti*. This explains why, from 1441, there is no mention of any boys in the choir of the Papal chapel or of the Sistine chapel, which originally consisted of nine men and six boys: the high parts, soprano and alto, were sung by *soprani falsetti* who came from Spain. (*Catholic Encyclopedia of U.S.A.*, V, "Sistine Choir.")

The falsetto soprano or high tenor was not necessarily an eunuch. The best proof of this is furnished by the actual singers of the Sistine whose admirable soprano or alto voices did not prevent them from having a wife and children.

Consequently, the absence of children in the polyphonic choirs does not imply the presence of eunuchs.

It is certain, however, that at the beginning of the seventeenth century, authentic eunuchs are found in church choirs, including that of the Sistine. The famous Orlando di Lasso conducted, in 1569, a choir of six eunuchs in the chapel of the Duke of Bavaria. (M. Delmotte: *Orlando de Lassus*, Valenciennes, 1836, p. 301.)

The reason for this was that the eunuchs had more than one advantage over the falsetti and even over the women. For two centuries, they had enjoyed tremendous success and had played an important role in the evolution of music.

"The singing of eunuchs adds to the timbre and the texture of boys' voices, special qualities due to the development of their lungs as grown men: an easy rendering of very long passages in a single breath, the extraordinary prolongation of the *messe di voce*. It is to eunuchs that we owe, in greater part, the development of the art of *bel canto* during the seventeenth and eighteenth centuries." (Hugo Riemann: *Dictionnaire de Musique*, Edition Française, Lausanne, 1913. *Castrat.*)

It was from the eunuchs that the famous singers, and sometimes composers, of the Sistine Chapel in the seventeenth and eighteenth centuries were recruited: Loretto Vittori (1588–1670); Steffano Laudi (*c.* 1629); Gregorio Allegri (1584–1652), author of the famous *Miserere* for nine voices; Giovanni Francesco Grossi, called Siface (1653–1697). At the end of the seventeenth century, the use of eunuchs was general in Italian churches. They were found, not only in churches, but in the royal courts and in the theatres. Carlo Broschi (1703–1782), called Farinelli, cured by his singing the melancholy of Philip the Fifth, King of Spain, and became his favourite. The eighteenth century marks their apogee. Eunuchs "have raised singing to a splendid art, to the detriment of music which is scarcely regarded as fashionable any more." The reason for this success, which was great, is due to the fact that boys destined for singing began the study of music very young, and exercised early a voice which preserved, through the years, the range and purity of youth. Hence that virtuosity and brilliance which charmed the theatre even more than the church. Hence, too, those careers which easily lasted for half a century. At eighty years of age, the eunuch Matteucci sang with so much flexibility and lightness that his audience thought they were listening to a young man.

After two centuries the fashion changed. Count Orloff, travelling in Italy and making researches on this subject about 1827, could find only five or six eunuchs in Rome and Naples. The *Gazette musicale* of June 9th, 1850, published a letter of M. Adrian de la Fage, dated March 13th, 1850, in which, speaking of an obscure eunuch pupil of the famous Crescentini, he writes: "He is now the only one of his kind. . . . He would give a rather feeble idea of those voices, so justly enthused over, which were formerly so common in Italy and which are found no more."

Leo XIII definitely closed the door of the Sistine chapel to them.

Voltaire, and many others after him, have lamented that the Church tolerated for such a long time, the presence of eunuchs in her choirs, even in the Papal choir.

Let us remark first and foremost: to allow eunuchs to sing in church, to use them for the greater splendour of the Liturgy, does not entail an approbation of criminal mutilation, because one can be an eunuch without having incurred any moral stigma thereby. Castration could have resulted from an accident or from a necessary operation. It must not be forgotten that the doctors of the Middle Ages and of the Renaissance found many therapeutic reasons for castration; for example, as treatment for hernia, as a cure or prevention of leprosy, epilepsy or gout.

An inquiry made in 1676 by the Royal Society of Medicine shows that, in the diocese of Saint-Papoul alone, more than five hundred children had been castrated for hernia. It was the same in Italy, where hernia patients were not uncommon.

It was no difficult matter to recruit from among these the six or seven eunuchs who were made members of the Sistine choir. Surely this was to offer to victims of a primitive surgery a situation which would make some compensation to them for their infirmity.

The admission of eunuchs to the church choirs did not necessarily imply an approval of criminal mutilation; it was merely the use, for choral singing, of a simple consequence of operations which were then frequently performed for purely therapeutic reasons. Moreover, more than one eunuch who became famous, attributed his castration to an accident in youth, or to a surgical operation necessitated by a hernia or some other infirmity.

Hence our conviction that the Church, without any lack of logic and in all fairness to the victim, could condemn all castration not justified by the necessity of saving a life threatened by a diseased member, and at the same time allow as members of her choirs those eunuchs whose mutilation was not necessarily culpable.

What is important in this matter is that the authentic doctrine of the Church has never authorized castration performed solely to ensure to the eunuch a melodious voice in accord with the tastes of the day.

Nevertheless, some theologians have held that parents could legitimately castrate their children in order to ensure that they should have a very pleasant voice and qualify for a situation which was then very desirable.

The first to defend that opinion as probable was a Spaniard, a hermit of St. Augustine called Michel Salon, author of a tract *De Justitia*, published in Valence, 1581.

One of his Italian confrères, Zacharia Pasqualigo, in 1647, brilliantly defended the same opinion. It was specifically opposed by P. Diana and forms part of a letter which is a whole tract, published at Dijon in 1655, by J. Héribertus Coemeliensis, with the suggestive title: *Eunuchi, nati, facti, mystici ex Sacra et humana litteratura illustrati, Zacharias Pasqualigus puerorum emasculator ob musicam quo loco habendus.*

Paul Laymann, in 1625, and Cardinal de Lugo, in 1652, take up an equally clear stand against the opinion of Salon and Pasqualigo. Apart from Tamburinus, Elbel and Mazotta, the majority of theologians rallied to the negative opinion of Laymann and de Lugo, so that Pope Benedict XIV, in his treatise *De Synodo* (1760) declares as the more common opinion: "*vicit apud plerosque et facta est communior opinio negans.*" (*De Synodo*, I. XI, VII).

"In effect," says Benedict XIV, "man is not master of his members to a degree which allows him to consent to the amputation of any one of them, unless he cannot otherwise conserve his body as a whole. A case in point, according to Aetius, is leprosy, from which mortal disease the victim can be delivered only by the amputation of his virility. And so, neither the pretended necessity of ensuring his livelihood, nor the laudable aim of serving the Church by fulfilling the office of chorister, can provide a sufficiently just reason or a motive which excuses from sin, for the voluntary emasculation of men."

Having thus condemned all castration not justified by the necessity of saving the whole body, but considering, on the other hand, the circumstances, the connivance of public powers which allowed castration, the long-established custom of hearing eunuch singers in churches, even in the chapel of the Roman Pontiffs, Benedict XIV advises bishops not to exclude from church choirs the eunuch singers. To do so would be to trouble the general peace, to foment hatreds and invite reprisals, without a sufficient motive. The evil to be condemned was the unjustifiable castration, not the singing of the eunuchs.

Clement XIV thought the same. He condemned, under pain of mortal sin, the euphonic castration of children, and he allowed in the choirs those who, on inquiry, were found to be merely the innocent victims of their parents or of the doctors.

In fact, the condemnations of Benedict XIV and of Clement XIV, as also the finally unanimous severity of theologians, was not without result. Castration was practised gradually less and less. Burney, who aims at accuracy in this matter, has recorded his failure: "I inquired through all Italy for the principal centre where young boys were prepared by castration for a singing career, but I was not able to obtain any precise direction. In Milan, I was told it was in Venice; in Venice, that it was in Bologna; but in Bologna, they directed me on to Florence." (Cited in *Dictionnaire de plain-chant et de musique religieuse*. Migne, 1860, V. "Castrat," col. 252.)

Moreover, medical science had reduced considerably the therapeutic indications for castration, and thus the number of eunuchs became progressively fewer. Numerous in the eighteenth century, they were but a handful in the nineteenth; the source had run dry, and the scandal of euphonic castration was ended. The Church was never a party to it.

THE PSYCHO-PHYSICAL CONSEQUENCES
OF CASTRATION

WHEN discussing the legitimacy of castration, some moralists regard it as just one among other mutilations, that of the hand or foot, for example. (Tamburini, Pasqualigo, etc.) The Ancients, however, had a less superficial idea of the effects of castration. In any case, the physiologists of to-day all agree that the removal of the testicles or the ovaries has a more profound repercussion on the evolution and stability of the human being, than that entailed by gastrectomy, nephrectomy, or even the amputation of a foot. They see in the suppression of the sexual glands a serious alteration of the personality and of the character.

It is a known fact, that the man and the woman are distinguished from one another by a complexus of morphological, physiological and psychological characteristics which constitute profoundly different types of humanity.

It is not merely by the organs and by reproductive function that the man and the woman are differentiated, but also by a sexual imprint which manifests itself beyond these: "there is scarcely a part of our body which has not its sex." (Pézard, Caullery, Lipschutz, Maramon.)

To the *primary sexual characteristics*, consisting of the organs and the functions directly appropriated to reproduction, are added certain *secondary sexual characteristics* which seem remote from generation, but which, in common opinion and in reality, are manifestations of sexual life.

In the woman, the hips are wider than the shoulders; the muscular system weak; the female bulkiness is in the lower half of the body; there is a scanty distribution of hair but the hair of the head is luxuriant and lasting; the larynx little developed. In the man, on the other hand, the shoulders are wider than the hips; the muscular system is very strong; the male bulkiness is in the upper part of the body; there is a generous distribution of hair but the hair of the head is short with a tendency to fall; the larynx is well developed and prominent.

These *anatomical* characteristics are supplemented by not less important *functional* characteristics. Libido towards the man; a slow sexual orgasm; an aptitude for conception; the maternal instinct; a very great sensibility to emotional reactions and less inclination for abstract

21

and creative work; less aptitude for active muscular activity; typical carriage and behaviour; a high-pitched soprano or contralto timbre of voice—such are the distinctive characteristics of the woman. The characteristics of the man, on the other hand, are: libido towards the woman; a rapid sexual orgasm; an aptitude for rendering fertile; an instinct for social organization; less sensibility to emotional reactions and a greater capacity for mental abstraction and creation; a greater aptitude for active muscular impulses and for passive resistance; the timbre of the voice deep (bass or tenor). (Cf. Pr. Gregorio Maranon, *L'Évolution de la Sexualité et les États intersexuels*, trad. française, N.R.F., Paris, 1931, p. 12.)

Now, all these characteristics, whose complexus creates such a real diversity between the sexes, are strictly conditioned by the existence and evolution of the genital glands, the ovaries in the woman, the testicles in the man. Their alteration or suppression entails a profound modification of the anatomical, functional and psychological characteristics of the individual.

The man

(*a*) *Before puberty:* The removal of the testicular glands entails a clear modification of the skeleton, which is lengthened, especially in the bones of the leg; the cranium remains small and there is a corresponding diminution of the brain; the pelvis is enlarged, while the shoulders remain slender. The larynx remains small, whence the high timbre of the voice, sometimes harsh and cracked as when "breaking" occurs in a boy. There is a total absence of virile pilosity—beard, moustache, pubic hair, axillary hair; but the hair of the head is abundant and lasting. There is a tendency to early obesity. Premature senility sets in: early wrinkles, an aged appearance and a scaly skin are characteristic.

From the psychological point of view: "The eunuch is apathetic, without strength of will or a strong and incisive personality. In character, he is volatile, sly, suspicious and irritable; he suffers fundamentally from a profound sense of inferiority which makes him jealous of others—of men, whom he envies, and of woman, whom he cannot instinctively dominate because of his condition. Some eunuchs have, however, been considered sweet-natured, affectionate to children, sometimes childishly susceptible to suggestion, supple and fond of play. In short, they are a mixture of the woman and the child, in which there survives, however, in those who were naturally gifted, an intellectual activity, often very brilliant, intuitive, and with a bias toward the arts, or supple and simply persuasive. (History offers many examples of highly endowed eunuchs; philosophers—Favorinus;

generals—Aristonicus; ministers—Photin, Eutrope; etc.) They appear
to be predisposed to psychic troubles and more or less neurotic."
(Dr. Hernard, *Traité de Sexologie*, 1933, p. 140.)

(*b*) *After puberty:* Castration performed on a man after puberty
scarcely modifies his stature, but it entails an exaggerated development
of the breasts and of the buttocks (E. Pitard). Hirschfeld has examined
two cases of castration performed on men between the ages of twenty
and forty-six years: the larynx was small, the voice high-pitched.
In four of the cases studied by Hirschfeld, and also by Lichtenstern, all
sexual libido has disappeared. However, other authors (Busquet,
Oberholzer) report that after post-puberal castration, erection and the
sex act are still possible.

Sixtus V, in his Bull *Cum frequenter* of June 22nd, 1587, informs us
on, doubtless, accurate reports, that in Spain many eunuchs of his
time, deprived of both testicles, "*qui utroque teste carent*," claimed that
they could still lead a conjugal life which, though sterile, was not
impotent,[1] "*quia impura carnis tentigine atque immundis complexibus cum
mulieribus se commiscent, et humorem forsan quendam similem semini, licet
ad generationem et ad matrimonii causam minime aptam.*" (Bull. Roman.,
Naples, 1883, VIII, 870.) Moreover, the predilection of Roman
matrons for the eunuch, "*in longam securamque libidinem exsectus*," is
inexplicable if castration resulted in complete impotence. More than
one surgeon has testified that after the removal of two tubercular
testicles, many of those operated on have been able to use the sex act
normally, at least for some time.

In this matter, concludes Lipschutz, "it seems that great individual
variations are met with."

From the psychological point of view, the same troubles listed
above may be doubled because of an inferiority complex. The eunuch
often becomes a violent "avenger," seeking to revenge himself on
society or on the surgeon who has performed the operation.

(Cf. especially A. Lipschutz. *The internal secretions of the sex glands*,
1924, pp. 5–75, and E. Pittard, *Le Castration chez l'homme*, Paris, 1934.
This latter is the result of minute observations carried out on 100
skoptzy, of whom 50 had been castrated before puberty, the rest after.)

The Woman

(*a*) *Before puberty:* Castration before puberty is rare in women. It
is practised among certain tribes of central Australia, in order to prevent
certain girls from becoming mothers. It seems to have been unknown
to Greco-Roman antiquity. The mutilation of the skoptzy women
leaves their generative organs intact. For these reasons, there is a

[1] The word "impotent" is here used in a purely medical sense.—Ed.

scarcity of data for the effects of pre-puberal castration on the woman. "The inversion of sexual characteristics appears, however, real in the case of the girl castrated when young. She acquires some characteristics properly male (narrow pelvis, a deep voice, masculine pilosity); but in this matter, the results of observation are not conclusive." (Dr. Hesnard, *Traité de Sexologie*, Paris 1933, p. 139.)[1]

(*b*) *After puberty:* The troubles and changes which the removal of the ovaries occasion in the women, are generally the same as those which menopause spontaneously brings about.

Post-puberal castration occasions the atrophy of the uterus, the vagina, the mammary glands, sometimes compensating by an accumulation of flesh in the region of the breasts. When castration is bilateral, menstruation is suppressed. An abundant down, like that seen on the faces of old women, is found. The diminution of basal metabolism has been discussed, but there is general agreement that superactivity of the endocrine, the suprarenal, the thyroid and the hypophyse glands results from castration.

Sometimes there is a diminution, or even a disappearance, of sexual desire and sexual sensation. In the majority of cases, the state of things remains unchanged: psychological conditions regulate sexual instinct more than the genital glands do, at least when these glands have made the nervous system erotic and have disrupted body habits. Functional habits have too much importance for it to be otherwise.

Often, however, when for several consecutive years after the operation, the "level" of sexuality has remained normal, it finishes earlier than in normal women.

It must also be noted that, in certain cases, there is an increase of desire and pleasure, which, most often, is an effect of the woman's no longer feeling the dyspareunia, related to salpingitis and other uterine and periuterine inflammations for which the operation has been performed.

Psychic condition: A fairly large number of women feel more or less diminished and depressed after castration.

Some are, on the contrary, excited, most often in association with a thyroidal reaction.

---

[1] A. Raciborski: *Traité de la menstruation*, Paris, ed. Baillière, 1868, p. 51. "In the report of Dr. Roberts, who was charged with a mission in central Asia, we find that there are relics in that land of the barbarities of the ancient peoples of Arabia and Egypt. The custom continues of removing the ovaries of a certain number of women in order that these women may serve as eunuchs. Dr. Roberts, who had occasion to meet several of them in the vicinity of Bombay, where they are known as hedjeras, said that they had no breasts, their pelves were narrow like those of men, the buttocks flat and the pubis denuded. The cellular tissue of the external, atrophied organs made these organs appear to be obliterated. At the same time, these eunuchs showed no uniformity, and had something of virility in voice and bearing." (Journal: *L'Expérience*, Fevrier 9, 1843.)

In the more serious cases, there are physical troubles of the depression type or the exaltation type.

There is no characteristic psychosis of castration, according to M. Combemale and his collaborators. That which dominates most often is melancholia, a depressive state sometimes caused by ideas of indignity, ruin, persecution; often, too, the subject manifests immoderate hypochondriacal preoccupations developing into delirium. But she also manifests, according to our observations, delusions of persecution, or else chronic hallucinatory delirium and even the manic-depressive psychosis. That which strikes us most, in thus considering the diversely morbid forms, is that all of them have their origin in mental degeneration.

The troubles which have been mentioned are the same as those we have enumerated in the normal menopause; psychasthenia, some reduction of affectivity, together with irritability, amnesia, mental confusion, melancholia.

Taken together, these are rather the troubles of the depressive type, as though castration has brought about a lessening of vitality.

In a recent work, Combemale and Demacon returned to this subject in connection with the examination of eighteen cases of ovariotomy. All the women, except one, showed more or less profound modifications of disposition, memory, emotion, will and the faculty of attention.

It seems very clear, therefore, that castration is an operation which is, from time to time, followed by serious psychological troubles, either as a result of the suppression of ovarian secretion, or as a result of the more or less conscious idea that one has been deprived of an important organ—the organ of sexuality.

The frequency and intensity of these troubles has been variously estimated by different observers.

Chroback (*Centralbl. f. Gynak*, 1896, No. 20, p. 521) writes: "The many troubles complained of by the majority of women from whom the ovaries have been removed, have at all times destroyed the satisfaction I experienced in having successfully operated on them." Picqué speaks of "very real troubles"; Tuffieret-Mauté of "profound troubles from which very few of the patients escape"; Champonnière of "serious complications . . . more intense and more persistent that in the normal menopause . . . some immediate, some delayed . . ."; Reverdin speaks of these troubles as constant; Bucura regards the symptoms as extremely painful.

On the contrary, some other writers make light of these complications.

These different complications are generally passing, not permanent;

an adaptation occurs in a year or two. The very keen reactions cease, and the women who had been castrated sometimes show, at length, a certain amount of vitality. However, life continues and old age comes to leave its mark on them. (H. Vignes, *Physiologie gynacologique*, Paris, 1929, pp. 315–316 and 370–392, 498. This excellent work summarizes the most recent work on the effect of castration among women.)

Impotence and sterility: Of all the psycho-physical inconveniences which the total removal of the genital glands can occasion in the man and in the woman, the most certain and most serious is undoubtedly the radical deprivation of the power of reproduction and of leading a normal married life.

When castration is complete or bilateral, that is to say when it involves the complete removal of the two ovaries or the two testicles, the woman and the man thus mutilated are definitely and irreparably made sterile. Even if they could still make a pretence and have the illusion of sexual potency, they are no longer able to beget or to conceive.

Moreover, at least in the man, the radical and decided sterility can be accompanied by a more or less complete inability to accomplish normally the sex act—*impotentia coeundi*—and this is habitually so in the case of prepuberal castration, and sometimes in cases of postpuberal castration also.

In the measure in which castration of the man or the woman entails not only sterility, but also complete and decided impotence, it excludes the possibility of a valid marriage in the eyes of the Catholic Church. Antecedent and perpetual impotence, at least that which the Canonists call *impotentia coeundi*, constitutes, in effect, a diriment impediment of the natural law which admits of no dispensation as long as it remains irreparable.[1] *Impotentia antecedens et perpetua, sive ex parte viri, sive ex parte mulieris, sive, alteri cognita sive non, sive absoluta sive relativa, matrimonium ipso naturae iure dirimit* (Canon 1068.)

---

[1] It is to be noted that many, though not all, Canonists require a certain quality of content or of origin of the male secretion before they admit the existence of a normal coitus. Without necessarily accepting their conclusions one must admit the weight of their authority when considering other and perhaps more satisfying opinions.—Ed.

THE MORALITY OF CASTRATION

BECAUSE of its physical, psychological and social consequences, the castration of the man or of the woman seems a serious mutilation of the human being.

When it is not due to a vital necessity, such mutilation is undoubtedly an offence against Him Who creates mankind in His own image and likeness, and "makes them male and female."

On the last page of his splendid treatise on anatomy in which he describes the human body to its smallest details, Leonardo da Vinci concludes with the cry: "What a crime and what an offence against the Creator it is, to do violence to such an admirable piece of work!" This sentiment of the artist coincides with the reason of the theologians, who consider mutilation as partial suicide, and deny that any man has the right to suppress any part of his body, any more than he has a right to suppress the whole.

Man is not his own master. As a creature, he cannot, without offending his Creator, lay aside at will his life, or those organs which are the integral elements of that life. Like suicide, self mutilation is a crime against the Creator; it is, moreover, an act against nature, an act of treason against that reasonable love of self which everyone ought to possess. It is also a crime against society which we ought to serve with all the faculties given to us.

These principles having been laid down, theologians are unanimous that, in virtue of the duty which he has of respecting, conserving and cultivating himself, a man should not hesitate to sacrifice some part of himself, if such a sacrifice is found to be an indispensable condition of bodily health. Hence St. Thomas on this matter: "Any member whatever, being a part of the totality of the human body, exists only for the benefit of the whole, as that which is imperfect is subordinated to that which is perfect; hence the reason why one ought to suppress a member of the human body, if such suppression is necessary to the health of the whole. In itself, every member serves the good of the whole body; but, per accidens, it may become hurtful to that whole, as when a corrupt member threatens to corrupt the entire body. Consequently, when a member is healthy and continues to function according to its nature, it cannot be suppressed without detriment to the whole body." (Ia, Iae, q. 65, a. 1.)

From this it is evident that, if necessary, a man can amputate the gangrened member which compromises the health of his whole body, since he is responsible for his own health, equilibrium and conservation.

"Therefore," concludes Lessius, "if cancer is eating away a member or it has received a deadly snake-bite, it may be lawfully amputated." (*De Justitia*, sect. II, ch. IX, dub. 14.) The good of the whole takes precedence over the good of the part. It is necessary, however, that this amputation should be a really efficacious means, and the *only* means, of saving the life and the health of the whole body.

Consequently, the only legitimate castration, in the opinion of theologians, is that which can claim to be the only efficacious means of preserving the individual from a worse evil than that of the castration itself.

The evil one wishes to prevent, therefore, must be more serious and not less certain and determined than the castration itself, which is, as we have said, a very serious mutilation with a train of psycho-physical consequences. There must also be a direct and necessary connection between the castration and the arrest of the evil one wishes to prevent; that is to say, it must be the only really efficacious means of preserving the individual from a worse evil than that entailed by castration itself.

If the evil to be avoided is in reality less serious, less certain, less decided than the castration, it is certainly not legitimate. Similarly, if there are other, equally efficacious means, less damaging to the individual and more respectful to his integrity, than such a mutilation, they must always be preferred.

It is immediately clear why castration could not be permitted under the pretext of avoiding incontinence. The sin of impurity is undoubtedly a great evil, but a mutilation of the body is neither the only nor the most efficacious way to preserve the soul from an evil which is entirely in the will. The Fathers of the Church have repeated, with Origen and St. Chrysostom, that the eunuch is not less tempted in his flesh or less subject to impurity because of his castration, while carnal emotion cannot stain a soul that stands firm in its will to purity: *"Non inquinatur corpus nisi de consensu mentis."*

Neither can it be maintained that the preservation of a soprano voice can be a legitimate reason for a mutilation of the individual as serious as that of castration. It is mere sophistry to maintain—as some have done—that, by euphonic castration, the eunuch is assured of a situation and preserved from misery. The common sense of a Lugo or a Laymann answered justly that there were many other means by which a man may avoid misery, and that, moreover, the advantage of an artificially preserved voice did not equal the pain of castration.

There is neither a just proportion nor a real relation of cause and effect between the misery one aims to avoid or the good one aims to achieve and the serious mutilation proposed, the effect being as remote and problematical as the mutilation is certain, immediate and irreparable.

On the other hand, castration is always legitimate if a conscientious doctor decides that it is indispensable for the health of the patient.

Since the Council of Nicea in 325, the Church has always distinguished and authorized castration performed by a doctor for the purpose of saving or curing a patient. She has always allowed a man, castrated under these circumstances, to be ordained a priest, and, if he is deemed worthy, to be promoted to the episcopacy: *"in Episcopum promoveri."* (C. 35, *De Corpore vitiatis.* See above: *The Church and Castration.*) Similarly, she has condemned all castration of healthy and normal men for purposes of asceticism and gain. The reasons of the theologians are backed by the authority of the Church which is infallible, not only in her definition of dogmas, but also in her moral discipline—in this sense, that she cannot by her laws either approve what is evil or condemn what is good.

Since the individual is forbidden to mutilate himself, or to consent to mutilation, without a vital necessity, it may be asked whether the state has not the power to inflict mutilation on the individual, seeing that it has the power to put him to death in the common interest or to decapitate him for reasons of public order.

If the individual may sacrifice one of his members for the safety of the whole body, may not society also demand that one of its members should sacrifice or mutilate himself for the common good? St. Thomas (IIa, IIae, q. 65, a. 1) answers that "every man being subordinated to the community as to an end, it may happen that the amputation of one member, when done to the detriment of bodily integrity, may be ordained to the common good inasmuch as it is inflicted on someone as a punishment for the repression of sin." In effect, it is only to the extent to which a man, through a moral fault, becomes noxious to society, that society can inflict repressive punishment on him, including capital punishment. But it is permitted to no man to kill or mutilate the innocent even under pretext of the common good. *"Nullo modo licet occidere innocentem"* (22, 2.64, a. 7, and 11a and 11ae, q. 108, a. 4).

The encyclical *Casti Connubi* has solemnly reaffirmed this doctrine: "Magistrates have no direct rights over the members of their subjects: they can never, either for eugenic reasons or for any other reasons, wound and injure the integrity of the body, when no fault has been committed and when there is no pretext for inflicting bloody punishment. St. Thomas Aquinas teaches the same when, having posed the question whether human judges can inflict evil on a man to prevent future evils, he concedes it for certain other evils, but rightly and with reason denies it for what concerns the cutting of the body: 'No one, according to human judgment, ought to be punished without having committed a fault; he can neither be killed nor mutilated nor beaten.' "

Moreover, individuals themselves have only that power over the members of their body which is in accord with the natural ends of those powers; they can neither destroy nor mutilate them, nor render them by any other means incapable of their natural functions, except when the good of the whole body cannot otherwise be attained. Such is the sure teaching of Christian doctrine; such also is the conclusion reached by human reasoning.

From this exposition of doctrine, it follows that castration can be legitimate in two cases only—

1. When it is impossible to secure otherwise the good of the whole body (therapeutic castration).

2. When the civil authority believes it to be indispensable, for the common good, to inflict it on criminals to ensure the non-recurrence of gravely criminal actions (penal castration).

Every other pretext is rejected by the common doctrine of the theologians and by the ordinary teaching and discipline of the Church. Neither euphonic castration nor eugenic castration is admitted.

We may add that the legitimacy of penal castration can, and has been, defended in theory. However, it would seem an appalling anachronism to us to-day, since all mutilation has disappeared from the penal code of every civilized state.

It remains for us to inquire whether the civil authority may castrate certain people who relapse into sexual abnormalities, both as an efficacious remedy for their perversion and as a measure of social defence.

The answer depends on our knowing—

1. If this remedy by mutilation is *the only efficacious one* for freeing the individual from an evil not less grave than the mutilation in question.

2. If the defence of society against sexual perverts cannot be as efficaciously assured by other means more respectful to human integrity, and which allow for the possibility of the pervert's return to normal living.

In the present condition of medical science, the castration of the sexually abnormal does not seem to be notably efficacious, and there are other remedies which succeed in curing these perverts or at least rendering them harmless. Hence it does not seem possible to hold as generally legitimate the therapeutic castration of the sexually abnormal.

A fortiori, the castration, as a therapeutic penalty, of people who are more or less irresponsible, cannot be admitted as legitimate (P. Gemelli, J. Lhermitte).

In fine, in answer to the problem of therapeutic castration in general and the therapeutic castration of sexual perverts in particular, the theologian and the moralist can but lay down a principle, which, however, is very clear: castration can be legitimately proposed or demanded only when it is the sole really efficacious means of delivering the individual himself from a physical affliction more serious than the mutilation of the sexual organs.

It is for the doctors to judge in each particular case—

1. If castration is the sole certainly efficacious remedy.

2. If this mutilation, with all that it entails, is a means proportionate to the result sought. A surely efficacious means of ending the raging pain of toothache is to cut off the patient's head, but it is a means clearly disproportionate to the end sought. A mutilation so serious as castration can also be a means disproportionate to the effect intended.

CONCLUSIONS

FROM the diverse studies, historical, theological, physiological, etc., which we have here pursued, it seems that at least the following conclusions may be drawn—

1. From the beginning and throughout history, castration appears as a humiliating mutilation which implies, with him who inflicts it, a humanity divided into two groups: that of the strong, the victorious, the masters; and that of the slaves, the weak, the vanquished. The first have all the rights, even the right to treat the others like animals. Without having the same physiological effects as castration, sterilization imposed by civil authority manifests the same conception of humanity. It is irreconcilible with the Christian doctrine which respects in every man the dignity of the person and the integrity of the individual.

2. Christianity condemns all voluntary mutilation which is not demanded by the vital interests of the individual himself; but it recognizes the perfect legitimacy of pure therapeutic castration. Moreover, looking on the unwilling eunuch as a victim, rather than as an inferior being, it does not hesitate to admit him to the priesthood and even to the episcopacy, if he is found otherwise worthy.

In the case of castration imposed by the will of the State, the dignity and integrity of man is sacrificed to the race or the collectivity; in the case of medical castration, it is the vital interests of the person himself which justify and demand the partial mutilation of his integrity. The first subordinates every man to the herd; the second respects above all else the human person.

3. Since castration, even therapeutic, occasions, in the man or the woman, serious troubles which have repercussions on behaviour and psycho-physical equilibrium, it is with the greatest prudence that a surgeon ought to decide on such an operation.

4. In the present condition of manners and legislation, penal castration seems a barbarous anachronism to us; nor does it seem that the castration of certain perverts is any the less unacceptable. In the latter case, it is not the only surely efficacious remedy; nor is it a justifiable penalty, since such perverts are not responsible; nor a legitimate action of social defence, since internment is a sufficient public security which does not destroy the possibility of a cure.

Note: Whilst accepting that a proportion of the sexually abnormal may be lacking in full responsibility for their acts, in a degree analogous to that of those whose passions, though normally directed, are or have become excessive in their demands, it remains our opinion that the majority of those with perverted sexual tendencies are under the same moral obligation to control them as any normal person whose circumstances of life impose celibacy, nor does there seem to be any evidence that they are less capable of doing so with the aid of Divine Grace.—EDITOR.

SECOND STUDY

THE CHURCH AND THE DISSOLUTION OF THE MARRIAGE BOND

By Rev. E. Tesson, S.J.

EDITOR'S FOREWORD

THIS little book is not intended to be a textbook for canonists or even for the parochial clergy, though it may sometimes be useful for these to get a sort of bird's-eye view of a subject that bristles with legal complexities. It is intended for the ordinary Catholic or non-Catholic who seeks a general knowledge of the subject or who is anxious to answer, with some degree of authority, attacks made against the Church in regard to her discipline in this matter. It may be worth while repeating, for the benefit of non-Catholic readers, the Church's teaching on Christian marriage. Marriage has always been a sacred and, in the true sense, a religious contract made in fulfilment of the original Divine Ordinance, "increase and multiply and fill the earth." Christ raised the natural marriage contract to the dignity of a Sacrament. This means that when two baptized persons enter into this mutual contract validly, they receive, at the same time, the *Sacrament* of Matrimony. This Sacrament by the power of Christ gives them a special grace, related to the needs of their new state of life and a right to the daily actual helps or graces necessary for the performance of their duties to one another and to their children; and this inpouring of grace into their souls takes place infallibly, unless they prevent its reception positively; this they do if they are in a state of mortal sin, which means that they have sinned knowingly and gravely against the law of God and have not repented adequately. From this it will be seen that the Sacrament of Matrimony does not begin and end on the wedding day on which they make the contract but continues as long as the marriage itself, which is a lifetime contract, and gives to each partner the graces necessary to secure the continued harmony of their mutual love and support and to enable them to bring up the children entrusted to them by God, as His loyal and faithful servants. In time these will become the parents of a future generation and it is well to remember that in founding a family one carries on the divine plan for peopling the world and that perhaps, several centuries after one's death, there will be people, one's own descendants in the world, and that in many respects they will be naturally better or worse Christians according to the goodness, or otherwise, of the example and training one gave to one's immediate sons and daughters. Sacramental marriage therefore, is something altogether higher and nobler than the purely natural bond. It does not exist where only one of the partners is baptized, but if the non-Catholic partner becomes a Christian through

37

valid baptism, their marriage becomes sacramental. Catholics who
have married baptized non-Catholics with ecclesiastical permission
have, of course, received the Sacrament of Matrimony but they
cannot have a Nuptial Mass nor receive the Nuptial Blessing, unless
and until the non-Catholic partner becomes a Catholic. If the non-
Catholic partner has not been validly baptized the parties do not
receive the Sacrament, though the marriage is valid if it has been
contracted with a dispensation for "disparity of worship (cult)".
"Mixed marriages" are permitted by the Church only by dispensation
and this deviation from her disciplinary law is permitted only for
adequate reasons. The Church does not favour such marriages
because, among other reasons, they so often lead to disharmony, as is
to be expected when the parties differ on a matter of so much importance as their religious belief and practice and because, through them,
it can so easily happen that the future generations may be lost to
Christ. There are selfish people whose only idea in entering the
married state is the indulgence of their passions rather than the formation of a Christian home, but true marriage exists where the parties
co-operate with God's plan for carrying on the human race, forming
a home in which the future citizens of His Kingdom will grow up in
an atmosphere of Christian love and example. To be born into a good
Christian home is an enormous blessing and, even in the purely
natural sphere, those are happiest who achieve this in their marrying;
whilst the one secure assurance of a happy, as distinct from an empty
and lonely, old age is to be found in a flock of grandchildren. They
do not fear to die who can go to Our Lord, saying that they have left
descendants on the earth whom they have brought up in the love and
grace of His service.

INTRODUCTION

Two contradictory criticisms are often levelled at the Church with regard to the dissolution of marriage, as about so many other matters. Some of the would-be critics point to the intransigence of the Church's doctrine, saying that she is incapable of understanding the drama of everyday life and therefore equally incapable of adapting her legislation to those concrete situations in which men find themselves through no fault of their own. The other school of criticism is as emphatically convinced that this rigidity of principle is mere sham which serves as a cloak for sordid venality; obstacles melt into thin air, and authentically sealed concessions are easily obtained, if one only knows how to pull the right purple strings and pay the right price.

We shall not concern ourselves with these prejudiced criticisms. It would be sheer waste of time, and utterly fruitless, to do so; for is it not indeed a fact, once and for all established, that in these matters the Churchmen stand in solid phalanx to hide the truth!

But there are men of good will who are disconcerted by the complexity of the theological and canonical system which meets them when they come to grips with this difficult problem, either in their own persons or when they are caring for others. It is for such as these that this explanatory essay is intended.

Some preliminary remarks are necessary.

The first rule which regulates the conduct of the Church in this matter is that she has no omnipotent right to decide. When God has established a law, no earthly authority, however high, can dispense from that law.

God has manifested His Will in three principal stages: by the Creation; by the Judaic Revelation; by the teaching of Christ and of the Apostles.

The Natural Law is constituted by the profound demands of the individual and social cohesion which is the very foundation of our being. The ensemble of these demands indicates the line we must follow in our conduct and in our relations with others, if we are to live worthy of the name of human beings. We recognize, however, that there exists among these tendencies a hierarchy which must be respected.

But God did not leave man, maimed by sin, to his own resources and to his own lights alone. He gave man a supplementary help, first extended to him through Moses and the prophets, and brought to its perfection through Christ. It was thus that man learned what he really is; what God has planned for him; what graces he can receive to purify him and raise him to friendship with God; but also what obligations he must accept in order to respond to that plan and to those graces.

The guardianship of the teachings of Christ has been entrusted to the Church. It is she who, with Divine assistance, must ensure the propagation, the integrity, and the ever increased understanding of those teachings, from century to century.

In the last analysis, the difficulties experienced by many Catholics to-day arise from their lack of faith in this primordial role of the Church. They are not convinced that, whatever defects may be laid to her charge, the Church is the voice of God Himself speaking to them on every occasion when she demands that the Natural Law and the Evangelical Law must be respected; nor are they convinced that, despite the weaknesses and miseries of the present life, man's vocation is to submit himself to this Divine Will.

Moreover, it must be equally borne in mind that the ecclesiastical authorities are also charged with organizing Christian society, and that they are therefore empowered to issue laws and regulations which are binding on all the faithful. Of course, these laws and regulations have not the absolute character of those which come from God, and he who made them can modify or even abrogate them; but it would be a mistake to minimize their importance. They are restrictive, and no one will deny that they are sometimes burdensome, but they are necessary. No human society can exist without laws which inevitably put a brake on the activities of the individual here and now, but which do so for the common good.

There is another aspect of these laws and regulations which must not go unheeded. The activity of the Church, taken all in all and despite its inevitable deficiencies, is organized to serve as intermediary between God and man; it follows, therefore, that ecclesiastical laws are made to conduct us more or less directly to our supernatural end. We must consider this Divine Good towards which these laws show the way, if we are to learn how to look on them in an objective manner and patiently bear the yoke they put upon us.

We should also note how pliant and considerate ecclesiastical legislation is, by comparison with modern civil codes. Excuses and dispensations are provided for and admitted, every time that such a procedure is not contrary to the Law of God or injurious to the common good.

Finally, these multiple powers possessed on various titles by the Church and which she exercises to teach and to govern, are also used by her for the administration of the Sacraments—those Divine actions hidden under human gestures—and especially of that most complex of all the Sacraments, the Sacrament of Matrimony. Here too, therefore, all that came from Christ must remain unchanged throughout the centuries; that is to say, the constitutive elements and the essential conditions for reception. In this matter, the Church is no more than a vigilant guardian of what is immutable; to which is added, as we pointed out above, what arises from the fundamental demands of our nature as created by God.

But when these essential conditions have been respected, the rest is submitted to the consideration and decision of the Church. Hence we find the modifications and changes which have been made in the course of centuries, because the Church, in her anxiety to place at the disposal of the greatest number possible those sources of grace which are the Sacraments, takes account of circumstances and knows how to adapt herself to the evolution of the various human groups. An example of this kindly understanding has just been furnished by the new discipline of the Eucharistic fast. We are not surprised, therefore, to see that changes are introduced with regard to the import and the number of matrimonial impediments, or with regard to the juridical requirements for the validity of the marriage contract.

* * *

It is in perspective with all this that the question must be asked: *Does the Church allow the dissolution of the marriage bond?*

We know the answer. When the marriage has been celebrated but not consummated by carnal union, it is still possible to obtain a dissolution which renders both parties completely free from the marriage bond. On the other hand, if this consummation has occurred, the bond is indissoluble as long as both the partners are alive. In this matter, even the authority of the Pope is powerless. With the sole exception of cases where physical consummation has not occurred, *there has never been a dissolution of valid sacramental marriage.*

How, therefore, are we to explain the existence of ecclesiastical courts where matrimonial cases are heard, and where verdicts are sometimes given which set people free to contract a new union who, up to that time, have been regarded as bound to each other by marriage, having already lived for many years a life of complete union? In verdicts of this kind, there is no question of the annulment of an existing marriage, but merely a *declaration of nullity*—that is to say, a declaration that people who up to then have been regarded as married to one another are not married at all. In their case, there has only been the appearance of marriage, not its reality; and the Court, as a result of investigation and discussion, simply states that fact.

But how can such a case occur? To understand this, we must remember that the act by which two people bind themselves to each other in Matrimony must fulfil several conditions if it is to be valid, as the legal term puts it—that is to say, if it is to exist in reality and not simply in appearance. If one of these essential conditions is missing, there is no marriage. To show, therefore, how a matrimonial union can be legally null and void, we must examine what are these fundamental conditions which determine the validity of marriage.

We can list them under three headings: capacity to make the contract, or absence of diriment impediment; regularity of juridical formalities; and consent which does not contain an essential defect.

ABSENCE OF DIRIMENT IMPEDIMENT

THE right to marriage is a fundamental right of the human personality. Pius XI, in *Casti Connubi*, and more recently Pius XII, have found it necessary to defend this right against certain legislative measures adopted by some countries. But, like all other rights, it is confined to certain limits. Impediments arising from the very nature of things, contracts already entered upon and other circumstances, can oppose completely or under some particular aspect the free exercise of this right. Consequently, such-and-such a person will find that marriage is completely forbidden to him, or that he must accept a limiting of his right by the exclusion of a certain category of persons.

These impediments have two very distinct sources. Some derive from the very nature of things as created by God; thus we readily accept that a natural opposition exists to the marriage of a mother with her son, or of a father with his daughter. Others derive from the authority of the Church, at least in their final formulation. For example, it is *per se* dangerous for a Christian to marry a non-baptized person, and therefore it is a duty dictated by prudence for the Christian not to expose himself or herself to this peril. It is the Church which has given the force of a diriment impediment to this situation.

As to the import of the prohibition thus constituted, the impediments are divided into two categories: *diriment impediments* and *merely prohibitive impediments*. The force of a diriment impediment is that if either partner was bound by such an impediment and contracted marriage without having obtained a dispensation, when such dispensation is possible, then such a marriage is null and void, and has never existed. Impediments which are merely prohibitive do not invalidate marriage, even if it was celebrated without the necessary dispensation having been obtained. In the remainder of our treatment, we shall deal only with the diriment impediments.

We have just spoken of dispensations, and it is necessary to be clear about what precisely they are. As we have already seen, the Church admits in her juridical system the possibility of particular exceptions to the general laws. Besides being based on some recognized motive for nullity, every case must be submitted to the judgment of the Church. There are, however, limits to her power, especially in what concerns matrimonial impediments where the prohibition derives from the very nature of things or from the Will of Christ, and where, as a result, even the Pope himself is powerless to dispense. Thus, marriage will never be permitted between parents and their children, nor will a second union be permitted in a case where the first marriage between Christians was valid and has been physically consummated, and the two partners are still living.

The Church has the power to dispense from other impediments which she herself has decided upon; but she sometimes refuses to exercise this power, or she lays down very strict conditions regulating its use.

According to present legislation which dates from May, 1917, there are twelve diriment impediments. They are invoked with very different shades of emphasis in cases relating to the nullity of marriage. For some of them, we shall content ourselves with a mere mention and waive further explanation.

Age. Marriage is forbidden before the completion of the fourteenth year in the case of girls, and the completion of the sixteenth year in the case of boys. In France, the *Code civil* lays down the age of fifteen for girls, and of eighteen for boys.[1]

Abduction (Raptus). This impediment nullifies marriage between the abductor and the woman held against her will, as long as she is not restored to complete liberty.

The impediment of crime or outrage against an already existing marriage. It takes several forms by reason of the diversity of the crimes envisaged. The most usual is the prohibition of marriage between accomplices in adultery who have exchanged a promise to marry after the death of the present spouse; and similarly in the case of accomplices in adultery who have agreed that they intend to marry, even if only by civil marriage or clandestinely. This form of impediment arises every time that Christians who have been civilly divorced and re-married, wish to regularize their situation after the death of the legitimate spouse.

Spiritual Relationship. This is the impediment which arises through Baptism, and which forbids marriage between the baptized person, on the one hand, and the person who has baptized him or her, the godfather or the godmother, on the other.

Impotence to consummate physical union, when such impotence exists at the time of marriage and is incurable or can be cured only by a difficult and dangerous operation. From the juridical point of view, impotence is to be clearly distinguished from sterility. The latter does not *per se* invalidate marriage, since it usually coexists with the normal capacity to achieve physical union.

---

[1] In England the age for both sexes is sixteen years since 10th May, 1929—before which date the age was the same as that now required by the Church.—Ed.

Sacred Orders. Bishops, priests, deacons and sub-deacons cannot contract a valid marriage—a prohibition which arises from their having received Major Orders. But in the Oriental Churches, married men are permitted to receive the sub-diaconate, the diaconate and the priesthood (but they cannot become Bishops), and to continue their conjugal life while exercising their ministry. Recently, Pope Pius XII has allowed several Protestant pastors, converts to Catholicism, to receive Sacred Orders without separating from their wives.

Marriage-bond. A person who is already married cannot contract a second marriage. The exception to this is the case of a converted pagan who has the right to use the Privilege of the Faith.[1]

The Vow of Chastity, pronounced by Religious, always constitutes an impediment to marriage; but this impediment is either diriment or merely prohibitive, according to the conditions laid down by the Church. Solemn Vows render marriage completely null and void. The solemnity in question here, it must be noted, has nothing to do with the ceremony at which the vows are taken, but refers to the value placed on such vows by the Church.

Consanguinity. The Church regards as null and void, not only marriage between kindred of the first degree, but also between relations descended in collateral lines from a common ancestor down to the third degree inclusive—that is to say, down to the children of first cousins. It does not matter whether the relationship is legitimate or illegitimate.

Dispensation is never given for marriage between persons related within the first degree, not even to a brother and sister who have only one parent in common.

Two other impediments must be added to those of consanguinity. The first results from the *affinity* or relationship by alliance which each partner contracts with the blood relations of his or her spouse. This nullifies marriage to the second degree inclusive in the collateral line. Thus, a widower cannot marry, without obtaining a dispensation, the sister, aunt, niece or first cousin of his deceased wife. Dispensation for the direct line, for example the mother or daughter (by a former marriage) of the deceased, is scarcely ever given; it is easily obtained for the collateral line. The second impediment is that of *public decorum*. This is the impediment which results from a situation analogous to affinity but created by a pseudo-marriage, either in the form of an invalid marriage or of public concubinage. But the impediment is

---

[1] St. Paul, in the First Epistle to the Corinthians, allows Christians married to pagans to separate if the pagan is not prepared to continue conjugal life in peace. This is the Pauline Privilege. The "Privilege of the Faith" is something of broader application, and applies to analogous cases. (See farther on.)

less extensive than the preceding ones, since it invalidates marriage only between the man and the blood relations (first and second degree) in the direct line of the woman who has been his accomplice, that is to say, mother and daughter. This applies equally, of course, to a marriage between the woman and the father or son of the accomplice. Notice in this connection, that the question can arise even while the pseudo-spouse is still alive.

These three impediments of consanguinity, affinity and public decorum, are designed to safeguard the natural modesty that should exist between persons constituting one and the same family, and to prevent disorders which could arise if such persons were in a position to envisage a future marriage. They also encourage the widening of family circles, and have therefore great social importance.

Disparity of Cult. Two impediments exist whose purpose is to protect the Faith. One is diriment, the other prohibitive, and it is with the first that we are concerned here. It prohibits the marriage of a Christian to a non-baptized person, if at any time in his life that Christian has been a member of the Catholic Church, even if he or she has since abandoned this membership.

The Church grants a dispensation, in this case, only on the strictest conditions. Both parties must enter into an agreement to have *all the children born of their union* baptized and brought up in the Catholic Church; and the non-Christian party must promise to allow the Christian partner full liberty to practise his or her religion.

Some people say that the Church, in laying down these conditions, exceeds her rights, since she imposes on the non-Christian decisions which may be contrary to his convictions. To reason like this is to misunderstand the bond which exists between the Church and her members. She has the right and the duty to protect the faith of her children. If one of them seeks *an exceptional favour*, she is quite within the rights of her authority when she lays down conditions which she considers useful. The non-Christian party is affected only in consequence of the fact that he or she wishes to marry a Catholic.

REGULARITY OF JURIDICAL FORMS

THE bride and the bridegroom are themselves the ministers of the Sacrament of Matrimony. It is their mutual consent which, by creating the bond between them, is the sign and the cause of matrimonial grace.

This doctrine is now well known among Catholics, but it could be used as the basis of an objection against the necessity for external formalities. Since the consent of the parties is sufficient to create the marriage, why is it indispensable that this consent should be given in conformity with certain regulations, and why should the absence of such publicity nullify the marriage?

The objection is easily answered by pointing out that the contract made by the two parties must necessarily have social repercussions. They are bound to one another, and it is important that this should be generally known in the interests of good order, as well as in the interests of the children that may be born of their union. And how can it be known unless there were witnesses to the promises exchanged? Moreover, a secret contract can always be denied by one of the parties. The stability of marriages and the good of the parties demand, therefore, that there should be witnesses and documents.

From the very beginning, the Church demanded this publicity; but for centuries the rules regulating it were not as precise as they are to-day. It was not till the Fourth Council of Lateran (1215) that preliminary proclamations or bans were instituted; and it was not until the Council of Trent in the sixteenth century that marriages without publicity, or as they were called, clandestine marriages, were regarded as null and void. It was the number of inconveniences arising from this state of affairs and the demands made by princes in the name of public order, which led the Council to modify the previous discipline and to lay down that henceforth marriages celebrated without observing the regulations of publicity which it established, would be invalid. Every marriage would have to take place in the presence of the proper Parish Priest or Bishop of the engaged couple or in the presence of a priest delegated by them, and in the presence of two other witnesses.

The Council did not specify who was the proper Parish Priest, but the regulation was unanimously interpreted as meaning the Parish Priest of the parish where the couple had domicile or quasi-domicile.

For reasons which would detain us too long here, this did not, however, put an end to clandestine marriages; and, moreover, the regulation that the marriage should take place before the proper Parish Priest or his delegate, raised difficulties which were often insurmountable.

One of the most famous cases of this kind is that of the marriage of Napoleon and Josephine de Beauharnais.

Napoleon Bonaparte, who had just been appointed commander of the army in Italy, and Josephine Tascher de la Pagerie, widow of General de Beauharnais, contracted a civil marriage on the 9th of March, 1796, at the town-hall of the second *arrondissement*. A few days later, Bonaparte left to join his troops. The rest is common knowledge. The civil ceremony had not been followed by any religious marriage, and it might well have been thought that this was the result of circumstances. Ministers of religion everywhere in France, and especially in Paris, scarcely appeared in public, even though some fifteen Catholic churches had been opened in the capital by the end of 1795. But later on, in Italy, when his wife came to join him, the conqueror of Arcole and of Rivoli seems never to have had the intention of seeking a priest in order to contract a sacramental marriage. This abstention is significant because, at the same period, he was adamant that his sisters Elisa and Pauline should be married in proper religious form to Bacciochi and to Leclerc at Mombella in 1797.

On the other hand, Josephine, threatened with divorce because of her sterility and attacked by the Bonaparte family, ardently desired the religious ceremony in order to consolidate her position. She regarded Napoleon's coronation as Emperor of the French (December, 1804) as an excellent opportunity for forcing his hand, and it is said that she herself explained the situation to Pope Pius VII.[1] The latter who, in connection with his coming to France and with the coronation, had to make numerous concessions to Napoleon, could not be otherwise than uncompromising in this matter. He refused to preside at a religious ceremony where Josephine, who was not the legitimate spouse of the Emperor, would be treated as such and also receive the imperial crown. Napoleon was forced to yield, but he wished the marriage ceremony to be reduced to the minimum. He demanded that there should be no witnesses, and that the only person present should be his uncle, Cardinal Fesch, *grand aumônier*, to receive the matrimonial consent and bless the couple. But Fesch was neither Archbishop of Paris nor parish-priest of the parish; and, moreover, as he himself pointed out to his nephew when he made this demand:

[1] As a matter of fact, there is still much uncertainty about what did occur on that December 1st, 1804. We follow the version accepted by the majority of historians.

"No witnesses, no marriage!" But time was pressing; it was the first of December, 1804, the vigil of the coronation. Fesch found a solution by which the whole matter could be settled. He went to the Pope, and, as he says: "I pointed out to him that very often I would have occasion to apply to him for dispensations, and I asked him to give me then and there those which would be indispensable, from time to time, for the fulfilment of my duties as *grand aumônier*. The Holy Father acceded to my request, and I went immediately to His Majesty the Emperor with the ritual for administering the nuptial blessing, which was duly given about four o'clock in the afternoon."

Time went by, and Josephine still did not give birth to the desired heir. Came 1809, and Napoleon decided to divorce her. A civil divorce was pronounced on December 16th by a decree of the Senate, the validity of which is questioned by some authorities. It remained to have the religious ceremony declared null and void. What court was competent to judge the case? Under the *Ancien Régime*, matrimonial cases were not usually taken to Rome, save in rare exceptions of which this was one, seeing that it concerned the marriage of a prince and that the Pope had reserved such cases to himself and also the right to appoint the judges. But, in 1809, Pius VII was Napoleon's prisoner at Savone.

The *Official de Paris* (Judge of the Diocesan Court), arguing from the extraordinary circumstances pertaining and from the impossibility of consulting the Sovereign Pontiff, and after having obtained the opinions of several bishops, declared himself to be competent. But it must not be supposed that the servility of the Parisian judges made them jettison all canonical regulations and bring in a sentence of pure complacency. Though the case was pushed through rapidly, it was seriously handled, and the arguments adduced for nullity were examined and discussed with great attention.

The arguments adduced were, first of all, the defect in consent on the part of the Emperor, who could never have had the intention of really marrying her—an argument we shall lay aside for the moment; and secondly, the absence of the proper Parish Priest. It is the second argument which interests us here.

This absence was a clear matter of fact, as was also the absence of the two witnesses. Therefore the necessary external formalities could not have been respected, and it was a decided case for nullity. However, the ecclesiastical authority which fixes these forms has equally the power to dispense from them; and the Pope, in this matter, is the supreme power for the entire Church.

Consequently, the question which was completely decisive was that of the pontifical intervention. Did Pius VII give a dispensation from the juridical form of Matrimony, on that First of December, 1804? Since the Pope had given no opinion on the matter, the only means of knowing whether he had or had not given such a dispensation was the evidence of Fesch which we have cited above—evidence which seemed to be quite embarrassing. *The grand aumônier* had requested from the Pope all the dispensations of which he might be in need for the discharge of his official duties, and his request had been granted. Did not that settle everything? No—because the whole point of the discussion was to decide whether it came within the official province of the *grand aumônier* to bless the marriages of the imperial family; which was equivalent to deciding whether he really had the power of a proper Parish Priest in this matter. The Parisian judges considered, with good reason, it would seem, that he had not such power, and that the dispensations accorded by the Pope were without relevance to the case.

There remains, it is true, the possibility that the Pope, knowing quite well what particular action Fesch had in mind when he made his *ex abrupto* petition, really intended to give him all the power necessary to render this marriage valid.

It emerges, therefore, from this brief discussion, that no one has succeeded in clearing up perfectly the question of this defect of form. The validity of the marriage was just as doubtful as its invalidity. But a doubtful marriage should be regarded as valid, pending clearer knowledge. The judges, therefore, had no right to invoke the defect of form as a reason for declaring the marriage null and void.[1]

Since a decision given by St. Pius X in 1908, and especially since the promulgation of the New Code of Canon Law, the conditions for the celebration of Matrimony are no longer the same as they were at the beginning of the nineteenth century.

Two cases are envisaged: a normal case, and an exceptional case.

In the first, the form known as "the ordinary form" is to be used. This requires that the consent of the parties should be given in the presence of a qualified priest and of two witnesses.

What qualifies a priest to assist at marriages as the representative of the Church, is either the office which he holds in the place where the marriage is celebrated—for the diocese, the Bishop or his Vicars General; for the parish, the Parish Priest—or the priest may be qualified because he has been delegated by either of these.

Moreover, it is specifically laid down that the priest is to take an

[1] The complete canonical discussion of this case, as well as documents many of which had not then been published, can be found in the thesis defended by M. l'Abbé Gregoire before the Faculty of Canon Law in Paris: "The 'divorce' of the Emperor Napoleon and of Empress Josephine, before the *Officialités* of Paris, 9th–11th Jan., 1810.

active part in the ceremony, by demanding and receiving the consent of the parties. This last requirement is recent. Formerly, the simple presence of the priest was sufficient at the moment when the parties exchanged their promises, so that he thus became a witness to the fact. But since merely passive presence was required, there was a danger that the priest might be tricked or forced into assisting at a marriage, thus making it valid by his presence. It is to preclude the risk of abrupt marriages and other possible inconveniences, that the new legislation has been introduced.

The exceptional case arises when it is impossible, because of circumstances, to secure the presence of a qualified priest.

This eventually can occur in two forms. The first is when at least one of the parties is in danger of death, and the situation is too urgent to allow of time in which to call a priest having the necessary powers. The second occurs apart from any danger of death when a man and a woman wish to marry and there is no qualified priest at hand to assist at the ceremony, either because of absence or of grave inconvenience, provided, however, that his absence or this inconvenience will last at least a month, as far as prudent calculation can foresee. This would be the case, for example, in a mission-country where priests are rare and can visit the faithful in their scattered settlements only at long intervals.

In the case of the two situations we have just indicated—the danger of death, or the absence of a qualified priest, such absence being estimated to last more than a month—two witnesses are still necessary for the validity of the marriage. But they need not demand the consent of the parties; it is sufficient that they are present at the exchange of promises. The drawing up of a written statement is, of course, required to meet the possibility of any future argument about the matter.

A most important point must be made, however, in order to avoid serious misunderstandings. Only those who have been baptized into the Catholic Church or who have adhered to that Church at any times of their lives, are bound to submit to the above formalities in order that their marriage may be valid; and they are so bound, no matter what may be the present state of their religious belief, or who the person may be with whom they marry—whether non-Catholic or unbaptized. Consequently, all Christians other than Catholics, and all unbaptized persons, are exempt from these formalities when they marry, provided the marriage is not with a Catholic. Therefore their contract fulfils the conditions of the Natural Law; they are validly married in the eyes of the Church, at least if there are no other reasons invalidating the marriage. Such a marriage is valid when the matrimonial consent is a free one given before a civil registrar or minister of religion, or even when the consent is exchanged freely in private. And when there is question of marriage between two baptized persons, such marriage is indissoluble as soon as it has been consummated.

Hence the necessity for issuing a warning to any Catholic wishing to marry a Protestant who has once been married to another, still living Protestant, but who has since been divorced. There is every danger that this project can never end in a marriage accepted by the Church.

Invalid marriages because of non-dispensed diriment impediment or because of defect of juridical formalities, are comparatively rare. We shall see that it is the subject of consent which ordinarily furnishes the matter for debate.

MATRIMONIAL CONSENT

A MAN and a woman, free from all impediment, come before a qualified priest, answer his questions with a decisive *I do*, in the presence of two witnesses. A marriage celebrated in these conditions seems to respect the requirements of the law with the utmost perfection; and yet, is it possible to find reasons for nullity in such a marriage?

Undoubtedly it is. Considered from the outside, everything is in order, but it remains to submit to examination the act itself which is the essence of marriage—mutual consent to conjugal life. And experience teaches us that sometimes the interior reality does not correspond to the appearances. The lips speak a promise which the will rejects or does not ratify.

It is these cases of invalidity by defect of consent that we must now study.

What, then, is necessary in order that a consent exchanged in proper juridical form should create a *per se* indissoluble bond.

It must comprise three principal elements. Each of the parties must *will*, must will *to marry*, and to marry *one certain person*. A defect in any of these three points would endanger the validity of the marriage.

(a) Must will

Nothing can take the place of the act of will, when there is question of engaging oneself. It is as essential in marriage as in other contracts.

But it is also necessary that it should be given with sufficient freedom.

That is why there is no marriage if the act of will is refused or if it is extorted. And since it is thus possible to distinguish between the act of will and the liberty with which such an act must necessarily be posited, these two aspects should be examined separately.

It can happen, then, that while a person is present at the ceremony of his own wedding and apparently taking an active part therein, he or she may nevertheless refuse interiorly to accept the contract. The words spoken do not express the real feelings, and the exterior consent is absolutely void. This is what is called in Law *total pretence of consent*.

Sixty years ago, a young priest was performing his first marriage-ceremony. When he asked the young man whether he took the woman standing by his side for his lawful wife, he received the expected answer: *I do.* He repeated the formula to the girl, who replied emphatically: *No.* There was general amazement. The priest took the girl into the sacristy. "You do not wish to be married?" he asked. "No!" came the reply. "But why have you waited till now to make that known?" "Because," she answered, "this is the first time anyone has asked me what I think about this marriage."

How many would have had the courage to speak out in such a public way at the last moment? In a like situation, many would have been content to speak this refusal only in the silence of their own hearts.

What are the motives behind such an attitude? As one can readily suppose, they are of very differing origins. Sometimes it is the fear of opposing the parental will; and it may also be, in some cases, a more sordid intention—for example, the advantages expected from this pseudo-matrimonial situation: fortune, social position, etc., etc.

Note that it is sufficient for one of the parties to abstain from the necessary act of will in order that the marriage may be nullified, since quite clearly the contract must be mutual if it is to be valid.

It was this defect of consent which was invoked as the second motive for nullity in connection with the marriage of Napoleon and the Empress Josephine, the former having accepted the religious ceremony only "to satisfy" the latter. The Emperor and Arch-Chancellor Cambacérès, who was directly in charge of the whole case, attached great importance to this reason for invalidity.

But the diocesan court could not decide to recognize "in favour of a man who makes us all tremble—as l'Abbé Rudermare, *promoteur général,* remarked—a reason for nullity which was never successfully invoked except by a deceived or oppressed minor."

That is why the first judgment made no mention of this defect of consent, and retained as cause of nullity only the absence of a qualified priest and of witnesses. On the other hand, the metropolitan ecclesiastical court,[1] before which an appeal had been immediately lodged as is the normal course in such cases, took up a more submissive attitude to the solicitations of the imperial representatives, and based its sentence of invalidity on the two counts put forward—

"Seeing . . . that, on the one hand, it is certain that the defect arising from the absence of the proper Parish Priest and of the required witnesses . . . presents a radical defect in the act of celebration of the marriage—a defect which nothing in the case was able to amend. . . .

That, on the other hand, it is not less certain that every contract,

---

[1] At that time, there were two Curias in Paris. The first dealt with the first instance, and judged only diocesan cases; the other, called the *officialité métropolitaine,* heard cases appealed from the first court and from the *officialités* of suffragan dioceses.

religious and civil, to which one of the parties has not given a formal and voluntary consent, does not contain the substantial condition which is the root of all contracts. . . .

That, in the circumstances of the case, the defect of a formal will to bind himself by a spiritual and indissoluble bond emerges not only from the reiterated declarations on this point made by H.M. the Emperor and King and established by the investigation, but by deduction from the striking fact of the omission of those essential formalities which are carefully attended to in connection with important actions when the intention is to ensure the effects which derive from the regularity of their external forms. . . ."

For these reasons, the metropolitan judge upheld the verdict of the diocesan official as to the principal disposition, namely the nullity of the Emperor's supposed marriage.

What value must we put on this second motive for nullity, put forward by Napoleon and definitely accepted by the ecclesiastical judge?

It must be admitted that there are strong presumptions in its favour. Up to December 1st, 1804, Napoleon had never manifested any intention of contracting a religious marriage with Josephine. Furthermore, though he was not "a deceived or an oppressed minor," he was placed in a situation by the Pope's demand which forced him to submit, at least in appearance; for it was this demand, and not the insistence of Josephine, which was the decisive factor in making him submit. Could he, on the very eve of the ceremony, cancel the coronation prepared a month earlier—a coronation whose sole purpose was to give a solemn consecration to his reign, thereby supplying for the absence of hereditary rights? Or could he agree that he alone should receive the imperial crown, even though the coronation of Josephine had been officially announced and prepared for?

Of course, when faced with the duty of marrying by religious ceremony, he could have accepted the situation and behaved as a good child of the Church should do. But taking into consideration his nature and his ardent desire to found a fourth dynasty, could one reasonably have expected that he would have acted thus and agreed to bind himself indefinitely to a woman who was almost certainly sterile?

Presumptions, however, are not proofs. It was probably not impossible to assemble such proofs, but the affair was pushed through too rapidly to allow of their being sought out and discussed. Although some witnesses had testified, the situation really was that Napoleon demanded the acceptance of his statements, and this was not sufficient to establish with certitude that a defect of consent existed. As in the case of the first reason for nullity, so here too the final outcome is a doubt; and a marriage should not be declared null and void as long as one has reached only the stage of doubt, and not that of certainty.

Such being the circumstances, one would be tempted to conclude that the judges allowed themselves to be overreached by the political pressure brought to bear on them by the mandataries of Napoleon, and that they were guilty of a serious failure in duty.

Certainly, if the case had been conducted with less precipitation, complementary information could have been obtained, and legal questions more carefully scrutinized. But one must not be in too great a hurry to condemn these men who, considering the difficult circumstances in which they were placed, brought in a verdict according to conscience. For we have reported the facts of the situation, to serve as an example, and we have indicated a modern court's solution, according to the present state of the Law and in the light of a doctrine which numerous cases in nullity during the past century have shaped to greater and greater precision; but our space did not allow us to deal with the juridical ideas of the Napoleonic era. To put it briefly, these ideas were still completely impregnated with Gallicanism, because the Revolution had changed nothing in this field. Now, Gallicanism "attached considerable importance to questions of form, and took account not only of canonical rules, but also of royal decrees." (*Leflon, Monsieur Emery: L'Église concordataire et impériale*, p. 423.)

Nearly all the French canonists of the period would probably have reached the same verdict as the Paris courts about the defect of form, and would have recognized Napoleon's marriage as null and void because of the absence of the proper Parish Priest or of his delegates, and the absence of witnesses. M. Emery, Superior General of Saint-Sulpice, whose independence of character is a matter of history, did not hold a different opinion and regarded the marriage as invalid from defect of form.

While consent is necessary, it must be freely given. There are two influences which can oppose freedom.

The first arises from mental alienation which, by affecting the power of judgment, diminishes or suppresses the use of free will.[1] And if this mental disease is serious, a real act of conjugal assent cannot be posited.

The case is relatively easy to judge when the person whose psychic health is in question has given indubitable signs of mental alienation shortly before or shortly after the marriage. For example, there was the man who had a crisis of insanity during his wedding reception; it can be legitimately supposed that at the time of the actual ceremony

---

[1] See *Dictionnaire de Droit Canonique* (Letouzey, Paris): Mental Alienation and Nullity of Marriage.

he was not in a condition to know exactly what he was doing, and therefore equally incapable of willing it.

The situation is more complex when the first recognized manifestation of mental alienation makes its appearance some time after the marriage. Because, in the case of *dementia praecox*, which is probably the source of the trouble which catches the attention of those about the patient, doctors are far from being in agreement about the incubation period. The slowest evolution seems to be a maximum of three years. Consequently, if the clear installation of the disease is not diagnosed until three years after the marriage, the validity of the consent will be practically impregnable.[1] But on the other hand, the nearer certain symptoms are to the time of the marriage, the more likely they are to furnish serious matter for a process in nullity.

Happily, these tragic instances are rare; ordinarily, the impediments to liberty of matrimonial consent are external factors. Canon 1087 declares invalid every marriage into which a person is drawn by violence or by serious and unjustly provoked fear of an external nature, such that in order to escape from it one is forced to accept the marriage. The fear in question, therefore, is that which is provoked by another person in order to compel consent to marriage, and not that fear which the subject may experience spontaneously because of the circumstances in which he finds himself.

In our times, physical violence used at the very moment of the marriage ceremony, is almost unthinkable. No priest would continue the ceremony in such circumstances.

On the other hand, moral violence, by threats and sometimes even by blows and wounds, used with a view to compelling consent to marriage, belongs to all ages and is not rare to-day. It is even one of the most frequently invoked reasons for invalidity. In the volume of Rota decisions for 1937, we find it invoked thirty-fives times out of a total of ninety-six cases; and, for 1938, forty times out of a total of eighty-eight.

Historical examples of this kind are not wanting. One of the most interesting is that of the first marriage of Jeanne d'Albre who was to become an implacable Protestant and the mother of the future Henry IV. Born on 16th November, 1528, daughter and heir of Henri d'Albret, King of Navarre, she was kept under close vigilance by Francis the First, who intended to make use of her as an important pawn in the political game. An opportunity to do so arose when she had reached the age of twelve and a half. To win Guillaume de la Marck, Duc de Clèves et de Juliers, from the party of Charles the Fifth, the King of France offered him the hand of the heiress of Navarre.

---

[1] We are not in full agreement with this opinion.—Ed.

After having vainly protested to Francis, Jeanne was conveyed to Tours, where she was strictly watched, and to Châtellerault where the marriage was to take place. But before the ceremony, and probably with the secret consent of her father, she sent for a notary, and, in his presence and that of two witnesses, drew up in her own hand this solemn declaration: "I, Jeanne de Navarre, continuing my protestations in which I persist, do say and declare . . . that the marriage arranged for me with the Duc de Clèves is contrary to my wishes . . . and that all that I may henceforward do or say concerning the matter will be under constraint . . . and from fear of the King of France, of the King my father and the Queen my mother, who have threatened me about it and have had me whipped by the wife of the bailiff of Caen, my governess. . . ."

On June 14th, 1541, the day of the nuptial ceremony, the unfortunate little girl was so weighed down by the heavy gold brocade of her garments that she made this the pretext for fresh resistance, and appeared incapable of taking a step. Francis the First, who also knew what she wanted, ordered the constable de Montmorency to take her by the scruff of the neck and compel her to enter the Church—an order which was immediately and quite literally obeyed.

Some years later, the interests of the political game had shifted, and everyone was very happy to be able to avail of the protestation of 1541. Pope Paul III, on October 21, 1545, decided that since Jeanne had accepted the marriage only "through force and from fear," and since, moreover, it had never been consummated, this marriage was null and void.

But what do we mean by "unjustly provoked fear"? In practice, and whatever the controversies about this subject, it seems certain that every fear which leaves no alternative except marriage, qualifies for the above description; because, even when reparation can be justly claimed, as in the case of fraudulent seduction or rape, this legitimate claim cannot take the form of a demand that the author of the crime must marry the wronged girl.

The gravity of the fear will be judged in accordance with the trouble caused and the strength of the pressure exercised. This means that the subject and his moral strength must be taken into consideration as well as the threats to which he or she has been subjected. Where a resolute character would be scarcely troubled, a weak one may be utterly cowed.

One of the cases where such comparison and assessment is most necessary and most difficult is that of reverential fear—an emotion provoked by the thought of the disappointment one causes to those people who have a right to one's respect and submission. Such a case arises, for example, when a girl of eighteen or twenty who has always lived with her family cannot oppose, without great interior prostration, the wishes of an authoritarian father who proposes to her, as a matter of course, that she should marry a man whom he considers in every way suitable.

It itself, however, this reverential fear is merely slight, and it will not impede the free expression of the will, despite all the circumstances. But it can increase in gravity because of the intensity of the disappointment caused—a disappointment which can show itself in renewed persuasions, reiterated reproaches, and even in threats to turn away and disinherit the disobedient child. In the case of a weak nature, where unquestioning obedience has become a habit, it is not at all impossible that reverential fear will end by binding and subjugating the will.

Among the Roman decisions for 1938 of which we spoke above, out of forty cases where fear was invoked as the motive for nullity, thirty alleged reverential fear, and sixteen of these were recognized as valid motives.

There is another modifying factor to consent which must be added to our list. It may happen that a matrimonial consent, given with full knowledge and complete liberty, may have a *sine qua non* condition attached to it—as for example: I will marry you, provided you have never been a patient in a mental hospital. What is the value of a consent expressed like that?

We shall confine ourselves to examining the most simple cases. A condition thus attached to the consent can concern the past, the actual moment of the marriage, or the future.

As regards the past and the present, the answer is an obvious one. The consent will depend entirely on that condition: if it is fulfilled, the marriage is valid; if it is not fulfilled, the marriage is null and void. A typical example can be found among the decisions of the Rota. A young lady, prior to the marriage, had said to her intended: "I agree to marry you, but on condition that you promise me that we shall never live in the same apartment with your mother." He agreed, and on their return from their honeymoon they spent some time in an hotel. Then they moved into an apartment contiguous to that of his mother, but, in spite of the young wife's protests, the communicating door between the two apartments remained always open, and an independent domestic life was refused her. The husband answered his wife's reproaches by saying that he never regarded her "condition" as anything more than a girl's whim, and that he never had any intention of being bound by it. An ecclesiastical process in nullity was introduced. The judges found that the formal condition laid down by the young lady before marriage, had not really been accepted by the man, at the actual time of the ceremony, and they declared the marriage to be null and void.

When the condition concerns the future, it can be suspensory, that is, the marriage will not come into existence until the moment when this condition is fulfilled; but it can never be resolutory, or in other words, there is no case in which the marriage can be considered as existing from the moment when the conditional consent is uttered, and then ceasing if, by a certain date, the condition has not been fulfilled.

(b) Must will to marry

We are no longer concerned with the act of will considered in itself, but with its object. Marriage is a state of life with its own structure, qualities and essential purposes, which are independent of human wills. This structure, these qualities and purposes, have been fixed by God when He created man, and by Christ when he re-established the primary meaning of conjugal society in order to raise it to the dignity of a Sacrament.

To wish to marry is, therefore, nothing other than an agreement to enter into this type of community as thus fixed. In order that a marriage may be valid from this point of view, the parties must not be ignorant of its essential characteristics. Consequently, ignorance and exclusion will be motives for invalidity, if they fulfil the conditions which we shall now lay down.

Of what must one not be ignorant, in order to contract a valid marriage? Simply this: that marriage is a permanent union between man and woman, having for its principal purpose the procreation of children, who are procured by means of certain special actions the nature of which is known at least in a general way. It is this last point which sometimes provides difficulty, especially in the case of the woman.

But, as several decisions of the Rota have pointed out in this connection, the two expressions *to know* and *not to be ignorant of* must not be regarded as synonymous. *To know* is to have complete or almost complete knowledge of the act in question; while *not to be ignorant of* means that one has some knowledge of the subject.

Canonical doctrine, like the decisions mentioned, teaches that, for the contracting of a valid marriage, it is not required that the parties should know the manner in which conjugal relations take place; it is sufficient that they should not be ignorant of the fact that children are born as the result of a special bodily action between husband and wife.

After puberty, non-ignorance is always presumed by the ecclesiastical courts. The burden of proof for the existence of this motive for invalidity, rests on the person who invokes it. Since the reorganization of the Rota in 1908, there has been only one verdict of nullity brought in on this head by the ecclesiastical court, and even this one was reversed on appeal.

We pass on to consider the cases where the deliberate exclusion of an essential characteristic is invoked; and such cases are more frequent and more complex.

To be validly married, as we have already said, it is necessary that one should be willing to accept the essential conditions of marriage such as they are fixed by the nature of things and by the teaching of the Church. But this essential willingness to accept is also sufficient, and as soon as it is given, the marriage contract comes into existence.

What, then, are the defects which spoil the consent, and with it the marriage itself, and constitute what is called partial simulation?

It must be noted that only a defect bearing on the will has this consequence, because, contrary to an opinion which is very widespread, simple error as to the nature or substantial properties of marriage does not render the marriage null and void. It is what one has willed or has not willed which counts, and that alone. Therefore, as long as the error does not affect the will to the extent of leading it to a positive exclusion, it provides no valid basis for a case in nullity.

For example, a person who believes that marriage can be dissolved by divorce has, in a certain sense, the intention of contracting a dissoluble marriage; but since this intention remains most often a general one, it does not impair the consent by which one intends to marry in the usual Christian manner.

There must be positive, explicit exclusion; but on what must this exclusion bear in order that the marriage can, in fact, be said to be refused?

We shall confine ourselves to the three principal cases: exclusion of children; exclusion of indissolubility; exclusion of unity.[1]

But before we examine each of them separately, a preliminary remark bearing on all three will clarify the whole matter by providing some clear general ideas.

Every human society inevitably establishes relationships of duties and of rights amongst its members. The conjugal community is no exception to this; to enter into such community is to receive rights and to give them. But it is one thing to take on an obligation, and

---

[1] It should be pointed out that a person who deliberately causes the nullity of his marriage, forfeits the right to claim the benefit of this invalidity and to begin a case before the ecclesiastical courts.

quite another to fulfil it. At the very moment when a person accepts the engagement, he may know that he will very probably be unfaithful to his promises, because he knows his own weakness only too well. It may even happen that, while having the formal intention of binding himself, a person may also make a deliberate mental reservation about not respecting the engagement he undertakes.

Does this prescience of probable infidelity or this deliberate intention to be unfaithful, invalidate the marriage? Not at all; because, as the word which we have designedly used clearly indicates, this is a question of *infidelity*, meaning that the person foresees as probable, or voluntarily accepts, transgressions of a promise which he really intends to make. He is fully aware that there will be some divergences between the promise he is now making and his probable or certain future conduct; but nevertheless the promise is made. Thus it is that a man can really will to marry a certain woman, while at the same time he has decided not to be faithful to her. The effect of the second intention is not to suppress the first, which remains the predominant one. The second intention does not, therefore, render the marriage null and void.

What must there be if such a marriage is to be nullified? It is necessary that one of the essential rights of marriage should be formally refused, with the result that the person refuses to accept that essential part of the marriage contract. He does not, in fact, regard marriage as a permanent association between a man and a woman for the procreation of children, but indulges his own personal conception of it. For example, he looks on it merely as a temporary association, or as an association from which the begetting of children is excluded *a priori*, and it is in accordance with this conception that he has the explicit *will* to engage himself, and not otherwise. We shall see examples of this connection with the three cases referred to above, and which we shall now discuss.

The first case is that of *the exclusion of children*. The expression is the current one, and that is why we have used it; but it is too vague to be immediately and sufficiently clear, and it is therefore necessary to supply its exact juridical meaning. By the matrimonial consent, the man and the woman give to each other a reciprocal and perpetual right to precreative actions, accomplished according to the order of nature.

What forms will the refusal of this right take—a refusal which nullifies marriage?

Sometimes it will take the form of a complete refusal of all physical intercourse, in the case where a person refuses to yield the right to such intercourse, even though, in other respects, he or she agrees to live with the marriage partner. It must be carefully noted that this attitude is altogether different from an agreement which may be made between the parties not to consummate the marriage, as history records as having happened between certain saintly persons. In such a case, the right is really conceded, and it is only its use which is excluded by mutual consent. If one of the partners later changes his or her mind, the other may indeed complain that this entails a failure to keep the agreement, but not that it is the claiming of a right to which he or she is not entitled.

In other cases, it is the order of nature which the person intends to thwart, and thus refuses the engagement which creates this right to fecundity. He or she will accept physical intercourse, but it is absolutely understood that precautions will be taken to ensure that pregnancy never results from it.

Finally, it may be the perpetuity of the right to normally accomplished precreative acts that is affected. The intention is to confer the right to these acts only for a limited time—for example, until the birth of two or three children.

The line of conduct which one proposed to adopt when the fixed time had passed, is of no importance for the juridical consequence—that is, for the invalidity of the marriage. Whether one has envisaged total abstinence, the exclusive use of the Ogino method, or the use of artificial methods of birth control, the result is the same if, at the moment of matrimonial consent, one had the intention of conceding to the other partner merely a right limited to a certain period of time.

But it will be readily appreciated how difficult it can be to decide, many years after the marriage ceremony, whether a negation of the right was involved, or merely the resolution not to respect it. That is why many appeals, based on this motive of nullity, are not acceptable.

In practice, when they are considering an exclusion of this kind, the ecclesiastical judges presume the refusal of the right itself if they are dealing with a case of total exclusion in which there is no question of limitation as to time or as to the number of children. On the other hand, if the exclusion is only partial or limited, the presumption will be that the right has been accorded but with the intention of contravening it—a presumption which can, of course, yield to conclusive proof for the defence.

It is according to the same principles that the two other cases—*unicity* and *indissolubility*—are assessed. Here, too, there is question of a right which must be recognized by the matrimonial consent: a man takes a certain woman for his wife, and permanently; a woman takes a certain man for her husband, under the same conditions. Only positive exclusion on one point or the other would render the consent valueless. In our day, the exclusion of indissolubility will not be rare.

A person reserves the possibility of ending the union if it does not fulfil the hopes expected from it. But as in the case of the exclusion of children, it is necessary, from the juridical point of view, to distinguish between firm and positive exclusion clearly willed at the time of the marriage, and often expressed in the form of a condition *sine qua non*: "I am marrying only on condition that I have power to divorce, if later on I wish to do so"; and the hypothesis, more or less clearly envisaged: "If things do not go well, there is always the possibility of getting a divorce."

The first is a case for nullity; the second is not.

(c) To marry a certain person

Whatever the love involved or the interests at stake or the complex of different motives urging towards a marriage, the matrimonial design always comprises a choice of partner. It is this woman or this man whom one chooses to marry, and once the consent has been given which publicly confirms this choice, there can be no further discussion about the matter. And yet one not infrequently hears from married people: "I deceived myself" or "I was deceived"; or they use a juridical expression which they believe fits their case: "There was an error as to the person."

It is true that error as to the person invalidates a marriage, but this term has not the meaning in law which is currently attributed to it. It must be understood as an error concerning the person "as such," and that is indeed to be expected, since the person is the substantial object of the contract, the idea being to enter into a contract with one definite person, and with no other. An error on this point nullifies the consent. In so far as one can be categorical in such a complex matter, it is an error as to the physical identity of the person which has the effect of invalidating a marriage, and there is only one exception to this. This man or this woman who stands at your side before the officiating priest, is indeed he or she whom you have decided to marry. You answer in the affirmative to the question put to you. Henceforward there is no going back on this; you have really bound yourself indissolubly to the person you have chosen.

If you afterwards discover that you were mistaken about *the qualities* which you thought you saw in the chosen one, what then? However regrettable your mistake may be, it has no invalidating influence. You have been mistaken about the fortune, the character, the health, the physical integrity of your partner, and you see a prospect of heavy consequences for you as a result of your illusion; but, once the marriage has been consummated, nothing can deliver you from your burden. It cannot be otherwise, because, if the indissolubility of matrimonial unions were open to such interested criticism, how many marriages would survive?

If you had known the truth, you say, you would not have married. That is possible, even probable; but the very form of words you use proves that your consent was fully given, for it implies that you *did* wish to marry. And even when one has married because of a quality supposed to exist in the other person—for example, that he or she is rich—and that quality is found to be non-existent, there is still no case for nullity.

The situation would be very different, of course, if there had been a condition *sine qua non*, clearly and explicitly formulated at the time of marriage, relative to a certain quality; for example: "I marry you only on condition that you are really of British nationality." This would provide a possible case for nullity, as we have seen above when dealing with *sine qua non* conditions. But if the condition was not deliberately formulated, there can be no such case.

We have said, however, that there is an exception to this.

A quality can be, at least in the circumstances of the marriage, such a determining factor with regard to the person one wishes to marry, that an error on this point, whether an honest error or a piece of fraud, would be equivalent to an error as to the person.

This can happen in countries, which are becoming to-day more and more rare, where betrothed couples meet one another for the first time only when they come before the priest, all the preliminary transactions being done by intermediaries. In such cases, substitution is not impossible—for example, the substitution of a younger for an elder daughter.

A particular case is provided for by Canon Law. There is an error as to determining quality, an error which nullifies marriage, "if a person contracts marriage with another whom he or she considers to be also a free person, whereas that other is a slave in the strict sense of the word." This case is clearly only of theoretical interest to us.

We must now deal with a final question which, in our day and country, arises with unhappy frequency.

Two betrothed persons, baptized and brought up in the Catholic faith, declare that they have lost all religious belief. If they were left to their own choice, they would go before a civil registrar; but their families would feel disgraced in seeing their children thus living in what they regard as mere concubinage. Under family pressure, and sometimes concealing their real sentiments, such a couple agree to go through with the religious ceremony; but for them the Sacrament is merely a rite, venerable and picturesque it is true, but purely human. In these conditions, are they really married in the eyes of the Church?

Emphatically yes. There can be no doubt about it, since they have really consented to take each other as husband and wife respectively, and have not qualified that consent with one of those exclusions we have dealt with above. Their marriage, after it has been consummated, is indissoluble, because it is a sacramental marriage. In the eyes of baptized persons, the contract is raised to the dignity of a Sacrament, and it is not within the power of the human will to separate them one from the other. Baptized persons who really consent to the matrimonial contract in sacramental marriage, receive the Sacrament whether they wish to do so or not—provided, of course, that no other invalidating circumstance exists.

The circumstances we have just described do not constitute, therefore, in any case whatsoever, a *per se* motive for nullity.

*   *   *

However summary our description of the factors which sometimes affect matrimonial consent, it is sufficient to give some idea of the difficulties which arise when they come for examination with a view to deciding the validity or the nullity of a marriage.

Besides the juridical aspects, the examination of which calls for outstanding acuity, questions of personal psychology arise here which are still more complex.

Attentive study is, therefore, the price that must be paid if one is to discover the truth in the jungle of uncertainties, suppressions, and intentions, where the person concerned in the case does not always know where he is. Neither is it surprising that months on end, and sometimes years, are necessary in order to reach a decision which is as objective as possible. It is this aspect of our subject to which we shall now turn.

CASES IN NULLITY

SINCE the very simple conditions for the validity of marriage can be subject to many defects—a score of defects, it has been estimated—the Church, as guardian of the Sacraments and of the good order of Christian society, as well as of the particular good of the faithful, takes all necessary precautions to ensure this validity and to ensure that it is not attained under false pretexts. Hence the preliminary inquiry before every marriage, and the procedure followed when the validity of a marriage is contested.

The preliminary inquiry, already fixed by Canon Law in 1917, accompanied by the publication of bans either from the pulpit or by the posting of a notice in the Church porch, has been still more recently the object of a Constitution by the Holy See with a view to clarifying and strengthening these regulations. Some people are surprised at the number of questions asked and at the details demanded, but in the perspective of what we have explained up to this point, such astonishment should certainly seem groundless. What is demanded of the intending parties is, first of all, that they should assist the priest to assure himself that no impediment exists to the marriage; and, secondly, that they should express their willingness to contract a true marriage, without exclusion of the essential properties which make it such.

This inquiry is really a step which is demanded by Christian loyalty and Christian sense. If there is a moment in life when these demands should be spontaneously understood, surely it is that in which a person is preparing to found a new family.

Nevertheless, there will still be matrimonial cases, either because impediments have not been discovered, despite serious investigation, or because the truth has been kept back from the inquirer.

It is therefore useful, with a view to clarifying the whole matter, to give a rapid sketch of the procedure used in these cases.

Contrary to what is commonly supposed, it is not usually to Rome that one directly appeals in a case of nullity. The first competent judge is the Bishop.[1] But for the exercise of judiciary power, as for other

---

[1] According to Canon Law, the validity of a marriage can be contested either before the court of the diocese where the marriage took place, or before that of the diocese where the spouse who is not the plaintiff is domiciled. Transference of competence is possible.

powers, the Bishop has his Vicars General, and in most cases it is to them that the applicant will have recourse.

There exists in each diocese an office known as the Curia, with a diocesan court presided over by a president or a vice-president.

Besides the president, it comprises, for matrimonial cases, two assessors chosen from among the synodal or pro-synodal judges (nominated in synod or outside the synod).

The active presence of another personage, known as the *Defender of the Bond* (*Defensor Vinculi Matrimonii*) is also always required. His duty, as laid down by Canon Law, is of the utmost importance. When a marriage has been celebrated according to the required forms, Canon Law demands that it should be regarded as valid. If is for the plaintiff and his or her advocate to establish the contrary, in all sincerity. On his side, the defender of the bond is charged with the duty of defending the validity of the marriage, or examining the arguments put forward against that validity, of showing their inherent weakness, of pulling into the light what the interested party would prefer to leave in the shade, and of demanding all desirable explanations.

Lastly, there is a notary or clerk of the court who will take the depositions.

When a person believes that he has legitimate motives for contesting the validity of his marriage, the first step he should take is to consult a priest who knows him, his Parish Priest or local Curate, who will send him to the diocesan Curia with a few words of recommendation. Perhaps it will also be useful to submit the case first to one of the advocates about whom we shall speak later on, because one needs to be a specialist in order to give a proper opinion about such difficult matters.

Some French Curia have the reputation of extending a very cold welcome to their visitors. If this reputation is not always without foundation, it must be recognized, nevertheless, that there are extenuating circumstances for those who are responsible for such welcome, because they are besieged to-day by a host of people whose matrimonial situation is in a bad way. Moreover, they demand that their visitors should not lose themselves in a cloud of irrelevant detail, and, in the majority of cases, they give in a few words the solution which is quite clear from the juridical point of view: "There is no case for nullity in your marriage." The unfortunate who thinks himself the victim of an arbitrary decision, insists; but others are waiting. Is it any wonder that each case is quickly dealt with?

If, in the diocesan administrations of our cities, a bureau of ecclesiastical and religious information is some day set up—and such a bureau would be a boon for many reasons—the preliminary work of discrimination carried out by the diocesan Curia would be greatly eased. Everyone concerned would gain by that.

If the case seems to have a sufficient juridical basis, it is accepted. The applicant is then invited to choose an advocate from the list of those approved by the Curia—which list is, in France, almost exclusively made up of ecclesiastics, since considerable canonical knowledge is required to fulfil this role; and then he is invited to present a written memorandum summarizing the facts, together with complementary documents and a list of persons whose evidence may be necessary or useful.

This memorandum is sent to the defender of the bond, who draws up a list of questions to be put to those who will be interrogated.

It is then only that the instruction of the case begins. The applicant is summoned before the examining magistrate, who in many instances will be one of the judges of the case. The defender of the bond is usually present at the interrogation; the clerk of the court records the answers. The deponent is put under oath to tell the truth and to maintain secrecy until the end of the inquiry.

In the final sessions, the other spouse and his or her witnesses are interrogated. When necessary, interrogatory commissions are sent to far away dioceses in order that witnesses who reside there may be heard in evidence.

If the case requires it, expert examinations are made by specialists designated by the judge.

When the dossier is completed—and of course several months will often be necessary in which to study the whole affair—it is sent to the plaintiff's counsel. The latter draws up *in writing* a statement designed to show that the invalidity of the marriage is proved by the depositions and the documents.

Both dossier and pleadings of counsel are then put into the hands of the defender of the bond who, *again in writing*, will seek to discover in the dossier everything which can be used to prove the validity of the marriage.

There will thus be several written discussions, in some cases, between the counsel and the defender of the bond. In every case, the latter will be the last to sum up.

All this is then handed over to three judges who each make a separate study of the elements of the case, and who each give his opinion in writing.

On the day fixed, the three judges meet together, bringing with them their written conclusions. They hold a discussion among themselves, which may go on for several sessions if necessary; after that they vote, and take a majority decision. The only question to which they must find an answer can be summarized thus: Has the nullity of the marriage been proved? And the sole answer: yes, or no; *constat* or *non constat*.

If the marriage is declared null and void by this first judgment, the defender of the bond is under an obligation to appeal the case. If the contrary decision is given, it is for the plaintiff, if he so wishes, to appeal it. The appeal goes to the Court of the Metropolitan Archdiocese to which the diocese in which the first hearing took place belongs. If the case has in the first instance been heard before the Court of a metropolitan archdiocese, the case is appealed to that of a suffragan diocese which has been designated once and for all to hear such appeals—Versailles for Paris, Auton for Lyon.

The appeal is conducted in the same way as the first hearing. Often, however, there is no fresh interrogation of witnesses, their previous depositions being regarded as sufficient although it is always lawful to hear them again, and it may even be that witnesses are called who did not give evidence in the first hearing.

After the discussions have taken place in writing between the counsel and the defender of the bond, the sentence is delivered by the three judges on a majority vote, just as in the first hearing.

If the two sentences are in favour of nullity, the case is closed and the marriage is declared null and void. This is at least the general procedure, though there have been cases where the defender of the bond demanded a new examination of the case.

If the two sentences affirm that invalidity has not been proved, a new appeal by the plaintiff is not possible.

If the two judgments are in conflict—one finding for validity, the other for nullity—appeal is inevitable in order to obtain a definitive sentence. In every case, this appeal is made to the supreme tribunal for matrimonial cases—the Roman Rota. The foundation of this tribunal goes back to the beginning of the thirteenth century. It is impossible to be certain about the exact meaning of its name, there being as many opinions as there are historians who have studied the problem. Some derive the name from the fact that originally the judges sat on a bench shaped like a wheel (*rota*); others regard it as deriving its name from a mobile desk which was pushed around to each of the *auditores* whose duty was to examine the documents placed on it.

In 1908, during the pontificate of St. Pius X, the Rota was reorganized. Since that time, it is specially known for its jurisdiction in matrimonial cases; but its jurisdiction is far from being limited to this domain. It extends to all cases concerning ecclesiastical laws.

The judges or *auditores* of the Rota form a college of fourteen members presided over by a Dean. Each case is, as a rule, studied and decided by three judges. This group of three is known as the *Turnus* or turn. These "turns" are drawn up according to seniority, beginning with the Dean. In this way, the following groupings are arranged: 1, 2, 3; 2, 3, 4; 3, 4, 5, etc., until the grouping reaches 12, 13, 14, and begins its cycle again.

Several instances are possible when a case comes before the Rota, but in every case the nullity of a marriage will be definitely recognized, in accordance with the regulations of Canon Law, only if two sentences are in favour of nullity.

Several times in the course of our treatment, we have mentioned dispensation for non-consummated marriage, in order to distinguish it from a declaration of nullity, and we have also spoken in passing about the Pauline privilege. A few words on each of these will be useful to complete our explanation.

According to the common doctrine of theologians and the teaching of the Church, only a marriage validly contracted between two Christians (whether Catholics or not) is absolutely indissoluble after physical union has occurred.

Since this absolute indissolubility depends on two conditions: baptism of the two parties and carnal consummation, the absence of either of these is sufficient to empower the Church to intervene and free the parties from the marriage bond.

Consequently, when physical consummation of the marriage has not taken place, the dissolution of the conjugal bond is possible, even in the case of a marriage between Christians. But in such a case, there is no question of a judgment concerning the nullity of a contract, but only of a favour given for the good of the parties, and liable to be refused if the separation is not justified.

That is why there is no legal case in such matters, but simply an inquiry and a decision. The inquiry is made by the diocese under mandate from Rome. Its purpose is to establish two points: the non-consummation of the marriage, and the value of the reasons which oppose the continuation or resumption of life together, with its natural expression—carnal union. The proof of the first point is very easy where there has been no cohabitation; but if there has been cohabitation, even if only for a few days, it will be appreciated how difficult it may be to prove a case of non-consummation.

When the inquiry is finished, it is sent to Rome—not to the Rota but to the Sacred Congregation of the Sacraments. The latter, after examining the dossier, gives its opinion on the question: Are there sufficient grounds for advising the Sovereign Pontiff to grant a dispensation? For the object of all this work is merely to prepare the

Pope's decision; it is he alone, by virtue of his supreme jurisdiction, who makes the decision and thus suspends, for a particular marriage, the general rule of indissolubility.

As regards the first condition, it can be realized only if neither of the partners has been baptized or because one alone has been baptized. In the second set of circumstances, as much as in the first, the marriage is not sacramental, and therefore does not symbolize the union of Christ with His Church. It can be dissolved.

But the ecclesiastical authorities will act only to protect the faith of the newly converted, and they will do so only very rarely and in certain definite circumstances. These circumstances arise when a non-baptized person who has been married to a baptized person under the necessary dispensations, later on receives Baptism, and serious reasons exist for separating from the marriage partner and contracting a new marriage.

Much more frequent, however, will be cases where the Pauline privilege is invoked, when two unbaptized persons have been married and one of them is later on converted and receives Baptism.

What are the conditions which make it possible to have recourse to this privilege? In the first place, the still unbaptized partner must refuse Baptism, or at least refuse to live peaceably with the newly baptized and allow him or her complete freedom in practising the Christian life. In the second place, it is necessary to question the non-baptized person, in order to discover what are his dispositions relative to these different points; whence the *interpellations* as they are called.

If, when thus questioned, the non-baptized person refuses at least peaceful cohabitation, the neophyte has the right to re-marry, and the first marriage will automatically end the moment the second is contracted.

These dispositions, of which we have given only the broad outlines, based on a text of St. Paul (I Cor. vii. 12–14), have for a long time had practical application only in mission countries. To-day, however, the number of non-baptized persons in countries officially Christian is increasing, and it is therefore not surprising that the privilege has sometimes to be used apart from its traditional use in mission countries.

*   *   *

Such, then, in a summarized form, is the procedure followed for matrimonial cases in nullity and for the dispensations granted in cases of non-consummation. But we think that the reader would feel cheated, were we to omit a consideration of two questions which are always raised in connection with these cases: the question of delay and the question of finance.

Cases relating to marriage which come before the ecclesiastical courts are long drawn out, with the exception of an insignificant number where nullity is quite clearly present. Some people must wait ten years or more after the introduction of their claim, before they can obtain the final verdict.

This delay has, in the first place, a profound reason which is connected with all that we have just said. The Church takes seriously her role as guardian of the Sacrament. The rules which she has established, and the industry she demands from all those who are concerned with a case in nullity—judges, counsels, defenders of the bond—have nothing in common with the frequently summary procedure of civil divorce. What reasonable complaint can be levelled against this? The Church is not concerned with settling a piece of litigation, or with liberating marriage partners who, to use the secular phrase, are "temperamentally incompatible." She is merely concerned with establishing whether the marriage in question has been concluded in conditions which render it null and void, and it can be readily appreciated that, in these involved matters, the truth is difficult to establish. Nevertheless, we may hope that, for the peace of mind of those concerned, these delays may be reduced to a minimum.

To this first reason for the lengthy nature of the proceedings, other reasons of a more relative kind are, it is true, added.

To-day, for a variety of reasons, requests for declaration of nullity are more numerous than they were in former times. Moreover, vocations to the priesthood are becoming more and more rare in France. Are we to divert a considerable number of young priests from the direct parochial ministry, so that they can specialize in difficult studies and devote themselves to this judicial work, while parishes and apostolic work are left in the hands of a more and more depleted personnel? . . . On the other hand, a case may be held up pending the hearing of witnesses who refuse to testify. The Church has no power of subpoena to compel such testimony, and when such lack of co-operation is shown, is it any wonder that the case drags on and on, perhaps never reaching its conclusion? However painful these situations may be, they present an obstacle before which the judges are powerless.

As for the question of finance, the first objection raised by many people is that one needs to have money to go through with all this. And some add a rider to this, that it is often the absence of financial resources which makes these cases so long drawn out.

It is true that such complicated cases cannot be handled without considerable expense being incurred, and we perhaps need to remind ourselves that not one of the numerous priests who intervene in these cases is paid by the State. Is it any wonder, in such conditions, that the service is not free to all, and that those who can afford to do so are required to meet the expenses necessary for the prosecution of their case?

In a brochure on this subject, published in 1932, M. Cimetier wrote—

"Let us consider, in a concrete example, the considerable expenses which the study of a matrimonial case in nullity involves. In the case X . . . Y . . ., the dossier of the first instance of which is before us, there were sixteen witnesses, nine of whom were questioned in other dioceses by rogatory commissions. To examine these sixteen witnesses, whose depositions fill 114 pages of the dossier, it was necessary to hold sixteen sessions averaging two to three hours each, at which three priests were in attendance: the examining magistrate, the notary, and the defender of the bond. . . . Add to this the cost of correspondence, the citations, affidavits, the dispatch of documents, not to mention the payment of expenses to witnesses or of honoraria to experts. Remember that it was necessary to supply four or five carbon copies of the 240 pages of the dossier. . . . Bear in mind, too, that to study the dossier five priests—the counsel who drew up the case, the defender of the bond who replied, the three judges who reached a considered decision—had each to put in several days of work, and sometimes even weeks. And what was the exact sum demanded by the Curia from X . . . for this enormous quantity of work? Two thousand one hundred francs—a sum which just covered these expenses calculated at a minimum rate. Add to this that counsel's fee for a case which he must have had to follow up for a whole year, was 1,000 francs, we arrive at a sum total of 3,000 francs for the first instance."

Of course, to-day the sum would be greater; but in proportion to what it was in 1932, to-day's cost is far from keeping pace with the general rise of prices. It can be said that, in France, the amount required to defray the expenses of two normal instances is generally not much more than that of one civil divorce, at least if the case does not present any special difficulties.

Moreover, *legal aid*, partial or complete, can be obtained for cases that come before the diocesan courts and the Rota, just as much as it is for those of the civil courts. It is given to all who can prove that they are unable to meet the expenses incurred.

There is no better proof that great wealth is not necessary in order to win a case before the ecclesiastical court, than the statistics of cases judged in Rome. Unfortunately these are the only available statistics, because diocesan ones are not published.

Of 146 matrimonial cases judged by the Rota in 1950—(notice that this figure is higher than the preceding years)—there were 108 negative sentences and 38 affirmative ones (i.e. 26 per cent).

Complete or partial aid was given in 43 of these 146 cases (i.e. in 30 per cent of them).

What is of particular interest, however, is that there were 17 cases of legal aid among the 38 affirmative sentences. Of 43 cases where legal aid was granted, therefore, nearly 40 per cent were decided affirmatively; whereas among 103 cases where payment was made, there were only 21 positive sentences—that is to say, only 20 per cent.

These figures can leave no doubt in the mind of any impartial and upright man. Even when a person is poor, he or she need not fear to begin a case for nullity of marriage, and, if it is a good case, there is no reason why the demand should not be granted by the ecclesiastical courts.

That is all very well, it may be said; justice is not refused to poverty. But the rich still have an advantage, because they can gain their ends, however flimsy their case may be.[1]

Let us be serious about this. We have described the mechanism of a case in nullity. At what point could bribery and corruption be used in this complicated organism?

What good would it be to "buy" a judge? Would not the only result of this be to hold up the verdict? Because if the motives alleged are worthless, one of the courts will certainly pronounce a *non constat*, and the case will have to be taken to Rome.

As to buying the complicity of two courts, not to mention that of two defenders of the bond—such an idea belongs to the realm of the utterly outlandish, and no sane person could for a moment entertain it as a possibility.

At all events, witnesses can be suborned and documents can be forged. Ecclesiastical judges are only men and they can be deceived. But they know to what lengths certain plaintiffs will go to obtain a declaration of nullity at any price, and they are on their guard. And who could possibly suppose that people usually get away with this kind of thing?

And yet, there are some plaintiffs who are persuaded that it was their wealth which was decisive in securing the success of their case. How can this persuasion be reconciled with what we have just said?

---

[1] A recent case again underlines what little credence must be given to attacks against ecclesiastical judges. Three Italian Communist papers: *L'Unita, Il Paesa* and *Noi Donne* had organized a press campaign to spread the idea that it is sufficient to hand over a large sum of money in order to obtain declarations of matrimony nullity from the Rota, even when there are no juridical grounds for such a verdict. Prosecuted for defamation before the Italian courts by the Rota, the accused could produce no proof in support of their statements, and sentences of imprisonment and of fines were pronounced upon them.

There are two possible explanations. It may be that their case was a good one, but they thought to strengthen it by giving a large donation to the seminary fund or to the education fund. Because they received an affirmative sentence, they imagine that their banknotes counted for something and, through vanity and perhaps from a desire to conceal the real motive for nullity, they boast to friends and relatives that *they* knew how to handle the Clergy and how to profit by their weakness for money.

But stories about nullification of marriage bought at a big price are not always invented, the persons concerned having indeed paid heavily for the document they obtained. It was not to the ecclesiastical judges, however, that this money went. Such people have been the more or less conscious victims of the corrupt practices of those who undertook to fabricate false attestations of nullity on payment of exorbitant sums. This is a profitable piece of swindling, examples of which are known to have occurred in former times, and which can happen to-day.

In the *Correspondant* for October 10th, 1904, Mgr. Pisani, who for a long time was a Paris Judge related the following: "A woman came one day to the Paris Curia to ask if she could be permitted to depose before the ecclesiastical authority for a matrimonial case.—'Certainly, Madame; where do you intend to be questioned?'—'In Paris.'—'It is to here that you are summoned?'—'No, it is the rue Bleue.' A pseudo-court was known to be in operation there, which investigated cases of nullity and which gave verdicts which only needed to be pronounced by a competent authority. I have seen proceedings which came from that quarter; they were so admirably drawn up that more than one person would have been taken in by them!"

Here is another more recent case which we quote from M. Cimetier. "In late December, 1927, a rumour spread through the town of Nîmes that Mlle. G. J., daughter of a well-known businessman and six years married to M.B., had obtained from Rome a dispensation or declaration of the nullity of her marriage. This appeared most unlikely . . . for in the opinion of those who knew the circumstances of the marriage and the disagreements later resulting from it, the marriage was perfectly valid. . . . How great, therefore, was the amazement of the priest who had married them, when the following document was put into his hands—

Archdiocese of Paris.

"We, the Officials of the Paris Court, attest and certify that, on the advice of the Congregation of the Sacraments, dated January 29th, His Holiness Pope Pius XI has deigned to accord, in his audience of

February 15th, the dispensation from her marriage requested by the lady, G. J."

At first glance, the document seemed authentic; the wording, signatures, seal and all else were apparently in order. But the priest to whom it was given had, as we have said, good reasons for being suspicious. It was sent to Paris where it was recognized as a clever and skilful forgery. It must have cost a good round sum. The author was arrested in consequence of a complaint lodged about the matter, and was sentenced for fraud.

The moral of these accounts and of other similar ones that could be cited, is that any Catholic who thinks that he or she has solid reasons for seeking the nullification of marriage, should approach the diocesan Curia where all necessary information can be obtained, and should choose counsel only from among those listed there.

* * *

To sum up—

1. Marriages contracted in accordance with the canonical forms, are regarded as indissoluble once they have been physically consummated. In certain circumstances, if this consummation has not occurred, dispensation for both husband and wife is possible.

2. Despite appearances, certain marriages can be non-existent, that is, invalid, either because of a diriment impediment for which a dispensation was not obtained, or because of a defect in consent.

3. In the above circumstances, a case for a declaration of nullity can be made out, but the nullity will be definitively admitted only if two sentences are in its favour, the judges having reached moral certitude about the existence of the alleged defect.

4. These cases are lengthy because they are conducted seriously with the sole purpose of discovering the truth.

5. The expenses entailed, reckoned at a minimum, can be considerably increased because of the number of witnesses called, the experts consulted, etc., etc.

6. But the Church gives legal aid to all those whose economic situation justifies it; and there is no case where money can be relied on to secure a favourable verdict which is not founded on clear legal right.

THIRD STUDY

PSYCHOANALYSIS AND MORAL CONSCIENCE

EDITOR'S FOREWORD

It must always be difficult to introduce a collection of articles which relate to an empirical therapy that by reason of its novelty has not yet founded itself on the sure ground of philosophical and scientific premisses, with the result, that some of its manifestations in practice depend on unethical speculation, or are unethical in their therapeutic application. Psychiatry suffers from these defects and perhaps even more, from the fact that some of its most enthusiastic exponents are devoid of any systematic training either in science or philosophy. It can, however, do only good to have discussions such as those reported here, between reputable practitioners and moralists of the standing of Père Tesson. From such discussions we may hope to evaluate the claims made now and expect that, at some future date, it may be possible to separate the cockle which, at the moment, seems to grow so much more abundantly than the corn.

Those who pursue these studies should bear in mind that the average psychiatrist takes no account of the human soul and that, ignorant of its faculties, intellect and will, he is quite incapable of interpreting his observations in terms of them. This being the case, it is hardly surprising that so many fall into error and that the end term of so much psychiatric practice is to devalue human liberty and to declare the sinlessness of the aberrations described.

We share our corporeal sensory life with the animal world and if there were in us no more than a highly endowed animal nature, we should be conditioned to the same instinctive conduct as the animal, who responds instinctively to the images presented to his consciousness by present or past experience. Disease in the physical organism or variation in the external environment determining the external sensory receptions, can vary the pattern of these images and therefore the instinctive response. In the human, on the other hand, the soul through the judgment of the intellect, after it has evaluated the picture presented, both in terms of its physical content and the concept of the thing itself, as distinct from its appearances, judges it by standards of good and evil and either moves the will to accept the good against the urge of animal appetite or to reject the good, thus granting domination to the lower desire. The human is the less a man according as he misuses his freedom of will to choose what he knows to be evil. This war, between what we recognize as right conduct and what our lower powers urge upon us, is that disorder in which is the penalty of Adam's

Fall. In this conflict success depends on the help of Grace. Temptation from whatever source it arises is not sin. We are required to recognize it as such, and to oppose our wills to it, as the condition of our successful probation in this life. This is not to suggest that all psychiatric practice is to be condemned, but it is well to remember that it is not proved—it is, in fact, incorrect—that the pansexual method of a certain school of psychoanalysis is an indispensable integrating part of psychotherapy which is serious and worthy of the name (Pius XII, Sept. 13th, 1952), nor "can we consider as lawful, without further explanation, the bringing to the level of consciousness of all the imaginations, emotions and sexual experiences which lie dormant in the memory and unconscious" (Pius XII, April 13th, 1953).

It should be evident that if the extroversion of past experience constitutes a temptation to present or future sin, it cannot be lawful to achieve that extroversion, nor may a patient reveal secrets entrusted to him indiscriminately. There is much in our disordered nature which must be inhibited or suppressed until sublimated into the whole service of God, which is the destiny of each one of us. Nor is it true that the highest state of man is one in which there has occurred a total surrender of the "ego" and its personal assertiveness. Pius XII says, "the thesis is formulated that the unconditioned extroversion of the ego is the fundamental law of congenital altruism and of its dynamic tendencies. This is a logical, psychological, and ethical error. There exists in fact a defence, an esteem, a love and a service of one's personal self, which is not only justified but demanded by psychology and morality. . . . Christ, then, proposes as the rule of love of one's neighbour charity towards oneself, not the contrary. Applied psychology would undervalue this reality if it were to describe all consideration of the ego as psychic inhibition, error, a return to a former state of development, under the pretext that it is contrary to the natural altruism of the psychic being."

The psychiatrist can probe into the depth of one's animal life and note the patterns registered and their deviation, if any, from what he considers to be normal but he cannot see into the soul; the most that he can do, and indeed may do, is to assist the patient to apply his intellect and will to achieve an ethical solution of the problems of his daily life and, whilst recognizing their import, to know that he is called upon to avoid the circumstances that render them urgent and to achieve their control by the help of Grace.

Every Catholic knows that sin deprives our souls of the presence of the Blessed Trinity, for we are Temples of God, and that it is our duty so to order and govern ourselves that the demands of our fallen nature are not acceded to, and that we achieve our highest mode of living when our control is so perfect that no sin opposes the activity of the Trinity in our souls. Those who have lost this Presence by gravely culpable sin, can know God only as one who is absent; the just know God within them and psychiatry has no proper function except when it assists men to that end.

PREFACE TO FRENCH EDITION

PSYCHOANALYSIS is still young and often totalitarian in its explanations, but it now occupies an important place among the techniques which deal with knowledge and investigation of the human psychism. Originally, it was spread abroad by those who were more enamoured of sensation-mongering than of the rigour of scientific truth, and as a result many of our contemporaries regard it with very understandable suspicion.

But it has now become imperatively necessary to confront Morality with Psychoanalysis, and Psychoanalysis with Morality. It is with this in view that the *Centre d'Études Laënnec* has undertaken a study of the relations between Psychoanalysis and Moral Conscience. The results published in this volume are simply the fruits of a first attempt.

MORAL CONSCIENCE AND PSYCHIATRY

IF there is one act in which man has long claimed the right to behave as a free, autonomous being, it is the act of moral conscience. What a unique prerogative it is to be able to say: "I see good and evil"—and to be thus enabled to shed light on one's way and to make one's decisions knowing their grounds!

More and more pointed and vigorous attacks have been made in the past fifty years on this originality which till now has been attributed to moral conscience. Though these attacks have come from different directions, they all agree in denouncing as an illusion the claim of moral conscience to be the product of the free and independent personality. When he thinks himself to be most free and most completely master of himself, it is then that man is most surely led by forces which have no spiritual character whatever, in the classic sense of the word.

When we decide: "This is my duty as my mind shows it to me"— the sociologists tell us that we are merely the unconscious interpreters of society, mere drops of water lifted with the ocean's swell.

The psychologists come in their turn, and if their statements are not so blunt, they are nevertheless formidable.

They say to man: "You think that it is in yourself that you find that high spirituality which affirms itself when you say that you recognize an obligation of conscience. But alas, the stakes have been played long ago. You think you have discovered the call of good and of duty, and perhaps you do no more than yield to a sentiment of guilt written in your nature because formerly you have desired the death of your father. What seems to you a victory of the spirit is no more than a desire for self-punishment."

We shall not enter into a discussion of sociological theories. However, we of the *Centre Laënnec* considered that it was important to attempt a study of the relations between psychiatry—and especially psychoanalysis—on the one hand, and morality and religion on the other. Many psychiatrists, indeed, have abandoned the philosophical doctrines of materialistic scientific thought, formerly accepted without discussion by Charcot and Freud, and they are attempting to fix the frontiers of these disciplines as well as their relations. Books like those of MM. Baruk, Odier, and Richard are very significant in this connection.

On the other hand, the defensive attitude of distrust which Catholic theologians and philosophers took to Freudian interpretations, is beginning to disappear. This attitude is not being replaced by one of blind acceptance, but by a desire for discussion and the interchange of ideas.

I. DESCRIPTION OF MORAL CONSCIENCE

This section is an introductory one. Since the words *moral conscience* will come up often in our discussion, it is indispensable to recall briefly its nature, to enumerate the elements which it gathers into a vital synthesis, and to examine the modifications or the contributions which psychiatry would make to this traditional description.

The first part of this exposition may perhaps seem at first sight superfluous; I do not doubt that it will be so for some, and I beg their pardon in advance. But I am convinced it will not be so for those whose whole philosophical equipment is merely the confused memory of their lesson in high school or college. We have the right to demand that the philosopher or the theologian who wishes to judge the value of therapeutic and biological techniques, should consult specialists in these sciences and learn to know what he is talking about. It is likewise desirable that doctors and biologists should not undertake to solve the most difficult problems of psychology, morality and metaphysics, with no equipment for doing so other than very rudimentary knowledge dressed up in ill-defined terms, supplemented by the common sense which we all possess. Conscientious work is necessary on the part of both theologian and doctor, if our collaboration is to have definite and practical results.

Conscience is a judgment of the mind

What is conscience in general and moral conscience in particular?

There probably survives from our philosophy class an impression of conscience as something static. It will be represented, according to one's fancy, as a spectator who watches a picture, or as a zone of light, very bright at the centre, shadowed at the edges and shaded into the night of the unconscious, with psychic phenomena moving about in that zone like pedestrians on a footpath. Modern psychology has happily laid this conception to rest. Conscience supposes activity of the mind. A characteristic of the mind is that it is transparent to itself, with the result that when it concentrates on itself in order to act, it cannot fail to see its action.

Moral conscience is the mind acting, but acting in a special province. What is this province?

Usually, when we act, we choose the means to satisfy a particular tendency, to attain a certain objective or to reach a desired result. A boy who wishes to begin his medical studies, first makes inquiries, applies to a college, enters his name, etc. But the presupposition of morality, whose legitimacy I do not aim to establish in this section, is that in all our free actions, we do not seek simply to satisfy a tendency or a group of tendencies, or to realize an idea; we act *as men*, in order to attain an end, to obtain something of value, which interests us as men.

From the particular viewpoint of the limited objective, of professional success, of artistic culture, we pass on to view things from the standpoint of our *whole* being. Once again, we judge as human beings.

But this viewpoint takes for granted that there is in man, behind the diversity of his functions and his activities, a profound unity, and that we are able to apprehend ourselves in that unity, and to perceive how we should conduct ourselves as human beings.

Now, it is the same element of *mind* that creates this unity in us, and which judges the value of actions and of things.

We must not think of the mind as something apart from other elements of which we are composed, but as virtually united to them. Many important consequences flow from this nature of man. Our mind can achieve its purposes only by using the other forces of our being. Our actions, even when most free, will be always complex, being comprised of corporal, instinctive, sentimental and intellectual elements. What constitutes the end of man *as man* are those spiritual purposes of which we shall speak shortly; but we can seek and find these only in particular activities. It is in his social relations, in his professional work, in his sexual, family and civic life that man is able and ought to behave *as befits man*. If you have grasped this, you will see immediately why morality intervenes to forbid euthanasia or therapeutic abortion. It is a mere chimera and an act of hypocrisy to attempt to place and to "zone" the moral and religious life outside all other activities. It is to pretend that man is an angel and a beast, and that this angel and this beast do not act in association but independently; whereas man is, in reality, a spirit which expresses itself in physical, sensible and social activities. Moreover, when we realize that, by this effort, we respond to our vocation as sons of God, it is clear what great value human life can have.

Yet another characteristic of our human condition must be pointed out. Since the human spirit is not separated but intimately mingled with lower elements, it is a cramped spirit, hemmed in on all sides, working out a destiny. And it is to this situation that it must adapt itself so as to satisfy its own demands unflinchingly. We do not choose our moment of birth, our country, our family, our sex; moreover, we are obliged to endure not only external events and their repercussions on us, but also our own inner drama and the deficiencies and weaknesses from which we wish, sometimes passionately wish, to escape. We need not recall in any detail the well-known pathetic cries of St. Paul, and the answer that was made to him: "My grace is sufficient for thee." We cannot repeat too often that man's consciousness is not a registering machine, carefully guarded against anything that might injure it. It is a spirit which is engaged in a hard conflict and which must judge in fever and fatigue, and lift itself to the light even when it is most tempted to turn away from it. It is this which marks our condition as created beings prone to sin. But in spite of these difficult conditions, it is the spirit that judges within us, and it is the spirit that must judge people and things.

For example, when a doctor realizes that he must husband the last moments of life in a dying person, and not treat him as a beast which has ended its days and which can, without more ado, be dispatched a few days sooner than its natural term, he makes a judgment which recognizes in the dying person a unique value which he cannot sacrifice.

We can now answer our question: "What is moral conscience?" It is, in the conditions which we have seen, a judgment of the mind; or rather, it is the mind in its judgment when it discovers, in an action which the subject is about to perform, what will respect spiritual values and human values and what will run counter to those values and tend to destroy them in oneself or in others.

Moral conscience is the mind realizing itself in a judgment of this kind.

The analysis of judgment

Psychologists have long taught us that judgment is a synthesis, that is to say, a unifying act which assembles diverse elements.

We find three principal elements in the judgment of moral conscience, which we shall examine in their order.

The first principle is that good must be done. Then come the definitions of this "good." Finally, there are the feelings which arise in us when we are confronted with good and evil.

Good must be done

However we define good, its primary and essential character is that it is *obligatory*. We are certainly not bound to accomplish all the good of which we have knowledge; but when we wish to act, we must do so within the limits of what is good. In certain circumstances, we have not even the choice between several good ways, one way only being open to us. Whence does good get this imperative character?

Only one answer seems possible to me, and we have seen what that answer must be. The human spirit appraises beings, and discovers their nature.

If this spirit is caught up in a social life and a life of the senses, and we have seen that this is so; if it directs the multiple actions of a subject in relation to other beings, persons and things, this spirit will necessarily demand, under pain of contradicting and denying itself, that the relative value of beings with which it enters into communication shall be respected.

The deep root of moral obligation is none other than a demand of the spirit which wills that each should be treated according to degree.

That is why, when we decide to act, if we are sufficiently clear-headed to recognize the nature and the import of what we are doing, we feel that we ought to act in such and such a way. Then, when we have acted, we have the satisfaction of being at peace with ourselves, or we have a feeling of inner contradiction, of irreparable loss, according to the manner in which we have acted.

What is good?

We possess a kind of spiritual instinct which lets us know what is good, but a work of elaboration is nevertheless necessary in order that we may answer all the questions posed by human life, especially when that life is as complicated as it is to-day. This work will be an investigation of values—an investigation so vast, so delicate, that we cannot hope to carry it out alone. To do good is said to be easier than to know good, and this is indeed true. To know what should be done is often difficult, as is sufficiently evident from the problems of conscience that arise for the individual and for the collectivity. Has one the right to torture a spy in order to discover the organization of which he is part? Is it lawful to commit suicide rather than risk revealing matters of national defence to the enemy? etc.

That is why, in this domain as in many others, we are the heirs to the social milieu and to the ideas that reign in our time. It is in the accepted language of the group that our spirit knows itself and expresses itself. Good will perhaps be discovered by us, but most often we receive our ideas of good from previous generations and from the life around us. Among certain tribes, aged parents are put to death; so too are little girls born into an already overcrowded family. What would a man of such a tribe answer if he were asked whether it is good or evil to kill his aged parents who can no longer follow the tribe? What possible answer could he give except to repeat and accept the judgment common to the tribe?

But ideas change with the passing of the centuries, and this is the result of two principal influences. Firstly, modifications in conditions of living cause things to be seen under a different aspect. Marx's theory is not completely false, which holds that the intellectual structure, that is to say the mass of ideas passing current in a social group, is a result of economic conditions.

Then there are the reactions, the moral inventions, of great personalities. One of the most important examples of this influence, which is often cited, is that of Socrates. He used to buttonhole people in the market-place with questions about the just and the unjust, so that afterwards, when they had occasion to speak of justice, they could not forget their conversations with Socrates.

In this connection, we must refer to the immense import of the Judaeo-Christian Revelation. More than all other currents of thought, it was to teach us what good is, and also many other matters of first importance for our moral life. In particular, this revelation shows us the real nature of man, because it reveals him in his relations with God —these relations being the solid basis on which we can build a whole system of morality.

We have, then, from this Word of God, absolute rules, definite light on certain points of human conduct; but it must be noticed that an effort of research still remains necessary. Christian reflection is always actively concerned with the great primary principles of charity, justice, the value of man as man, his value as the adopted son of God, etc. Such reflection will also be subject to the influence of external circumstances: economic or social conditions, current philosophical systems, newly discovered problems. From one century to the next, in the very heart of the most authentic Christianity where the rules of the Catholic faith are most faithfully obeyed, there will be changes of perspective, new unions between ideas, just as there are differences of temperament and of spiritual tastes among the saints. Thus, in the eighteenth century, we find, even among the least Jansenistic thinkers, ideas about the small number of the elect, which will certainly not be those of the nineteenth century.

But whatever variations of light there may be, the Christian has a considerable advantage over the non-Christian. He is guided by the Church and by the Gospel as taught by the Church. In many circumstances where the unbeliever remains in ignorance and in doubt, the Christian can know what he ought to do. Our weakness finds this a nuisance, sometimes, because we are tempted to prefer darkness to light. Nevertheless, it is very consoling, because we know that God Himself shows us the road we must follow.

I have spent what may seem a disproportionate amount of time in describing our dependence, in our search for good, on the human situation of which we are part. This is not, however, a digression, and I have not forgotten our question: How are we to define good?

So far from being a digression, these few historical reminders show us that we always decide on what good is in accordance with our general conception of the world and of man. Thus we shall find as many doctrines of morality and as many ways of defining good, as there are systems and philosophies of nature and of human destiny.

For our part, we take up immediately the position of the Christian faith, and we can define good only by reference to the doctrine and to the Person of Christ. The fundamental need of our nature incites us to realize more and more the manhood in us; and the only finished model of manhood we know is Christ.

But, you will say, this is to separate us at once from those who do not share our beliefs, and to refuse to build a human system of morality acceptable to all men of good will. This is not so, because it is man and all real human values that Christ came to save. However, let us face up to the fact that the truths which Christ teaches us about man are baffling to our minds, darkened and weakened by sin. We can scarcely look ourselves in the face and recognize ourselves for what we really are. The reform of our being which the Gospel proposes to us, implies the abnegation and death of "the man of sin" who is in each of us. Those who are not of the Faith will not consider such transformation necessary. We must renounce the hope of getting all men to agree on a common moral doctrine. All that one could hope to achieve is agreement on the most general principles and on some particular points.

However this may be, we can distinguish three zones in good: the social zone, the zone of values, the zone of liberty.

Man is a social being, and however primitive the society in which he lives, he will have at least a family. Order is necessary if life in society is to be made possible; and order is the regulation of different activities, which will be determined by custom, manners or laws. The good which imposes itself on the conscience will often be that of the social, legal order—for example, to pay one's taxes.

We are heirs to our social environment, but the obligations imposed by that environment do not cover the whole of the moral field. Far from it. The pharisee is he who identifies legal prescriptions with morality. Underlying the social order is the world of values; and if I am willing to obey the law, it is because the law is the guardian of certain values.

A *value* is something worthy of being sought, and there are several kinds of values.

Essential moral value, according to M. Le Senne, is that of the militant *ego*, of the *ego* which desires to build itself and to build its world, and not allow itself to be pulled along by determinism, by passion or by social forces. Let us at least bear in mind that a routine observance of rules and of precepts is not sufficient to attain to the moral life. A struggle is necessary against externals and against one's self; the direction of one's life must be taken firmly in hand, so as to give to that life the desired meaning and preserve it in spite of obstacles and of failures. All this supposes voluntary effort. The human value of a man is first judged sincerely according to the answer he would give to the question: "What *are you making* of your life?" Here we emphasize the creative initiative implied by the verb *to make*.

But movement is towards a goal. We wish . . . but for what? It is here that we come back to what I said earlier: we wish for human qualities in ourselves and in others.

And it is this which constitutes the most profound zone of morality, the search for, and the growing affirmation of, liberty.

There is within us an initial liberty, but it too must be won. Liberty, it has been said, is at once the instrument and the end of moral life. To be free is to be drawn only by the attraction of good, or, in Christian and more exact language, by the love of God.

And thus the problem arises for every man of winning liberty by discovering moral values and by devoting himself to carrying these values into practice, as well as by fulfilling his due obligations to the society of which he is a member.

All this does not go smoothly. Laws sometimes run counter to values, or appear to do so. Values clash with values, and a man must stand up against fixed ideas, collective passions, and tyrannical powers. But let us sidestep these discussions which would carry us too far.

The emotions

An affective movement accompanies every tendency which seeks to satisfy itself within us, and every activity which we exercise. Moral life does not escape this general law, for an important factor of affective elements enters into all its degrees and all its phases.

Here, in very brief outline, is the process which results in the production of a feeling. A feeling is the affective echo which is provoked when we perceive the object of a tendency, either directly or as recalled to mind. But the perception of an object can undergo ceaseless modification, can be enriched and strengthened, or on the contrary can lose its liveliness. The affective reaction will be coloured by all these variations.

The first consequence which results from the nature of affectivity and from its mechanism, is that it links the Ego with the world and

makes the universe present to us. The mind discovers the qualities of
beings and fixes their hierarchy; but it is the affectivity which
evaluates them for us. What does not interest me does not exist
for me.

In certain psychoses, the patient is capable of establishing perfectly
logical chains of reasoning and of seeing clearly what he should do;
but he decides: "I utterly scoff at it!" He has no longer any personal
links with the world which surrounds him.

It can therefore be said, as something of the utmost importance,
that our affectivity, our feelings, will determine our psychological
positions in relation to persons and to things. "For children," writes
Maurois, "words have no definite meaning. They signify more or less
extensive zones of emotion with vague boundaries; and in this respect,
many adults remain children all their lives" (*Memoires,* 1, p. 18). It is
true, not only of words but of all the beings which surround us and
with which we come in contact, that they signify for us zones of
affectivity. We could be defined by the totality of our zones and of our
affective reactions, their correspondences or their oppositions. *X* is this
man who detests this, admires that, is insensible to pity, is at times a
prey to such and such fear, etc.

The great discovery of Freud has been that concerning the genesis
of our affectivity, for up to his time, it had scarcely gone beyond the
state of description. Nothing or almost nothing was known about the
awakening of our affective reactions, their fixation and their association
through a mechanism analogous to that of conditioned reflexes. It is
to Freud that we must trace what is called, in Germany, depth
psychology.

Our affectivity puts us, so to speak, in a certain place in the world,
and it will therefore necessarily have a very great influence on our
judgment, since one sees things from the point of view commanded
by one's position. It is a well known fact that, in order to reach truth,
the mind must take up a very critical attitude to those decisions which
tend to arouse personal reactions of an emotional kind.

These few general ideas will help us to understand better the role
of affectivity in the moral life, and especially in the judgment of
conscience. But we must first examine more closely the word
affectivity which we have employed, and notice that it is equivocal or
at least lacking in precision. Although, like our personality, our
affectivity is *one*, it cannot be denied that it changes its nature, so to
speak, according to the activity which it accompanies and according
to the object which awakens it.

In the highest reaches, there will be an affectivity corresponding to
the motions of our mind, to our spiritual *élan.* When we perceive

what befits us as free beings, and what it is towards which we are directed by our creation and by our vocation as beings made in the image of God, we cannot fail to be profoundly moved and to feel, at the same time, a desire to respond to this appeal. It is therefore in this higher part of our being that we shall find sentiments of love of God, love of good, moral obligation, selfless love of others, etc.

Then a zone opens up where the variety of sentiments is almost infinite, whether they show themselves in a positive form, or—as is more frequently the case—take on a negative appearance: "the fear of destroying or of injuring . . . the fear of violating a rule," etc. (Le Senne, *Traité de Morale*, p. 327).

On the other hand, because of the unity of our life, sentiments of diverse origin will sometimes interfere with moral sentiments, properly so called, either by way of addition or even of substitution. The intervention of social sentiments will be particularly important, since the moral conscience is nearly always aroused by contact with the prohibitions and prescriptions emanating from the family or the group. The fear, admiration or respect provoked by the authority of the family or of a wider community will easily insinuate itself into the judgment of conscience.

Moreover, we shall never experience such and such a refinement of affectivity in its pure state, but it will be experienced as dominant notes accompanied by multiple harmonies of a very varied nature. Thus it is that even in the soul of a great saint, the most exalted, the most purified love of God will not entirely suppress the seeking of his own happiness, and will even allow the fear caused by Divine Majesty to exist side by side with it.

Hence, thanks to this intercommunication of affective zones, we can explain the contamination and the substitutions revealed by Freud. The instinctive sentiment of guilt will succeed in confounding itself with the sense of sin. We shall reproduce unconsciously, in our attitude towards God, as well as towards the holders of political or religious power, the attitude which we have taken up towards our father.

We gather, therefore, that there is no moral life, nor any judgment of conscience, without affective irradiations, and that there are mysterious relations between the multiple currents of affectivity, because man is a living *unity* and not a simple association of functions.

The living person

To conclude this first part of our article, we shall draw some conclusions about moral life and the judgment of conscience, from this idea of the biological and psychic unity of man.

We judge of good and evil with our whole selves—with our past (the past for which we are indebted to others, the past for which we are ourselves responsible), and with our whole present personality—when we take up a position towards good, towards others, towards God. An effort to mobilize our good will, is therefore necessary to discovering true morality. Our mind is, of course, by nature prone to judge. But to do so correctly, in the moral as in other domains, it will be necessary not only to be *aware* of the elements of emotion that may exercise an influence, but also to free oneself from their danger. Moral truth is often reached only at the end of a road of ascesis and painful searching, as the reward of generosity in seeking. A moral problem is never solved in the cold light of exclusively intellectual principles, like a problem in mathematics. Every time we are faced with the making of a free decision, the question arises for us: What do you wish to become? Light will be given to us or withheld from us according to the answer which we give.

Now, it happens that we refuse to place ourselves at the precise point which commands all perspectives, where the adherence demanded of us takes on sense and meaning; and nevertheless, in turning our back on the source of light, we still pretend to see clearly. This is the false conscience—the conscience which lies to itself and blinds itself with a false clarity. The expression "false conscience" is of recent origin, but the old spiritual writers knew the reality very well, and have devoted many pages of analyses to the ruses of the man who, half-voluntarily, deceives himself.

From this it is clear what must be thought of the excuse so often invoked: "I have my own conscience, and it allows me to act in this manner." Our conscience is indeed our supreme authority in the order of action; but we are, to a great extent, responsible for our conscience. We see what we wish to see.

The rectitude of our moral judgment depends, principally, on two preliminary conditions—serious information and a generous desire for good. It is no matter for wonder, therefore, if our judgment is modified with the passage of time. Indeed, the moral and religious life is too often regarded as a series of decisions and of actions which, succeeding one another, have only a very loose connection one with the other. This is wrong. While it is true that the unification towards which we tend is never perfect, and is indeed very sketchy for certain people, nevertheless there is gradually created within us a deep current, taking one direction or another, which ends by investing all our free actions with a common character. Our moral and religious, or our amoral or immoral behaviour-pattern emerges and strengthens its features ever more and more.

II. Psychiatric Elements

What we have said above shows that the rectitude and the strength of the judgment of conscience are precarious, that they are always evolving and always menaced by a host of enemies. They are subject to the attacks of disease—a fact known long before our day. It has long been recognized that organic diseases have more or less extensive repercussions on the strength of the mind, and that there are demential conditions in which the mind more or less completely founders.

Nevertheless, scientific psychiatry came into existence quite recently. Since of all psychiatric methods, it is the methods of analysis which have made the most abundant contributions to psychology and which raise the most difficult problems for us, it is of them that I shall speak almost exclusively.

I shall deal with two questions—with one which concerns psychoanalysis, and with one which concerns the psychoanalyst.

The first can be worded like this: Have not the discoveries of psychoanalysis overthrown our idea of moral conscience?[1] No, I do not believe they have. Psychoanalysis brings us new elements of which we must take account; but it is not difficult, I think, to integrate them in the description of conscience I have given above.

The great work of Freud and of his followers was the discovery of the dynamism of the unconscious, and the invention of means by which this unconscious could be known and investigated.

The psychic unconscious, like the conscious part of the mind, develops from the first moments of life.

In the period of infancy, as Dr. Odier says, the instinctual tendencies often behave violently towards the first object capable of satisfying them, and attach themselves passionately to that object. But this passionate *élan* and this affective fixation do not fail to create conflicts with the milieu. The older, generally adult, group of human beings which receives the child, has already its ideas, its customs, its reactions, a complete system of behaviour in which the newcomer must take his place; and as he is malleable, in process of formation, totally dependent on others, he must perforce undergo these influences without being able to put up an active defence against them.

[1] The object of this conference—primarily, to describe moral conscience—does not allow us to treat with necessary completeness the relations between psychoanalysis and the moral life. We shall content ourselves with indicating the remarkable work of Dr. Odier: *Les deux Sources consciente et inconsciente de la vie morale*, which deserves to be fully discussed. With scarcely any qualification, we find ourselves in easy agreement with the principal theses of this book, and our divergence concerns almost exclusively the use of certain expressions. But it is well known how important are questions of terminology. However this may be, all directors of conscience ought to know this book thoroughly, and those who are *au courant* with Catholic spiritual tradition will not be perplexed by it.

For example, the child who desires that his mother should be with him cannot have her always to himself, for he is obliged to share her with father, with brothers and sisters, with strangers even. . . .

Again, the first sexual impulses of the child are freely expressed, but the family reacts against this. The baby is told: "That's dirty, naughty. . . ."

Since the child's tendencies may not be spontaneously followed and are not destroyed, they cloak themselves. They are repressed; they leave the field of consciousness.

Does this mean that they will no longer intervene, that they are as though dead? Not at all; they are simply masked. They seek their satisfaction by hiding behind other tendencies, and in so doing they deceive the subject himself.

Not only have certain forms of tendencies become unconscious, while remaining active, but the prohibitions of which they were the object in early infancy have followed the same course of evolution. Thus is formed a whole system of censures and of prohibitions condemning the instincts and impulses of the person. This totality of prohibitions is the masked custodian of the *Ego*, and is called the *Super-Ego*.

And henceforward we can trace the pattern of what will happen. One believes oneself to be acting from generosity, from a spirit of asceticism, of religion . . ., while in fact an unconscious motive is playing the principal role in this action. Hence the unconscious motivation which is the cause of the act, and the conscious motivation which is simply a pretence.

"The purpose of analysis is to reveal us to ourselves: on the one hand, our needs, our desires, our unconscious tendencies; on the other, our unconscious rules of morality. It is between these two groups of forces that our conflicts take place." (Richard: *La Psychanalyse et la Morale*, p. 19).

What does the moralist think of these statements?

When the facts have been correctly studied and exactly described, we must recognize the value of the contribution which is given to us towards knowing human nature. Moral science can be constituted only by reference to metaphysics and psychology. All those, therefore, who are students of the elements of our personality, the genesis and play of its activities, must be duly grateful to these sciences.

We have already seen that our moral judgment can be false. Thanks to psychoanalysis, we learn that a real substitution can occur, that we can regard as a judgment of conscience what is really not one at all. This is a new acquisition to our knowledge, and we shall not refuse to take it into consideration.

We are also told that it is possible to rectify these errors by an appropriate treatment.[1] We rejoice at this. Every method capable of re-establishing or of strengthening our interior equilibrium is of immense value; for, although the moral life can co-exist with psychic deficiencies and disorders, it will have much to gain from the re-establishing of psychic health.

But some remarks are nevertheless called for.

The first is very general, and concerns an important view of Freudian psychology. At the very time when he discovered the dynamism of affective growth, Freud, I think, subscribed to the associationist and materialist psychology of his time, which regards the human psychism as an assemblage of phenomena and of functions. The Master of Vienna considered the child only as a being entirely composed of instinct, whose tendencies develop such and such habitual reactions according to whether they are accepted or opposed by their milieu. But the child is not solely a mass of affectivity, for he is already a human being. From the beginning of his life, his mind is at work within him, with all the complexity which its presence implies. That his affectivity is often injured by contact with others is undeniable. May we not believe that his need to understand is also often baffled by the conduct of grown-ups, and that the little man will have secret scars as a result?

At a very tender age, at three years, sometimes at two years of age, certain children have some realization of religious values, not only of their imaginative, sentimental or social expression, but of their spiritual reality. But in order to notice this, one must oneself be sensitive and responsive to the spiritual life.

However comprehensive may have been the Freudian inventory of infancy, will the psychologists blame us for saying that it appears to us to be incomplete? Freud's work falls into three sections: his metaphysics, his psychology, his therapy. The first is rejected as obsolete, but the other two are jealously preserved. However, it seems to me that his psychology itself calls for correction and supplementing.

The second observation concerns the *Super-Ego* and moral conscience. Many psychoanalysts regard these two terms as synonymous, but this is a confusion which must be cleared up completely if we wish to enter on discussions profitable both to morality and to psychoanalysis.

This confusion rests on a false idea of the nature of moral life, and it is easy to discover its origin. The psychoanalysts have taken their conception of the moral life from certain sociological theorists, for whom the moral life is an adaptation of the individual life to the social

---

[1] We leave to psychiatrists the task of discussing the value and the limits of this treatment.

milieu. Man, a bundle of instincts, can live in a group only if he curbs and sacrifices his impulses so as not to trespass on the domain of his neighbour. When we control our instincts in order that life in society may be possible, we are acting morally, and the very society which greets the new-born person, proposes to him and imposes on him rules which will shape his activities.

Since the *Super-Ego* is the first depository of family influences, it is regarded by many psychoanalysts as an instrument of adaptation of the individual to his group, as a moral conscience, when this is not regarded as a revelation of divine origin.[1]

I do not think we have under-estimated the importance of the social contribution in the formation of our moral being. It is quite evident that a training which teaches us self-mastery will be of considerable assistance in the practice of justice, benevolence and charity. But it is liberty which characterizes the moral life, properly so called—liberty with regard to external impulses and automatisms; liberty which is not absolute, but which uses all these subordinate forces for its own ends. It therefore appertains to the free person either to establish his relations with his entourage, or—as more frequently happens—to enter into conscious relations with others which result from his past and from his present situation. The mother of a family is drawn by nature to love her child, to work hard for her child, to risk her life for her child. But these acts have moral value only if they are understood, willed, purified, so to speak, and lifted from the natural order to the order of conscience.

To-day, following Kant, a distinction is very often made between morality and religion, the first being regarded as obedience to law, to duty, while the second is regarded as belonging to the order of feeling and of belief. And since law is enacted by the authority which has charge of the common good, there arises that equivalence between the social and the moral which we repudiate. As against such equivalence, the quasi-unanimous opinion of Catholic theologians holds that the moral life is to be defined according to the relation of our being and our activities with the last end—with God. It is the attitude which we consciously and freely adopt towards the divine image written in ourselves and in others, which will make our life moral or immoral.

For all these reasons, we cannot accept the idea of an "unconscious

---

[1] "Is this individual or collective Super-Ego"—writes Dr. Laforgue—"otherwise than the representation of what is above the Ego, that is to say, above man, and from which his sensibility cannot hope to escape because the Super-Ego is an integral part of it? Is not the Super-Ego the concretization of all the educative influences of the past, and therefore a sort of incarnation of the same forces which the believer calls 'divine'?"—*Psyché*, No. 6, p. 397. Is there any need to point out how such summary assertions, so destitute of objectivity, make all serious discussion impossible?

moral system"; such "system" consists of impulses and unconscious motivations which disturb the judgment of conscience.[1]

Much can also be said about another identification—that of the sentiment of guilt with the sense of sin.

The sentiment of guilt results from the attack on, or from the infraction of, unconscious censures by tendencies which have become equally unconscious. Although the subject, unaware of the origin of this malaise, may trace it to a real or imaginary fault, the sentiment of guilt is simply an affective reaction and only seems to be a deliberate evaluation.

Now, the sentiment of moral guilt necessarily implies a deliberate evaluation, and the sense of sin, in the Christian meaning of this term, can be given only by faith; for it is revelation alone which can teach us what we are in the sight of God—sinners and redeemed.

We must dintinguish, therefore, between *the sentiment of guilt, the appreciation of moral fault*—which every man, whether a Christian or not, experiences when he fails to obey the prescriptions of his conscience —and *the sense of sin.*[2]

Finally, and here we are in accord with some psychoanalysts, when psychoanalysis has revealed to the person the hidden cause of his reactions and has delivered him from their infantile form, the moral problem still remains untouched. Psychoanalytic liberation does not signify enfranchisement from the moral law; it signifies the ferreting out of unconscious motivations. It is a preliminary work. When it has been done, it remains for the moral life to be formed according to its own laws.

We have little time remaining in which to speak of the *psychoanalyst* and of the moral problems raised by psychoanalytic cure. I shall confine myself therefore to a few rapid observations. It is the psycho-analysts themselves who present the principal difficulty here, for they are not in agreement as to the attitude which the doctor should adopt towards his patient. According to Dr. Pasche, the therapeutist ought to abstain carefully from passing judgments and from giving advice of a moral kind. His role consists in revealing to the subject whom he analyses the hidden mechanisms which enslave him, and in severing

---

[1] Moreover, these interventions of the Super-Ego do not entirely suppress moral life. This is quite clear, for who is there among us who is completely freed from it? And there are great saints whose psychism was subjected to strong neurotic influences.

It can even happen that a badly resolved complex is contained in a whole attitude which is profoundly moral and religious. And we, psychoanalysts and moralists, shall have to make some adjustments of focus which will probably contain many surprises for us.

[2] There remains the question of education. Many educators are tactless and provoke morbid fears in the child by calling up the fires of hell for every peccadillo; but a healthy religious and moral education cannot exclude the idea of sin or of the consequences of our faults.

affective associations dating from infancy, precisely because the patient is unwilling to co-operate in his own cure. He does not agree to be substituted, by the mechanism of transference, for the object which has formerly determined the fixation. He is simply a blank screen which refracts the light.

If this is so, we have nothing to say, because the personal ideas and personal attitude of the psychoanalyst will have nothing to do with the treatment. Whether he is Christian, Jew or unbeliever, his treatment will depend only on his professional worth. He acts simply as a technician, as a cardiologist or as a phthisiologist.

But we do not believe that this impossibility and this neutrality hold good for all psychoanalysts. On the other hand, certain philosophers or theologians are loath to admit that the psychoanalyst can prescind from his conception of man and of his own moral position, when he is treating cases which involve deep human and spiritual values. The discussion remains open. However the case may be, would it not be possible, at least provisionally, to reach agreement on the following two points?

Firstly, it would be desirable that a moral or religious counsellor should, in his turn, deal with a person subjected to psychoanalytic treatment, every time that this cure runs the risk of provoking, for the believing subject, profound repercussions, in the moral or religious domain, or is likely to result in a real modification of the personality. This will be the case especially when the patient is made aware of the real motive of actions which, till then, he regarded as being inspired by his beliefs; or again, when it is shown to him that his responsibility is not as great as he thought it was. Such revelations can be the occasion of overwhelming crises of conscience, even if they attain their object by freeing the subject from infantile reactions. Psychoanalysis cannot dissociate itself from the most immediate consequences of its intervention.

Secondly, it would be of interest to decide clearly what judgment is demanded of the psychiatrist on actions contrary to the moral law, for example on masturbation or homosexual practices. The psychiatrist's concern is not to give a moral evaluation or condemnation or an ironical absolution, but a technical judgment. It is sufficient that the actions we instanced should be regarded as indications of a maladjustment incidental to growth. And how could they be regarded otherwise than as such, since the patient comes to us to be cured of behaviour in which they are one of the factors? The rest is the moralist's concern. And it is, moreover, according to the abnormal character of these actions that he will establish their opposition to the moral law.

Our conclusion must be a very brief one.

We are still convinced that no satisfactory psychological and moral synthesis can be reached while regarding as a blind alley the doctrine which generations of philosophers, theologians and Christian spiritual writers have gradually developed from the teachings of the Gospels and from the data of reason.

But we just as readily admit that this doctrine is not completed—indeed will it ever be completed?—that contributions from other civilizations, and discoveries newly made, can enrich it, and can throw light on those regions of the human person which the doctrine had, up to now, glimpsed only in a confused manner. We, psychoanalysts and moralists, have therefore a great work to do, and we shall succeed in doing it only through a constant effort to achieve mutual understanding and collaboration.

REV. PÈRE TESSON, S.J.

PSYCHOANALYSIS AND MORALITY

I AM concerned with the vast front which psychoanalysis presents to morality, and morality to psychoanalysis, and I therefore lay down clearly at the outset that I am dealing, on the one hand, with Catholic morality, and, on the other, I am taking into account only the work of Freud, and deliberately ignoring his orthodox or dissident disciples, however important their contributions may be.

The mere fact of studying the relations between psychoanalysis and morality would seem paradoxical, if psychoanalysis were a simple scientific discipline. In reality, the word psychoanalysis embraces several ideas which it is important should not be confused. To understand the ideas of Freud and to support them or validly criticise them, one must know how to distinguish the three planes, each arising from original disciplines, on which these ideas exist. It cannot be denied that Freud himself sometimes passed from one of these planes to the others, without warning and even without appearing to notice that he was doing so; and this has resulted in ambiguities which a healthy method should know how to dissipate. In Freud's doctrine, there are a psychotherapeutic technique, a psychology and a metaphysic. It behoves us always to make clear on which of these planes we are when we discuss psychoanalysis.

The historic point of departure of Freudian procedure is above all medical and therapeutic. This *therapy* is directed exclusively to neuroses, that is to say to those psychic affections which are placed below psychoses: mental diseases, mental alienations, such as delirium, dementia, melancholia, etc. Neuroses and psychoses are separated by a wide gulf which is rarely crossed. Neurotics correspond to what, in everyday speech, are called serious and mild "nervous cases." And if there is a wealth of gradation between these different nervous types, it must be recognized that one passes insensibly from the mild nervous type to the balanced man who, with rare exceptions, does not reveal some mildly neurotic traits at one time or another. Freud holds that these neuroses correspond to maladjusted conflicts of infantile life, which, while they remain unconscious, are present as a permanent thorn which has disturbed later psychic developments. The psychoanalytic cure is obtained by verifying this hypothesis: that an unconscious conflict, restored to its original strength and lifted again into consciousness, dissipates itself and loses its morbid power. The term *psychoanalysis* is reserved, properly speaking, to this particular therapeutic technique, which is of a purely psychological order and which ends an unconscious conflict by making it a conscious one.

This investigation of unconscious life has led to the discovery of a *new psychology*. The Freudian unconscious is something quite different from our collection of memories which have been apparently forgotten but which the memory can evoke, more or less easily, according to the needs of the mind. The Freudian unconscious cannot be spontaneously evoked, however sincere and intense the introspection may be. It corresponds, in general, to the development of infantile affectivity from birth to the sixth or seventh year. This new psychology is of a very great interest which can only be retrospective. It is not a simple archeological chapter to be added to knowledge already acquired. It is new data of which account must be taken in all adult psychological activities. This development of our first years is indestructible, and it is the foundation on which all our psychic development is built. Our psychic development keeps the indelible and dynamic seal of this early development whose original imprint, though hidden, can remain as a painful wound.

Because of the importance which it gives to the first few years of life, this data has led to the easy temptation of sketching *a general conception of man*. Freud has indulged in these philosophical speculations even if not always in an explicit fashion. In general, he remained faithful to a certain empirical materialism, current at the end of the nineteenth century.

It is absolutely necessary to distinguish these three planes—therapeutic, psychological and philosophical. It is on each of these planes that we must study the moral problems which can arise; but all discussion would be of little interest, if I did not put before you, as a preliminary, some elementary ideas about these different planes.

*   *   *

In order to familiarize you with these three planes, I would like to begin by considering at their own level the *resistances* which the scientific world has generally made to the Freudian theory. The essence of that theory has been formulated between 1895 and 1923. These resistances are understandable, but you will allow me to remain sceptical as to their value, especially in what concerns the first two planes.

There was clearly no reason for taking Freud at his word when he boasted about the results of his analytical therapy. In scientific matters, one does not discuss an experiment; one re-enacts that experiment on one's own account. You will readily understand the difficulty of re-enacting on one's own account the experiments of Freud, when you realize that a psychoanalysis requires easily 150 to 200 hour-sessions, and this is not possible for all and sundry. You cannot experiment with psychoanalysis as you can with a new medicine, especially since it is not anyone at random who can risk analysing a patient without incurring danger. The analyst must be thoroughly conversant with this particular technique, which means that he himself must have been previously analysed for months on end.

Resistances to Freudian psychological data can be explained by the considerable role which it gives to sexuality. It must be admitted that Freud has never sought to sweeten his somewhat embarrassing revelations for the public. The reader, acclimatized to classic works on psychology, was repulsed by a plain and unvarnished vocabulary (Oedipian incest, parricide, homosexuality, penis-regret, etc.). He did not take into account that, in describing these vital situations of the child, language had only adult terms at its disposal, coined to meet analogous but in no way identical situations. Trouble began when they were read with the same social overtones as accompany the adult context, and *a fortiori* with the same moral overtones. On the other hand, it was inevitable that there should have been resistances in the analytic sense of the word. These somewhat garish lights on the affective and sexual development of the child, frequently embarrassed the most sincere critics who were unable to surmount the uneasiness caused by an unconscious reference to their own development. It is precisely to dissipate this unconscious resistance to understanding the patient's conflicts, that the analyst himself must undergo analysis. These conflicts demand that account should be taken of them in all the psychological and psychopathological problems which can be uncovered. And this entails an effort, sometimes ascetic, to call in question many acquisitions which seem established.

Resistance to the materialistic metaphysic of Freud was clearly to be expected from religious milieux. Everyone, in this domain, is of course free to take up a position according to his preferences. Nevertheless, this necessary distinction of three planes which I have proposed to you, should obviate the serious methical error which consists in throwing discredit or distrust on a therapeusis or on psychological data, simply because one holds metaphysical opinions differing from those of Freud. It seems that, in Christian circles, much ambiguity is born of this confusion.

*   *   *

A comparison is valid only when the two terms of comparison are perfectly understood. I freely concede that you have nothing to learn from me about the theoretical requirements of Catholic morality. I do not think I am lacking in courtesy towards the majority of you, however, if I do not consider it superfluous to outline the main ideas of the Freudian theory. I shall refer constantly to these three planes, and I ask you not to overlook the important distinction there is between them. I shall now begin with the second plane, the psychological plane, because it will help you to understand more thoroughly the other two, that is to say, the analytical cure and the speculations of Freud.

1. *Freud's analytical psychology* is centred on the development of affectivity in the child. This development obeys precise laws, results in the stable and living organization of personality, and persists in a more or less unobtrusive, more or less imperious, manner during the whole course of life. This psychology has been discovered through the psychoanalysis of neurotics, and through the didactic psychoanalysis of analyses; it is confirmed by the observation of children, and even of adults, when they are studied with these ideas in mind.

In a general way, Freudian psychology emphasizes the importance of affectivity—that is to say, of the love-hate couple. These terms, especially the second, have too close an association with adult morality, while we are here concerned with the infra-moral infantile stage; they are sometimes replaced by the more general and more psychological terms: affection and aggressiveness. Love and aggressiveness make their violent appearance in the adult, but they date from the cradle. Between the greedy love of his sucking-bottle and, later on, the serious love for his wife; between the toy which he tramples and, later on, the rival of whom he is jealous, man seems to progress by an insensible transition only, but it cannot be denied that this progressive continuity does not exclude the authentic enrichment which comes from this development. What is of particular importance is that a whole harmonious organization of his impulses ought to be completed before the age of seven years. There follows a latent period after the age of seven, in which all the lived data of the equilibrium thus established sleep in oblivion; but that equilibrium is as an unconscious schema which remains the basis of later development. And it is the stability or the instability of this early equilibrium, built up during the first years, which will determine the nervous equilibrium of the entire life.

The infant is born weak and unarmed, while his instincts immediately demand their satisfaction, that is, they demand pleasure. An interior tension demands the possibility of relaxation, and this narcissistic[1]

---

[1] "The finest of mortals can love only himself" (Paul Valéry).

need for satisfaction comes into conflict with reality. The "pleasure-principle" joins battle with the "reality-principle," and a progressive and tolerable adaptation becomes necessary. This reality is two-fold: there is the reality of the external material world which resists; and there is the reality of parental and social commands which now permit and now forbid. The latter is at first an exterior reality, which then impresses itself on the very inner life of the subject in the form of habits and of more or less differentiated automatisms. There is also a reaction of discomfort to the forbidden, a reaction which is the mysterious root of anguish and the feeling of guilt, and which shows itself with as much intransigence as that other equally mysterious datum—the thirst for happiness. A delicate equilibrium must be constantly established between these three factors: the instinct which demands its pleasure; the social and moral world which demands renunciation as the price of its acceptance of the individual; and the anguish which is always apt to be born from the conflict of these two demands.

The thrusts of instinct, the impulses, are vital forces which cannot disappear. Hunger and thirst will allow no compromise, and they witness to a need that cannot be deferred. If they are not satisfied, death quickly follows. The affective impulses, love and aggressiveness, are more malleable. Derivatives and compromises are possible, and satisfaction can be postponed or directed towards another object. A whole metamorphosis which is called "sublimation," makes it possible for renunciation on one plane to be compensated for by gain on another plane where equilibrium is more viable, where anguish is tolerable, even if the renunciation has been a very severe one.

It must be noticed that love is much more susceptible to sublimation than aggressiveness is. Enemy number one of social life is not sexuality, the infinitely malleable life-force. The implacable enemy is aggressiveness, the destruction-force, the force of death, whose uneasy preservation, ill-repressed, ill-sublimated, even cleverly disguised, is the drama of neurotics and of collectivities. Aggressiveness would even seem to have a real life of its own, demanding its satisfaction through a positive dynamism which would be more than a simple absence of love.

What, more precisely, therefore, is this essential equilibrium which should be established before the age of seven years? This equilibrium can be expressed in such simple terms that the complexity of this happy outcome is often left hidden. The child should love both his parents tenderly and equally (I do not say in an identical way); he must accept without anguish the real inferiority that belongs to him as a child; and—which is less clear—he must have repressed his sexuality in such a way that it will necessarily make an harmonious appearance at puberty. And all this should prepare and impel him to become an adult to the full extent of his sex.

We notice that the way in which the child atttaches himself to the objects he loves during his first years, has certain definite characteristics. We have already spoken of that narcissistic, self-centred love, which seeks in the object loved only that which feeds its own satisfaction. Moreover, the absence of the object loved, the fact that he or she hides from the child, causes a particularly painful show of frustration. What is refused appears as something which is due. Finally, the child's love cannot have any nuances in it, because he desires everything, and when he has not everything, he feels that he has nothing. He can understand only complete satisfaction or complete frustration.

It will be readily understood that such imperious demands quickly leave the field free to aggressiveness which lays siege to the objects preventing the child from getting "all." The jealous rivalry of Cain for Abel, this younger brother who dispossesses the elder, is written in some form or another in the personal origins of each of us. Aggressiveness hurls itself against him who takes the mother, and against the mother who dares to usurp one of his glances. But above all, the mother's warm love must be preserved, and this compels the child to repress his too crude hostility. Thus, from the very beginning, we discover this idea of ambivalence, this mixture of aggressiveness and of love towards an object which often discourages the free play of our passions. Moreover, this remote jealousy, however buried it may be, is very rarely altogether liquidated, and will easily become active again in a nostalgic feeling of abandon, when the difficulties of life present themselves.

An important stage in the child's affective development is reached about the age of three or four. The Oedipus Complex, a name familiar to everybody, and the Castration Complex make their appearance. The Oedipus situation arises through the child's attachment to the parent of the opposite sex, with the aggressive desire to eliminate the other parent who then appears as a rival. Since this rival cannot be eliminated, the child attempts to take the parent's place, that is, to imitate and to resemble him or her. The child attempts to identify itself with the "rival" parent. Finally, by making himself "Dad," or by making herself "Mummy," the child recovers in itself the love of this parent, and at the same time keeps in line with its own sex.

It must be again understood how he has accepted the weakness natural to him as a child and which is the essential condition of his being able to become a fully developed adult. In reality, the Oedipean adventure, even schematized, is more complex. Let us attempt to analyse it more profoundly by taking into account the Castration Complex.

The real inferiority of the child is something which he quickly feels to be uncomfortable, as though it corresponds to some guilt. The child feels himself straitly subjected to his parents' power, a magic power of giants, which he regards above all as malevolent when it takes the form of numerous and painful educative "don'ts." Through affective association, to feel oneself inferior is to feel oneself dependent, and this is already to feel oneself guilty. On the other hand, the child regards the parents' power as the omnipotent cause of everything he sees, even of the difference between the sexes. It is they, therefore, who have castrated the little girl as a punishment. The little boy dreads the same punishment, whence an uneasiness about possible mutilation, felt very early in life. All the real inferiority felt by the little boy will revive this very profound uneasiness, if the latter has not been successfully liquidated.

Successful liquidation is very important, if this feeling of inferiority is not to be left in the child, and later in the adult, as an ever open wound which can make all the real setbacks of life intolerable. To escape from this menace of mutilation, the child feels a natural urge to assert his masculine quality; and this results very early in a double parallel attitude towards parents, even before the formation of the Oedipus Complex. The boy likes to take up the attitude of "the little man" towards his mother, in his affection for her. He is unhappy if his attempt to do so goes unnoticed. The mother will hazard the future virility of her son, if she demands, as the price of the love he claims from her, that he should be good "like his sister." He will already have begun to identify himself with his father, whose real qualities he exaggerates, as his model of the "big man." He will try to imitate him, to please him and to gratify him.

This flight from the dread of castration cannot continue when once Oedipean competition begins. This loved and imitated father is also the husband, the possessor of the child's mother, and therefore a rival. The child cannot help feeling inferior to the father in relation to the mother whom he wishes to conquer. His dread of castration comes alive again when faced with this father who, while he encourages the naissant virility of his son by being his model, threatens that same virility by his power as a rival—regarded as the power to castrate.

The liquidation of the Oedipean conflict is crucial. The boy must achieve a two-fold sublimation: he must renounce his mother, definitively and for ever, as an exclusive and total love; and he must renounce aggressiveness towards this "rival" father and accept his superiority, by no longer attempting to please him passively nor by

8

trampling on his authority, but by showing a virility which will win him the esteem of that father and of other "grown-ups" whose equal he wishes to be and feels that he is becoming.

With the little girl, the same situations arise in a somewhat different way. The Oedipean schema is the same: attachment to the father and rivalry with the mother. But whereas in the boy's case, the Castration Complex endangers the successful liquidation of the Oedipean conflict, this dread of castration, in the case of the girl, should be over and done with before the Oedipean situation arises, the latter indeed having been an aid to the termination of the Castration Complex. In the case of the daughter, indeed, the Oedipus Complex ought to detach her from her mother to whom she has clung since birth, whereas this reversal of situation does not exist for the boy in his Oedipean attachment to his mother. Moreover, castration is not a threat but a fact. The little girl lives in expectation; she must learn that her expectation is vain, and that she must renounce for ever any idea of being a boy. Where there are normal parents (a virile father and a mother who is not neurotic), the Oedipean situation will aid the child by directing her towards her father, and by leading her to identify herself with her mother, whose apparently mutilated sex she will accept as her own.

You can now appreciate the essential line of this harmonious development, and the importance of necessary, final renunciations of narcissistic love and of aggressiveness, on the plane of pure instinct. It opens the way to a more oblatory love, a love which makes a gift of self. Sexuality, repressed and detached from parental objects, reappears at puberty, with its own life and its freedom to choose. But the force of love, while it frees itself from original narcissism, can be directed to a multitude of desexualized objects, can open out wide to the neighbour and can become enriched in authentic and original ways. Aggressiveness, having finally abandoned its primitive unconscious objects, sublimates itself in competitions, in victories, in bodily and mental exercises.

These brief ideas enable us to draw up a certain plan of the whole of the physical equipment, which takes into account all those forces whose development we have just traced.

At the apex of the pyramid is the "Ego," which is composed of our thinking, conscious and pre-conscious personality.

Below this comes all that unconscious life which remains an irreplacable psychological hypothesis, whatever may be the metaphysical difficulties which its existence raises for certain people. The unconscious is two-fold: there are the repressed demands (the "Id"), but there are also the repressing prohibitions (the "Super-Ego").

The "Id" represents the instinctive urge which is composed of our brute impulses, our most elementary needs and desires, and of more evolved impulses which have been repressed. It is the domain where interested love, sexuality and aggressiveness remain indestructible. It is not by a simple, tyrannical repression that the demands of these elementary forces are denied, for this would leave the uneasiness of badly fettered power. It is a permanent, dynamic metamorphosis of these impulses, which remain comfortably sunk in a mysterious oblivion, while only the good fruits of this metamorphosis reappear in clear consciousness and inspire concrete conduct.

This unconscious censor is called the "Super-Ego." It opposes a barrier to profound impulses, while at the same time it is in a certain sense porous to their dynamism which it allows to filter through to fecundate both physical and moral life. The "Super-Ego" corresponds to the introjection of the first parental and social prohibitions into the psychic organism, and therefore corresponds to an extremely primitive infantile morality. It is really a pseudo-morality which the automatisms of the infant construct in order to be in accord with the taboos of the clan. This unconscious pseudo-morality is later capable of contaminating the natural development of true moral conscience, of which this must be regarded as being only a pre-moral, rudimentary first sketch. The improper persistence of this system of unconscious and primitive reference, can be particularly disastrous[1] to an autonomous moral life.

* * *

2. *Psychological treatment* logically intervenes when the equilibrium between the Super-Ego and the Id is defective, and there results an intolerable malaise for the conscience. The repressions have not been successful, and unconscious conflicts persist. The analytical technique will attempt to revive, with their primitive emotions, the situations through which the adult has passed in his childhood, in order to lift these anachronistic conflicts into consciousness and thereby to end them. But in order to make conscious what is unconscious, one must succeed in getting at the repressing forces, and one must end by destroying the psychic resistances which are opposed to repression. It must be clearly understood that it is not a question of a simple intellectual recollection of remote situations. To make a conflict conscious is to re-live it in all the unconstrained pathos of its original vehemence. This explains why an analytical cure necessarily involves episodes which are dramatically painful.

[1] See Dr. Ch. Odier: *Les deux sources consciente et inconsciente de la vie morale*, 1 volume, 273 pages, 1943–1947. *Cahier de Philosophie: "Être et penser."* Edition de la Balconnière, Neufchâtel.

To achieve the reintegration of forgotten elements in the field of consciousness, the fundamental rule of analysis is to demand that the patient should take up a relaxed attitude, and should give full play to all the free associations of ideas or of images which come into his mind without choice or trickery. This free evocation will sometimes be disturbed by an unconscious curbing; and the analysis of these resistances thus encountered is of very great importance. Dreams are necessarily encountered in the course of the unburdening, and their analysis will uncover a lightly masked unconscious. A whole work of careful interpretation, whose opportuneness and management are matters calling for dexterity and experience, will help the patient to reach progressively the decisive point in all the analytical material which he reveals to his doctor. Finally, the analysis of the reactions of transference will be an equally essential part of the treatment. By the reactions of transference, we mean the whole pattern of conduct which the patient shows during his analysis, both towards the treatment and especially towards the doctor. These reactions are very important, because, through a need for repetition which Freud has shown to be a constant factor in neurotics, the human psychism tends to re-create the same emotional states when placed in analogous circumstances. In other words, the emotion provoked by a situation, by a deception for instance, is out of all proportion to the event which has apparently caused it. The reason for this is that the present set of circumstances has caused a recrudescence—a recrudescence of which the subject is unaware—of a much older, unconscious, analogous deception which was never completely liquidated. "It is thus that the neurotic will very naturally reproduce unconsciously, in relation to the doctor, the conflicts which have set him in opposition to his parents, and also the reactionary, compensatory attitudes which resulted from these conflicts: revolt or love, homosexual passivity, aggressiveness or masochism."[1] The very special role of the analyst is therefore clear. He must be simply an impersonal figurehead, and he must avoid all that would create an attitude of real sympathy or antipathy between him and his patient, in order that the latter's behaviour towards him may be as technical as possible, so as to lay bare the original conflicts which it is the object of the analysis to seek out and clarify.

3. *Freudian speculation* of a philosophical kind, is above all reductive. Freud has shown rare genius in analysing the lowest part of the psyche. He has pointed out with very objective pessimism, how often the life of the adult contains elements of an infantile life, more or less magical

---

[1] Dr. S. Nacht: *La thérapeutique psychoanalytique*. In *Médecin Français*, February 25th and March 10th, 1947.

and scarcely outgrown. It was an easy temptation to affirm the essential universality of this explanation of the higher in terms of the lower. The highest values—art, morality, religion—were traced back, when their references were analysed, to primitive infantile activities. And the analysis, which until then had been unduly pushed to the point of psychological determinism, inclined perhaps still more towards the unwarranted assumption of metaphysical determinism.

Freud's position is that of a logical and integral materialism, against which only arguments of an equally philosophical order must be opposed. We emphasize insistently that the psychological discoveries of Freud are completely apart from the philosophical perspectives in which these speculations sought to integrate them. It is a question of two completely different planes.

* * *

We believe that the clearing of the ground in what we have just written, will allow us to pose with greater precision the moral problems raised by psychoanalysis and the analytical problems raised by morality. Keeping strictly to our original distinction, we shall consider the problem of Psychoanalysis and Morality as it appears on the therapeutic, the psychological and the philosophical planes.

1. It cannot be denied that *analytical therapy* raises a moral problem. It causes a revival in the patient of seething infantile conflicts of sexuality and aggressiveness, which will reappear and express themselves in adult terms. The situation of transference, in its actual appearance and in the rigours and implacable analysis which must be made of it, is certainly a most unusual social situation. I do not wish to evade the difficulty, but I can only express a personal and sweeping conclusion by saying that I find no real contradiction between psychoanalytical treatment and the sincere desire of patient or analyst to remain faithful to strict Catholic morality. To discuss the basis of such a conclusion, it is necessary to have a clear idea of what is in question, by having an understanding both of neuropaths and of psychoanalysis. Previous experience, slowly and laboriously acquired, is necessary in order to understand neuropaths. A knowledge of psychoanalysis is acquired in one way only—by oneself having undergone analysis. I can only wish that certain Professors of Moral Theology would undergo analysis, and this for reasons of much greater moment than the simple discussion of this delicate point. They will smile, no doubt, at my totalitarian demand. I do not dare, however, to go the length of wishing them a manifest neurosis to compel them to undergo this essential experience. I hope they will pardon me my apparently haughty and intransigent words.

Apart from this delicate question which I refuse to discuss, I believe that the idea of transference can render great service in the analysis of the cure of souls. In the course of a psychoanalysis, a clear amelioration is always noticeable as soon as the transference takes place and the patient becomes conscious of it. This amelioration arising from the transference is only an apparent cure, and it would be a serious matter to rest content with it. This particular behaviour, viewed by the analyst in a dry psychological light, is capable of explaining certain happy enterprises open to a confessor, a director of conscience or a doctor. It is perhaps an excellent spring-board; but the spring-board must not dispense with the effort of leaping.

2. It may seem paradoxical to bring questions of morality into a psychological science. It is an important problem, however. In the first place, every moral act expresses itself in terms of psychological behaviour. But above all, Freudian psychology has shown that there existed in the child, before the moral age, certain patterns of psycho-logical behaviour in which "everything happened as though" there were such things as the permitted, the forbidden, the malaise in face of the prohibited. The whole adult vocabulary borrowed to express these vital infantile situations, is really borrowed from morality. The whole successful liquidation of the Oedipus Complex, and of the Castration Complex, takes place under the guise of renunciation. This whole progressive passage from self-centred behaviour to oblation occurs below the moral level. The important point is that this pseudo-morality, which is the *Super-Ego*, provides an unconscious instance from which moral conscience will only progressively emerge, and in which moral conscience will find its first outline and its first incarnation.

It is debatable whether, in cases of particularly successful equili-brium, the *Super-Ego* disappears entirely. It would not seem that subjects of this type have been often met with in analysis. But one thing is certain: this pseudo-morality of the *Super-Ego* persists, though hiddenly, into adult life, and can unconsciously contaminate true moral life. This contamination is often slight, sometimes considerable, and it can become tyrannical. It is therefore necessary, in the case of every psychological act, and *a fortiori* in the case of every moral act, to distinguish its double motivation: the conscious motivation, authentically moral and adult; and the unconscious, pseudo-moral motivation, which is regressive and infantile.[1]

The presence of these unconscious infantile elements in our moral life would in themselves demand long treatment; and it is here, I believe, that the collaboration of moralists and analysts would be

[1] Ch. Odier: *Loc. cit.*

especially fruitful.[1] I cannot develop this point, and I shall therefore pass on to give some examples of everyday instances of contamination by the *Super-Ego*.

Take, for example, the idea of penance. Regarded as a Christian virtue, penance is a painful detachment which is willed and accepted in order to prepare the way for attachment to something of higher value. For the majority of people, this detachment has nothing spontaneous or instinctive or, to use the popular term, "natural" about it. Nevertheless, it must be taken into consideration that a hidden instinctive tendency to penance does exist, and shows itself in an instinctive satisfaction taken in the endurance of pain. This is "masochism," whose grossly perverse manifestations only must be taken into account. When a spiritual director finds a tendency to penitential maceration in one of his penitents, he should realize that such an attitude may have a double motivation. It may have a redeeming virtue; and equally it may be contaminated by masochistic pseudo-virtue. The director must not await the appearance of a neurosis with distinct characteristics, fifteen years later, to decide the matter.

Unconscious motives, having nothing to do with authentic virtue, may also be found in another type of behaviour—that of chastity. Where there has been an unsatisfactory liquidation of the Oedipus Complex, the *Super Ego* which inherits it introduces an unconscious reference to the taboo of incest (homosexuality or impotence) into sexuality, whereas sexuality should be free from reference of any kind. Here again, we find the constant and latent pressure of a perturbation dating from the parental prohibitions of early infancy. It behoves us therefore to be very much on our guard when dealing with a chastity which is both effortless and without curiosity. Before regarding as God-given the ease with which an adolescent avoids the entanglements of the flesh, it is necessary to discover how much is to be attributed to real conquest through virtuous habits, and how much to a too rigid *Super-Ego*.

"In the last analysis, the Christian's love of God should be an original and transcendent attitude. The child is led to love his Heavenly Father, through a process which begins with the earthly father whom he sees and loves. But is it sufficiently appreciated that the first term of the comparison may be a highly equivocal one? The child runs a great risk of forming his idea of God too much in the image he has unconsciously formed of his father, or in the contrary of that image if he is reacting against it; and this is also true of the adolescent who so easily preserves his childhood impressions, especially in the religious domain. Is not the attitude to God often a kind of heavenly

[1] See Dr. G. Richard: *La Psychanalyse et la Morale*. 1946, Payot, Lausanne.

transference, in which the adult's behaviour towards God, from whose Almighty Power he expects magical and miraculous presents, is like that of a child towards his father? And expressions such as "the way of childhood" and "abandonment to the Lord," which have a proper context and a precise sense, can sometimes be used with serious though unconscious equivocation."[1]

3. This is not the place to determine to what extent precisely the materialistic reductive attitude of Freud towards spiritual matters, is incompatible with the Christian metaphysic. However, analytical psychology leads the Christian to very fruitful philosophical pondering on the unity of psychic life and the necessary hierarchy of its different planes.

It must be affirmed that this psychology is in no way opposed to religious speculation of all kinds, especially on the role of sanctifying grace. The affective development of the child, as we have described it, takes place on the empirical plane of observation where the doctor can accept no restriction. But, by definition, there can be question only of tried mechanisms, of trodden paths. All questions of origins lead the doctor to a philosophical plane. He must not find that he has unwittingly strayed into that plane, nor once there, find himself without a method fitted to that plane. Psychoanalysis, inasmuch as it is a psychological science, does not explain the liberty of the soul, any more than it explains the capacity for sublimation of instinct. The life force and its potential germinations remain an irrational factor where metaphysics gives itself plenty of elbow-room. Moreover, Christian theology has always maintained that the action of grace, whose existence is de fide, is psychologically indiscernible from the mechanisms of natural life created by the Saviour.[2]

On the other hand, this possible contamination of adult moral life by the inclusion of infantile pseudo-moral elements, should be more closely examined. It is understood that only the first register—that of adult life—involves moral responsibility. This intimate and mysterious relationship of these two registers—that of adult moral life and that of early infancy—may perhaps lead to the suspicion that they are a continuity, even a unity on a metaphysical plane. I shall put it to theologians whether, indeed, one would not be justified in speaking of "analogous" ideas.[3] This lifts us immediately to the plane of the specific and incorruptible human soul, which would progressively, "analogically," inform this organism in full evolution

---

[1] Dr. Ch. H. Nodet: Vie affective infantile et vie morale adulte, notions analogues. Supplément de La Vie Spirituelle, February 1948.

[2] In whose image man is made and makes himself. The supernatural is not to be regarded as a garment, however rich the material. The grace of God is also the grace of man.

[3] Dr. Ch. H. Nodet: Loc. cit.

called the body—this body which is, say the Thomists, the very principle of our individuation. And a Christian cannot ignore the fact that "analytical psychology reaches to depths where the ideas elaborated by metaphysics appear to us, not as simple hypotheses, but as vital phenomena."[1]

The whole man is one, possessing unity of substance. His highest activities cannot escape at any time from the weight of the flesh. But his moral experience is perhaps not a unity, and therein lies its great novelty. In a form difficult to define, all our past is present in our actions. The moral act we posit, preserves a connection with the unsuspected dramas of our first infancy. But, in the two registers, it is seen that love can progress, can enrich and give itself, only at the price of final renunciation. The destiny of man is perhaps to make his way, fully and harmoniously, from the state of infancy to that of the adult.

DOCTEUR CH. H. NODET
Ancien Chef de Clinique à la Faculté de Médecine
de Paris, Médecin des Hôpitaux Psychiatriques

[1] Dr. Parcheminoy: *L'angoisse humaine et Civilization.* Psyché: September 1947. (A propos of Jung.)

PSYCHOANALYSIS AND MORAL
CONSCIENCE

THOSE who are directors of conscience, in the religious or the political field, are well aware that it is difficult to rise above self-interest and to remain above it. How can they be blamed, therefore, for taking up an attitude of prudent distrust towards every innovation which appears to question the traditional foundations of morality, and in particular towards psychoanalysis?

The best among such directors rightly demand that things should be clearly set forth. They consider that if a therapeutic method cannot be *proved* in an external way, its principles at least should be capable of being clearly formulated and discussed. We are very much of this opinion, and that is the reason why we would like to state clearly, in this article, our position with regard to psychoanalysis.

At the outset, we emphasize that we are dealing with *classic* psycho-analysis—that is to say, with Freudian technique—and not with any other. It is to be regretted that the word psychoanalysis has taken on so many different meanings. The psychotherapeutist, Jungian or otherwise, the literary critic and the film critic, the advice columnists in so many women's weeklies, all "carry out" psychoanalysis. This results in most regrettable confusion for the public, and also for us. We would willingly search for another word if the public would excuse us from using that one.

Meantime, let us recall the essential characteristics of the technique with which we shall be dealing in this article.

The patient is lying on the couch and the doctor is seated behind him. There is only one rule for the patient: he must keep nothing back, he must give full liberty to the flow of his ideas over which he must exercise no conscious control. No modesty, no shame, no obligation of the law of charity, can justify the omission of a single fact of consciousness. The idea may be absurd, disgusting or injurious in the eyes of the doctor, and yet it must be said.

If the doctor is able to give a greater precision to the business in hand, he must do so without guiding the free associations of the patient. *He must give no advice*, except perhaps the preliminary advice to post-pone every serious decision until the end of the treatment. *He must pass no judgment on the value* of the conduct revealed to him, and he must be especially on his guard against the implicit judgments which his own known conduct would lead him to make. Similarly, he must shun all personal relations with his patient, and he must never treat any person who has been even remotely concerned in his own private life. It would even be desirable that his political, religious, and philosophical opinions should be a closed book to his patient.

What, then, will be his role? *To interpret* and never to go beyond the limits of a strict interpretation. To interpret means to seek out a constant behaviour-pattern, or the smallest possible number of behaviour-patterns, in the apparently extreme diversity of the material submitted to him: actions, speech, dreams. It is a work of induction whose proof is furnished immediately by the reaction of the patient, and in the long run by his cure.

All other psychotherapy, however spectacular or even efficacious it may be, must be clearly distinguished from the one we have just outlined.

We must also distinguish it from historical, sociological and biographical extrapolations. It is these works, often very interesting but always somewhat venturesome, and certain aspects of the Freudian doctrine, which are disturbing to Christians. Such works are representative of a sordid and outmoded materialism, and are deceitfully propagandist.

Now, all *classic* psychoanalysts remain faithful to the Freudian *technique*, such fidelity being the touchstone of the "classic"; they are not defined as those who accept *en bloc* the doctrines of their master. Some are Christians, others are Marxists, others are Hegelians or Existentialists, but all use the same technique; for, while proselytism is a duty for the conscientious Marxist or the priest, it would be a serious fault in the exercise of our profession.

Our own didactic analysis, the controls which we underwent at the beginning of our career, the frequent comparison of our points of view, the reserve which we imposed on ourselves, and finally our formation and the practice of our profession, all enable us to reduce the personal factor to a minimum. It cannot, of course, be entirely suppressed, but I know of no other discipline which gives a greater guarantee of objectivity.

* * *

If it is admitted to us that our personal system of metaphysics and that of Freud can be distinguished from one another, it is less easily accorded that our psychology is not "pansexualist."

"You degrade man; you see the sexual in everything." It is a comical accusation, as though one were to tax the confessor with pandiabolism because he grapples with sin, or the socialist with pancapitalism because he studies trusts in order to conquer them. It is too readily forgotten that we concern ourselves with sexuality because neuroses are sexual troubles, just as the ophthalmic surgeon deals with the eyes of a patient whose sight is not good. It is not we who emphasize the sexual element, but the patient himself; and it is to enable him to integrate an obstructed sexuality, to suppress it as such, that we treat him.

To say that every superior human aspiration is the end of an evolution which had a biological origin, is not to reduce it to the level of that origin. Neurosis retards the subject at the first phases of this evolution and psychoanalysis aims at enabling him to resume his normal development. The idea of sublimation is Freudian.

It will be objected that when "good-living" patients, "pure" women, "chaste" men, and so forth are confided to us, they find that in the course of treatment they are accused of nourishing the most disgusting instincts. Psychoanalysis would pervert them.

It must be recalled, therefore, that there are such things as pseudo-virtues. One may be continent through inhibition, through frigidity, through obsessional disgust; one may be devoted and scrupulously exact through masochism, idealistic through homosexuality, irreproachable through sadism. All these false neurotic qualities are merely the symptoms always discovered in a pathological ensemble of regression or emotional retardation: characteristics which are oral, anal, narcissistic, etc. As a result, it can indeed be maintained that the apparently "pure" heart and mind of our patient are infected by the most rudimentary instincts. His conduct is entirely "eroticized" against his will, and he is not able to admit this to himself. When cured, he will finally attain to genuine impulses, not by "repressing" his impulses, but by getting to know them, by conquering them, and by rising superior to them.

*   *   *

"We are indeed convinced," it will then be said to us, "that you unmask and exterminate pseudo-good sentiments. But how can you hope that the genuine ones will remain intact? Is it not at the price of spiritual gifts that you root out anguish? Do you not change the Socrates dissatisfied into the swine satisfied?"

This is a serious accusation. To meet it, we must recall some ideas of infantile psychology which are regarded as classic. All the interest and all the energy of the newly-born child are centred on the mother, in order to obtain the milk of which the child is in great and urgent need. This need is satisfied as much as possible. As yet, no constraint is placed on excretory functions. But soon discipline is gradually imposed on the child, and forbidden pleasures are met with threats or even with punishment. At the same time, other objects take their place with the mother in the child's consciousness: there are father, sister, brother, etc. Each of these inspires love and its contrary, in varying degrees, in the child.

During those first years, his conduct is above all utilitarian. His weakness, his growth, demand this. Normally he is egocentric. Convinced of his parents' omnipotence, he expects to receive from them much more than they can give, in the way of nourishment, caresses, full scope to indulge his pleasures; but he *fears them* to the same extent. If we compare the conduct of the child with the sublimated conduct of the completely adult person, we find that the child's conduct consists in striving to obtain material advantages and to avoid material discomforts. For, in the best cases of development, the evolution takes place in the direction of the purification of primitively instinctive energy. The man then weighs his values in reference to others and to the world in general, and when he does so in a supreme fashion, he is a Saint or a Genius. The neurotic, on the other hand, has not progressed beyond the first stages or he has returned to them. In spite of appearances which are due to "rationalizations," he remains the little child with his unlimited requirements and his anguish. Now, we act in such a way that he re-lives the emotional situation of his very first years. He makes the same urgent requests to us, returns to the same tactics in order to escape imaginary punishment, and shows the same fears. Every one of his initiatives has for its objective to obtain something or to remove a danger, and each is abandoned because we have unmasked it, have failed to respond to it—in short, *it does not pay*. It is also abandoned because it is seen to be obsolete in relation to an adult personality in possession of a body and a mind shaped to other objectives. But how can a superior activity be dissolved by our interpretations? Morality is above all *disinterested*, not utilitarian, because one is not moral just *to gain something*. And how can it seem anachronistic when it even advances the evolution of the person who devotes himself to it?

*   *   *

Our intention was to show that morality has nothing to fear from psychoanalysis, not even a new moral theory. We aim at giving his liberty to the patient, by allowing him to become aware of his conflicts and to resolve them. When, in our opinion, he has been cured, he is at liberty to choose. He can opt for the genuine or for the false. The mere idea of a mental hygiene which takes the place of moral responsibility, nauseates us. Psychoanalysis is simply a pre-morality, and there is no necessity to raise an objection against it.

DOCTEUR F. PASCHE
Chef du Laboratoire de Psychothérapie à la
Faculté de Paris

PSYCHOANALYSIS AND RELIGIOUS SYMBOLISM

FROM its outset, psychoanalysis encountered religious symbolism in the patients which it treated, and attempted to interpret religion in terms of psychoanalytical findings. There can be no question in these few pages of dealing with a subject so immense, but only of making a few remarks which may serve as an introduction to a wider study of the relations between psychoanalysis and religious symbolism.

In order to avoid discussions which would carry us too far, we begin with a completely empirical definition of symbolism as religion itself would define it. A symbol is any religious object, image, or activity of the sensible order, which signifies the mystery of the Divine and causes its believers to participate in that mystery: the image of the Heavenly Father, of the Blessed Virgin, the angels; sacramental rites, etc.

Psychoanalysis meets these symbols at two moments of its practice: (1) With patients, as symbolism which is lived by a given neurotic subject, and inasmuch as that symbolism is therapeutic; (2) With religions, as a human phenomenon, in so far as symbolism can be erected into a explicative science. This double point of view, the practical and the theoretical, suggests the division of this introduction.

Psychoanalytical treatment and lived religious symbolism

The question of psychoanalytical treatment bearing essentially on religious symbolism, arises when a given subject shows in his religious life, in the use which he makes of the symbols of the faith, certain disquieting perturbations against which all the efforts of the spiritual director, and above all of the subject's own free will, are powerless. What is most striking in these cases is, for example, the inability to live the *whole* of the dogma itself. The patient fastens on to the Divine Wrath, to Hell, and shows himself deaf to any appeal concerning the love of God and Redemption in Jesus Christ. He seems incapable of realizing in a practical manner, the synthesis of extremes which is one of the characteristics of complete faith. He is also subject to irresistible impulses which urge him, for example, to confess ceaselessly; but in spite of what he is told and in spite of what he himself wishes, he is incapable of admitting the efficacy of the Divine Pardon, which he receives through the medium of the Sacrament. There are always those inspirations, those visions, those inner voices, etc., which ordinary criteria cannot authenticate, and which resist every effort to dominate and to ignore them.

Psychoanalysis, when faced with these subjects, has its interpretation and its cure ready for them. All this religious symbolism used by the subject is not to be taken in a transcendent sense, and seems to psychoanalysis to express something quite different from the participation of the believer in the Divine Mystery. It suspects, for example, that the ideas of God and of Confession have a latent content behind their manifest content. They reveal an affectivity arrested at or returned to the infantile stage. To the question: "What does God or Confession signify for such a subject?"—psychoanalysis answers: "I know nothing of its signifying transcendent reality or divine pardon; but I certainly know that it signifies the terrible father of the Oedipean stage, the repressed *Super-Ego*, the neurotic sentiment of guilt."

There was the case of a curate, for example, who, when he thought of God, was obsessed by an intense feeling of guilt and assailed by thoughts of damnation. One day, he had the following dream. Passing a butcher's stall, he saw suspended there a great piece of meat which seemed to be a joint of beef. He approached and discovered with dismay that it was not a joint of beef, but his own bishop. This had the effect of deepening his anguish. Now, it is quite clear that his image of God did not represent the authentic God of the New Testament, any more than the image of his bishop, towards whom he felt a violent resentment, represented his Bishop. In fact, analysis showed that he was transferring to God and to his bishop, a strong, repressed aggressiveness towards his father. It was therefore a case of an imperfectly resolved Oedipus Complex.

Here is another case cited by Odier. A young lady was converted through the influence of one of her friends who was given to mysticism and to sacrifice. She conceived a boundless admiration for the ideas and beliefs of her friend. She shared her religious life, and sacrificed her whole fortune to it. After a while, she fell into a depression from which she could not escape. Despairing doubts assailed her, and she felt that she was losing the faith. What was the significance, therefore, for her, of the religious symbols she had adopted? Analysis showed that there existed in this woman an unconscious homosexual attachment for her friend. It was therefore clear that her conversion had been for her an unconscious means of satisfying this attachment in a disguised way. The feelings of doubt and of loss of faith were merely a defensive reaction against latent homosexuality.

These examples are sufficient to show the fertility of psychoanalysis, which discovers in lived religious symbolism a completely immanent meaning, and shows how such symbolism is being used for purposes of neurosis. They allow an instructive parallel to be drawn up between the analytical method in psychology and the Marxist method in history and in sociology. In both cases, we are considering religion in its relation to a given individual or a given class, in order to discover the unconscious motives which lead that individual or that class to adopt religion, and in order to discover the meaning which more or less conscious affectivities give to it. Freudianism and Marxism are at one here in sharing the same existential perspective.

These examples also permit us to define exactly the object of psychoanalytical treatment in cases of manifestly religious neurosis, and to fix its limits with regard to theology.

Psychoanalysis does not consider *faith* at all, in so far as faith attributes to a given symbol the value of mediation between man and transcendent reality. It considers only *affectivity*, in so far as affectivity provides an unconscious content for religious symbolism. The point of application for psychoanalytic therapy is not therefore belief as such, but unconscious affective disturbances, fixations and regressions which will hinder faith in its concrete exercise by charging its lived symbolism with every kind of abnormal significance. By re-establishing affective normality, therefore, psychoanalysis would help to set faith free from parasitical growth on religious symbols.

This implies that religious symbolism has always two meanings: on the one hand, it has a transcendent significance, in the degree to which it leaves to faith the Divine Mystery; on the other hand, it always preserves a relation with human affectivity, from which it springs and in which it continues to take root. Thus, the image of the father, applied to God by faith, allows the worshipper to reach God; but it still preserves a relation with the father-image from which it comes. The normality of the life of faith implies, therefore, the normality of an affectivity which has passed, in the course of its development, through stages which mark its evolution, notably the Oedipean situation and its solution.

We shall not enter into all the questions which the idea of affective normality raises. It will be sufficient to remark that this morality exists, and that we can distinguish it from abnormality. In any case, we have said sufficient to allow the theologian to speak.

Lived religious symbolism is, therefore, the meeting-place of the theologian and the psychoanalyst, but they do not approach this symbolism from the same point of view. The theologian will not deny the legitimacy of the analyst's undertaking, if the latter acts as a doctor who concerns himself, not with faith, but with the neurotic affectivity which uses the symbols of faith. He will not accuse him of trespassing into spiritual direction because he concerns himself with the apparently religious life of the subject. He knows, indeed, that the significance for the theologian is completely different from the significance for the analyst. They both see the same conduct and the same images, but they differ in their interpretation of what they see.

The theologian, however, will not deny the usefulness of psycho-analysis in cases where it has a chance of success. Where true faith is found in conjunction with neurosis in a person, it must necessarily seem good and sane to the theologian to free that person from the infantilism which interferes with faith. Psychoanalysis is here similar to every undertaking which seeks to ensure a certain temporal good, useful to the religious life. Just as social action, for example, seeks to ensure to each person the minimum of well-being necessary for the practice of virtue, so too does psychoanalysis seek to ensure to neurotics the minimum of balance which is not less necessary to the autonomy and to the fullness of the religious life.

However, given that psychoanalysts and theologians, neurosis and faith, meet together in the same field of lived religious symbolism, it is necessary here to state precisely the conditions that must be fulfilled in order that psychoanalytic treatment may not prove injurious to a faith impossible to separate from the symbolism which is its medium.

The fact that a person's religious behaviour reveals a neurosis does not imply that he lacks faith. Nay more, its presence must be supposed *a priori*, because in a sense it was faith that possessed the person in the first place. And experience shows that, even in cases of incurable neurosis, a life of faith can exist which is very often the only thing that makes life endurable for the person. This should cause the psychoanalyst to proceed with great respect and much prudence, when he is dealing with questions which involve religious symbolism.

The greatest possible collaboration between the psychoanalyst and the priest or the spiritual director is desirable, because the analyst's skill causes the patient to realize the neurotic content which he projects into his chosen religious symbols, and it is then that someone should be at hand to help him to find other symbols previously overlooked by him, in order that a serious crisis may be avoided. A subject, sufficiently instructed from the religious point of view, can of course find for himself, in the course of his cure, substitute symbols of which he stands in need; but the help of the priest is nevertheless very useful. Neurosis, indeed, introduces real selection into a religious symbolism which ought to be regarded as a *whole*. Now, this restriction of the field of symbols is not without danger for a faith which simply cannot do without symbols, and for which the *whole* of Christian symbolism must serve as medium, if it is to be a full faith. The cure almost inevitably involves for the patient a temporary lessening of the value he had set on religious symbols chosen by his neurosis. It implies the necessity, therefore, of helping him to carry out a process of construction conjointly with his cure, if his whole religious house is not to tumble. A Freudian psychoanalyst, jealous of his objective approach, will find such an undertaking repugnant. A Jungian would employ it to a greater extent, beginning with symbols spontaneously furnished by the unconscious. In every case, the role of the priest or spiritual director is clear. A psychoanalyst really respectful of a faith whose practical value he must recognize, cannot refuse to consider this aspect of the problem.

Ought we to go further, and ask whether it is possible for a non-Christian to act in this matter with all the skill it requires? An affirmative answer is sometimes given to this, based on the possibility of distinguishing adequately, in the world of psychoanalysis, between the man who has his own philosophy of life, and the technician who envisages only a cure. But is such a division possible? Do not the ideas and even the religious life of the analyst unconsciously influence his treatment? If he respects faith but is himself an unbeliever, can he consider symbolism otherwise than as relative? He will think of it as a body of beneficent beliefs and practices, which could be replaced by others, and which are even unnecessary. Has not he himself got along without them? In these conditions, it seems very difficult for him to give sufficient attention to the reconstruction of this integral symbolism of which we have spoken, altogether apart from the fact that he himself is often incapable of understanding the meaning and the value of certain fundamental religious sentiments. A whole study remains to be made, in this connection, of the manner in which many psychologists to-day seem to deny the sense of sin. They rightly desire to free the subject from agonizing sentiments of guilt; but in doing so, they run the risk of diminishing in him a sentiment which is as fundamental—that of a redeemed sinner. It is here, we consider, that belief in Jesus Christ alone permits the recognition of the essential value of the sense of sin. Unbelief would hide a dimension which is essential to religious conscience.

For all these reasons, I am inclined to think that, as a general rule, only a truly Christian psychoanalyst can safely deal with manifestly religious neuroses among believers.

Such, then, are the elementary remarks called for when we consider analytical therapeusis as applied to religious symbolism lived by neurotics. We present them without any pretence to their being complete or definitive.

We have had Freudian psychoanalysis in mind. It would be

necessary to consider also the therapy of Jung and his disciples, whose point of view and methods are notably different from those of Freud. To be adequately dealt with, the subject would need a conference entirely devoted to it. We therefore prefer to pass on immediately to the theoretical use which psychoanalysis has made of its discoveries in the interpretation of religion in general.

The psychoanalytical theory of religious symbolism

Not wishing to enter into an historical study which would carry us beyond our scope, we shall recall simply the idea of religion which Freud fabricated in one of his last works: *The Future of an Illusion* (1927).

The task of civilization is to protect us against a nature which is antagonistic to us. This can be efficaciously done only by restoring, in face of life's deceptions, those protective and good powers who were our parents. Hence the gods, and especially the Father-God with his Providence. "As man grew up, he saw that he remained a child, and so he created gods for himself."

But the task of civilization is also to protect man against man, that murder may be avoided. Now, the man of the primitive herd murdered his father. This crime, which originated in the Oedipus Complex, resulted in a strong feeling of guilt, and, by reaction, in the imperative and efficacious command: Thou shalt not kill.

Thus, like the child, humanity passes through neurosis in order to repress its anguish and its asocial impulses. "Religion is the obsessional neurosis of humanity. Like that of the child, it derives from the Oedipus Complex, from the relations of child to father." This collective neurosis is good for the individual, because it protects him against personal neurosis. It has been useful at a particular stage of his development, but this stage has now been passed. Science makes it possible for man to dominate a hostile nature and to unite himself with his fellow men. From henceforth, human attention should be concentrated on earthly tasks, in order that nature and civilization may no longer crush anyone. Intelligence must take the place of religion.

We shall not enter on a detailed criticism of this conception of Freud's. Indeed, it is out of date to-day. The disciples of the old Master of Vienna readily admit that the father of psychoanalysis was not himself analysed, that he did not progress beyond the Jewish idea of God, that he relied too much on the science which was in vogue twenty years ago, and that he saw religion in the manner his clientele revealed it to him. It is equally true that we have here an attempt at reducing religion to instincts, which appears to us to be characteristic of psychoanalytical theory. It was doomed to failure, and it has been generally abandoned. More interesting for us is the use of analytical psychology to throw light on certain aspects of religion, not in order to degrade it, but to find therein a certain conditioning.

Since, as we have seen, religious symbolism preserves, even in transcendent significance, an essential relation with the affectivity of its laws, it is possible to study it from this second point of view, not only in a given individual, but in humanity and in history. We are concerned with examining briefly *the unconscious affective attachments of religion*.

It is certain, for example, that the family symbol—paternity, filiation, maternity, birth, fraternity, love, etc.—in which the Divine Mystery communicated to man is expressed and revealed, preserves a reference to the fundamental patterns of affective life. It is also certain that St. Paul represents the development of Revelation in the Judeo-Christian consciousness as an evolution from infancy to the age of manhood in Jesus Christ.

Moreover, psychoanalysis notices many analogies between the situation of man under the Old Law and that of the child in presence of its paternal *Super-Ego*. There is the ambivalence of Yahweh, now the "ideal father" calling men to him, and now the "terrible father" whose anger is unloosed against those who attempt to rival him; there are aspirations towards the satisfaction of instinctive impulses expressing themselves in maternal symbols such as the tree of knowledge of good and evil, and the tree of life; there are the anguish entailed by the violation of the interdict, and the beginning of a process of aggression which turns either against the subject or against others; there are rites of expiation of every kind, from washings to sacrifices for sin, with the transference of guilt, etc., etc.

We shall not continue these analogies any further. There is, however, a problem which we would like to pose simply and accurately, and answer it by indicating to analytical psychology its limits and its possibilities in the religious sphere.

The Divine Mystery cannot be brought under any category of human experience, either within the framework of the affective life or within that of the intellectual life. Everything which enlightens the affective life or the intellectual life, is also a light on religion. We can probably expect a great deal from psychoanalysis towards the elaboration of a satisfactory theory of Redemption by the blood of Christ, as also towards a better understanding of the efficacy of rites and of Sacraments. For example, Yahweh cannot in any case be identified purely and simply with the *Super-Ego*. In Himself, He is already the transcendent God who reveals Himself in His sovereign autonomy and undertakes to give Himself to man. Similarly, the

Jewish consciousness of sin cannot be reduced to an unconscious feeling of guilt towards the *Super-Ego*, because there is in it the consciousness of a position taken up against God Himself. Consequently, and whatever analogies may be drawn up between the religious history of Israel and the affective history of the child, the first is not reducible to the second.

This observation is general and is valid for every application of psychoanalysis to revealed religion. Every explanation in terms of experimental categories must stop short on the threshold of Mystery.

We must also point out the normal character of Jewish religion before Christ. It was still an infantile religion, but certainly not a religion made infantile by fixation at or regression to a past stage, since it was orientated by Messianic hope and by faith in the Promise, towards something more excellent than itself.

Finally, we must ask psychoanalysis to moderate its appetite for religious explanation which often leads it to defy all scientific rules and to seize intemperately on religious data, which it then investigates precisely in order to give a certain interpretation to that data. Psychoanalysis shows the propensity common to all sciences which are still young, to put forward sweeping generalizations with disconcerting ease. It would be better if it occupied itself with elaborating for us a good anthropology of unconscious affectivity, and did not rush forward to link itself with religion.

These remarks on the foundation and on the method of psychological analysis serve only to reassure us that theology could find in such analysis a precious ally.

Theology cannot neglect to take account of psychoanalysis, since psychoanalysis has left a more or less conscious impression on too many minds. A current of thought can be Christianized only if we adopt its schemes in so far as they are admissible, while at the same time we clearly mark their insufficiency.

For all these reasons, we consider that the moment has come for psychoanalysts and theologians to go into serious conference together. No progress can be made in this matter by prattle of lay opinion. It must be the work of specialists who mutually enlighten each other on the methods and the results of their respective disciplines. It is desirable that this should happen as soon as possible.

REV. PÈRE LOUIS BEIRNAERT
Professeur de Théologie,
Enghien (Belgique)

PSYCHOTHERAPY AND PHILOSOPHICAL VALUES

THERE has never been an epoch so preoccupied with psychology as ours, for in our days the influence of psychology reaches to all philosophical, biological and anthropological disciplines. The different schools of therapy and the various systems of that general psychological tendency which the Germans call "depth psychology" (*Tiefenpsychologie*),[1] are ample evidence of this preoccupation. Major schools of "depth psychology" each comprising a psychoanalytical school and its inheritors have been formed in recent decades; and their appearance is explained as much by the growth of general interest in psychology, as by the fact that psychology has won its place of recognition as an independent science. Thus psychotherapy, as a recognized autonomous branch of "depth psychology," is now accepted by the scientific and lay world, in spite of more or less legitimate prejudices of all kinds which still attempt to oppose it. Nay more, we consider that our epoch is heading for just such a crisis as makes necessary a still more developed application of psychotherapy, and demands therefore an especially deep theoretical study of the "depth psychology" of man.

When we consider all the data presented to us by our epoch, the question occurs to our minds: How is it that such a significant development of psychology should have occurred precisely in these recent decades? However late they may be, it is clear that the delay in the discoveries made in this field is not to be explained by the same reasons put forward, for example, to justify *a posteriori* the late arrival of the great discoveries of civilization. In other words, psychological discoveries are not simply subordinated to the progress of technical knowledge or to the application of that knowledge. The treatment of the soul belongs to all epochs. It did not wait until our century to be successfully applied. In every epoch, the great religions and the great philosophical systems have made an attentive study of the soul. It would be a crass and serious error to regard the observations recorded in earlier times as less acute and of less value than those of modern psychology.

However, the point we would make here is that formerly psychology was a subordinate discipline, whereas in our days it has become an

---

[1] The psychology of the whole man, and in a very special way, that of the unconscious.

autonomous science. As such, it uses empirical methods and even methods borrowed from the natural sciences. In its beginnings, psychology was more dependent on subjective data than was any other branch of philosophy; and the significant difference in modern psychology is that it seeks to ground itself on an "objectivity" proper to the natural sciences. In our days, indeed, the proponderating influence of the natural sciences disposes us to accept only what is proved. This attitude contains embryonically the extremism which decrees that "thou shalt believe only what thou knowest, and thou shalt regard as known only that which has been proved to thee." Now, what is universally accepted is considered as proved—in other words, "objective." This gives rise to the enormous importance of the concept of objectivity in the field of contemporary thought. The following pages are, therefore, an attempt to fix the boundaries of the concept of objectivity in the exact sciences, on the one hand, and of the concept of ontological objectivity, on the other.

*   *   *

The concept of objectivity in the exact sciences

The results reached by the exact sciences are "objective." In the final analysis, this implies that the psychic life bears a character of subjectivity, that it unfolds itself within the *Ego*, and that we must sharply distinguish between it and the knowledge which is directed towards the external world, in other words communicable knowledge, also called scientific, exact or objective knowledge. Hence "subjective" becomes a synonym for *intra*-individual impression. On the other hand, "objective" becomes a mode of *inter*-individual impression, which gives us a means of understanding our neighbour, without, however, allowing us to grasp the very essence of things. Indeed, the essence of things cannot be vitally reached by even the most advanced methods of the exact sciences. We can only interpret this essence by a universally admitted scientific language. Consequently, we must take great care not to confuse the *terminology* of the exact sciences with *Ontology*, the science of Being.

Thus, for example, in discussing the principle of causality, it is necessary to distinguish, on the one hand, the terminological concept "phenomenon" which *logically* implies the terminological concept "cause"; and, on the other hand, our juxtaposed perceptions which, at most, allow us to conclude with *probability* to an analogy of relations, on the ontological plane, between certain phenomena. A relation exists to which we cannot attribute absolute value, between the logical, conceptual pair: "cause-phenomenon," and the probable, ontological isomorphism suggested by the connecting of our impressions. This is a "coincidental correspondence," to use the term of Prince Alfred Auersperg.

Let us not confuse concept with being. While terminology ought to be as clear and as exact as possible, it must not, however, be confused with the essence which it implies. Energy, electricity, the atom and other analogous concepts of physics, must not be made into idols; they originate merely in a "coincidental correspondence" with isomorphic perceptions. Thus, when I say that the temperature of the room in which I write these lines is 17° Centigrade, I do not yet know anything specific about the essence of heat, nor about my own perception of heat. And when, in psychoanalysis, we say that "religious sentiment is a product of sublimation," we must be on our guard against any specific conclusions about the essence of God or about the characteristics proper to intense religious feeling; for we have reached nothing more than a systematization of the presumed relations which would exist between certain structural aspects of the soul considered as object, and it is this which is known as the "psychological law."

An "objective" statement, therefore, is an interpretation which is as exact as possible. It is a simplificative interpretation dependent on method; a "coincidental correspondence" which exists between intra-individual perceptions and the inter-individual hypothesis. This is not an exhaustive identity.

The touchstone of our knowledge is, for example, given by physics, which is the science most adjusted both as to its content and its method. Physics is a science of observation and experimentation; it is both an *a posteriori* science and a methodology which serves to co-ordinate our perceptions according to certain purely structural points of view. Certainly, by that very fact, it is the best preparation for a philosophy; but, in itself, it possesses no power of philosophical proof. Its concepts cannot be hypostatized. In short, the objectivity of the exact sciences, as the "Viennese Circle" of Moritz Schlick had already recognized, is *not* that of Metaphysics. The method of the exact sciences does not reach to the substance of things; it co-ordinates the inter-individual substratum of our perceptions in accordance with certain structural rules.

Now, there is confusion, in the general tendency of our epoch towards "objectivity," between the inter-individual objectivity of the exact sciences and ontological objectivity. From this there also arises the error of being willing to "believe" only what has been "objectively proved." Humanity seems to have lost the certitude and the assurance that come from faith, and we have here perhaps one of the reasons for the contemporary crisis—and, at all events, for that spiritual uprooting—which has made psychotherapy a necessity.

*   *   *

The alienation of man and the hypertrophy of the ego

The corresponding tendency in psychology to a narrow "scientism," is causal determinism. Here, again, there is the pretence of having discovered, in an "objective" way, the relation between "effects" and "causes," and even *of thus explaining the whole of human conduct and man himself.* It is by the so-called objectivity of "exact" data that man is drawn away from the whole knowledge of himself, and that he becomes as an *atom.* He loses contact with authentic objectivity. And what results from this? There results the anguish of being thrown into a discontinuous world,[1] where man, now a part, a fragment, an atom, a complex of all pieces, struggles in the midst of an artificial world. And this is what is known to-day as "existential anguish. . . ."

This uprooted man is constantly seeking for some stability, for some immutable value. But because he is "atomized," thrown into a discontinuous world, he chooses for sole criterion his own *feelings* and he makes them absolute. This short-circuiting deprives him of the ability to think beyond himself. Love, humility, God, cannot any longer be regarded by him as abstract values. Feeling (*das Erleben*) is made absolute in the welter of the discontinuous. It incites, of course, the wish to feel (*erleben*) only what is agreeable and to fear above all what is painful. It is thus that the pleasure-principle, understood in its widest sense (*Lustprinzip*), is raised to the rank of the supreme principle.

The discontinuity of the world, the anguish, the rendering absolute of his own impressions, inevitably leads man to *hypertrophy of the "Ego,"* simply because the sole criterion is sought in the quality of his own sensation. The fall, or if Heidegger's term is preferred, "existence-thrown-into-the-world-of-anxiety," results in a coiling up within oneself—with anguish as its fruit. Herein lies the tragedy of every promethean adventure: *eritis sicut Deus.* This "hypertrophy of the Ego" can wear the mask of an ideal (an absolutized objective) or of wisdom (absolutized knowledge).

We have here a very serious problem, of great importance for our conception of the world; a problem which is destined to become central in psychotherapy. This problem may be stated as follows: "*Depth Psychology attempts to discover criteria in the depths of the individual*

---

[1] *Zusammenhanglose Welt*, as M. Max Picard so happily calls it in his book: *Hitler en nous-mêmes.*

himself, for man's growth to full maturity. For that very reason, it cannot go beyond the individual. The full realization of the "Ego," its "individuation" (C. G. Jung), all this aims at gathering an experience which should put us in a position to determine our ethical conduct by means of the consciousness of self. Thus the aim of a "Tiefenpsychologie" which has become autonomous, is no other than the full development of the Ego alone.

But here, "Depth Psychology" meets with a blind alley. If man wishes to make absolute his own impressions, he is led to hypertrophy of the "Ego." The apparent aim certainly remains the perfection of the "Ego"; but this perfecting cannot go beyond the individual as long as it is not bound up with authentic objective values. There must be renunciation, in order that it may be possible to go beyond the individual; in other words, man must be prepared to abandon egoistic values in favour of the values of love.

Sôren Kierkegaard, when making a study of the different types of men, sketched the consequences and depicted the results of this "absolutization" of relative aims (even exalted, yet still egocentric, aims). Ahasuerus—eternally seeking; Don Juan—eternally feeling; Faust—eternally knowing. All are withdrawn from the kingdom of objective values, eagerly seeking an absolutized egoistic value, without ever finding in it the expected sense of fulfilment.

The hierarchy of objective values

In this existential anguish, this rending, this discontinuity, this dictatorship of feeling, one last safety plank remains: the hierarchy of objective values. "Objective" is used here not in the sense of a result inter-individually established according to the method of the exact sciences, but in the decided sense of an existential, *lived* truth. I am able to *know* a truth, while I do not possess that truth. Even though I possess it, the truth remains inactive within me as long as I do not make it *my* truth, as long as I do not confess it. But here we meet the point at which it is no longer possible to turn back. My activity is completely penetrated by this known, lived truth which I have made my own. One could certainly not be too much on one's guard against the desire to impose on another person that personally accepted truth; for my neighbour himself must begin by first accepting truth as *his* own. But when a truth has become *mine*, I can no longer regard it as a simple hypothesis which I can set aside as irrelevant when it suits me to do so. On the contrary, it becomes the *constant support* of my convictions, even when I am talking about the weather. It will be even more so when I am dealing with the management of the soul or the educative formation of character.

Since I would not force anyone to accept *my* truth, I must certainly know how to remain silent sometimes. But even without bringing up the question of my own truth, I will remain none the less penetrated with it. For my part, I can no longer achieve a *volte-face*, and it is only in accordance with *my* conscience that I can truly heal and educate, because every education is grounded in stable values. And nevertheless, the results achieved show such a diversity. The art of education consists precisely in presenting these values according to a growing progression, in such a way as to lead man towards a conscious choice which will cause him to *confess* these values. It is something completely different from the training of animals.

Within due limits, the same is true of psychotherapy, because neurosis is always a flight from an "either—or" situation; it is an indecision, a bad compromise, a complete lack of inner criteria. And psychotherapy, also, should be based on firm, immutable values. It should set man free from neurosis by helping him to lead his life in accordance with authentic values.

If one is never sufficiently on guard, therefore, against statements, against theory, against dogmatic constraint, against rigid authoritarianism, is it not less illogical and dangerous of us to halt on the very threshold of superior values—even of those which, by their essence, are placed *at the centre* of the world of values. And if it is agreed—as many contemporary psychotherapeutists do agree—that neurosis presents us with a spiritual problem for solution; if it is even recognized that this spiritual problem is posed by the fact that man turns from the absolute in favour of the relative, it must with equal logic be proclaimed that *the educative aims of psychotherapy, like the aims of all education, can be fully realized only on the spiritual plane.* It was not by mere chance, therefore, that for thousands of years the care of souls was reserved to the priest. Nor can it be explained as a result of mere chance that the totalitarian regimes confide the direction of consciences to medical, pedagogical and political functionaries. . . .

Let us make ourselves perfectly clear. We live in the present, and the requirements of the present are binding on every man who is not a Utopian. We are therefore fully convinced that psychotherapy, as it exists to-day, appertains to the doctor. *But since psychotherapy shares in a vast, spiritual, religious problem, it follows that the practitioner himself is a kind of substitute for the spiritual director or confessor.* Unfortunately, the discontinuity of our interpretation of the world and the progressive specialization which results from this in the domain of knowledge, were and still are the reason why, not only directors of conscience, but still more representatives of the Medical Faculty, are completely at a loss where there is question of dealing with the problems of psychotherapy. But, in principle at least, there can be only one direction of conscience and one integral way of treating the soul, since there is but one soul in every man. And the cure of the soul, directed by the practitioner, ought to be the preparation of a *metanoia*, of a return to "vital orthodoxy." Moreover, the term in vogue, circulated in Austria by Dr. Frankl, is "medical direction of conscience" (*aerztliche Seelsorge*), and could not this be accepted in more than a figurative sense, as meaning "medical assistance to the director of conscience"?[1] And yet again, to use another term which we owe to M. Gallus Jud of Zürich, we say that it is *a technical* complement necessary to "pastoral psychology," which we would like to see entering into a really universalist psychotherapy.

We have just seen that objective truth, in order to be operative, must become subjective. We use "subjective" here in the clear sense of "personal." This is possible only through perpetual choice. And when a man makes his own objective values, in the sense that he can no longer not confess them, he ought also resolve to *transcend* his own existential problems. We give an active sense (*Transcendierung*) here to the verb "transcend," somewhat as Sôren Kierkegaard conceived the "existential categories." The inferior stage would be formed by the *esthetic* category, that of feeling; the second, built on law, would be the *ethical* category; the third, by far the superior, the *religious* category. This last stage would involve the recognition of a personal affiliation through relationship with a *personal God*. Each trait of character, each failing, each trial, each joy, each experience, every temptation too and every vice should be transposed from an inferior stage to a superior stage, in order that it may bear its fruit.

As a stay to our argument, we can recall here what Kierkegaard himself says about his melancholia, which he diagnosed as hereditary. According to the pathography made by the Danish psychiatrist Hjalmar Helweg, Kierkegaard belonged to the depressive type of manic-depressive psychosis, and therefore to the melancholic type. Indeed, it seems to us that Kierkegaard's condition was considerably masked (in the sense of a neurotic psychogenesis) by the results of his historic evolution (*lebensgeschichtliche Entwicklung*), especially of his education which was conducted against the dictates of common sense. But, however this may have been, we are dealing here with scientific, psychiatric or psychological analyses, and these analyses do not approximatively exhaust the richness of existence itself. For Kierkegaard himself saw in his "melancholia" a trial and an expiation which should not be considered except in the chiaroscuro of original sin and

---

[1] *Seelsorgehilfe*, according to the emendation of the first term by Dr. Albert Niedermeyer, Director of the Viennese *Institute of Pastoral Medicine*.

of personal infection. This man was the creator of a grandiose lesson on melancholia.

Melancholy, especially in the form of anguish, is inherent in every limited existence in this world of incertitude. It shows itself with particular acuteness in certain cases, and this in three ways. In the first place, there is *esthetic* melancholy, which affects the man who seeks his absolute in feeling and in pleasure. A Nero would be the very type, though bestially defaced, of the esthetic melancholiac in this plan. Secondly, there is *ethical* melancholy, which makes its appearance when we become conscious of what there is of the equivocal in every nature, and how narrow and menaced our existence is by its very nature in a universe which is itself ephemeral and limited. Finally, there is *religious* melancholy. This takes the form of nostalgia for a higher world which rends every creature torn between sin and grace. Melancholy and anguish are inherent in the confession of Christian values, because the Christian feels how the *homo animalis* is liable to experience a painful tension.

All his life, Kierkegaard waged war on his melancholy to illumine it, to give a higher meaning to himself, to lift himself up step by step. He had suffered cruelly, because he doubted that this elevation served him in each concrete case, at every moment of his existence, in every situation of "either . . . or." And we have the right to ask ourselves whether it is the modern psychoanalysts, or more properly Kierkegaard, who penetrate more profoundly *the very essence of melancholy* and who grasp its *significance* most surely.

* * *

The dialectic of spiritual progress

It is quite clear that we can reproach the believer with the discrepancy which exists between his convictions and his way of living. We certainly would not attempt to exalt and to exculpate the man who recognized truth as *his*, but did not live in accordance with that truth. However, life in truth and according to truth is precisely the goal aimed at. The attraction of this goal sustains our hope in the midst of an existence entirely composed of struggle. As long as we are not progressing towards that goal, truth remains in part a dead letter for us.

But it is equally true that the mere existence of a goal already implies the possibility of a direction, of a line of conduct. This is of the utmost importance; for it becomes possible not to "absolutize" our sensations any more, but to recognize the existence of objective criteria, to apply them, in order to forge our way ahead, however painful the effort may be.

To be pledged to something without being convinced of its truth involves a terrible decision. This is no fanciful idea. It is thus that, to keep the balance, there arises a tension at every moment, born of the disharmony which exists between conviction and way of life. But the mere existence of this tension may be sufficient to show that the soul has made some progress; and this is something which the psychotherapy founded on pleasure (*Lustprinzip*) cannot understand. The positive character of the conflict resides in the fact that the believer recognizes objective criteria and that he attempts to find in objective truth an end to be attained. Thus, *it can come about that in simply causing a conflict to disappear, in "dissolving" it by means of psychological analysis, one thereby neglects the depth of the spiritual problem which lies at the root of the conflict.* This problem would thus be left without an adequate solution.

We see, therefore, that in the case of the believer, whose outlook is not in accordance with truth, the tension is the result of knowledge, and this tension gives rise to a bad conscience. But is not the *bad conscience* here *repressed* in the *unconscious*? On the contrary, indeed, this man finds himself placed in a very difficult situation; for his conscience says to him: "You must make up your mind; no man can serve two masters at once." On the other hand, neurosis makes its appearance in the case of the man who, in practice, has lost contact with immutable values, and lives henceforward in accordance with the superstitious values placed on sensation. Such a man has indeed the feeling of not having reached the right decision, and he suffers because of this. But he has not at his disposal the criteria which would enable him to make a suitable decision. Even if he has a surface knowledge of these criteria, they are still only abstractions for him. In that case, this punishment which he inflicts on himself and which is represented by the bad conscience remains inoperative, and, according to the economy of the *Lustprinzip*, it is repressed in the unconscious and causes neurotic symptoms to appear there. Man is never so deprived of help, never so torn, as when he becomes an "atom." He can find rest only in a renunciation of self, by a loving adherence to the "Absolute Thou" (Gabriel Marcel) because he is a child of God.

To be a child of God means, according to Kierkegaard, the taking of the supreme decision of our existence at the meeting-place of being and non-being. But this decision is a conquest, because, to make it a reality, I must make the decision in every alternative that presents itself in my existence, and this involves an incessant "dispute" with myself. Always drawn as I am towards the abyss of non-existence, I must surmount defeat and torment. Human principles and human feelings are all ephemeral, relative, uncertain, ambiguous. Spiritual progress can be conceived only dialectically, in an ever renewed discussion with self, an uninterrupted dialogue pursued through doubt, and even through scandal.

*   *   *

Analytical unmasking and existential synthesis

It is precisely these theories, apparently so high flown, which give us the directives we must follow in the practice of psychotherapy. For if we return from these regions of principles to that of psychotherapy, we discover that, in the light of these premises, the aims of psychotherapy cannot be other than *existential*. (Here we have just used a word which is unfortunately assimilated to a philosophical fashion of the moment, and is very often understood and interpreted in a contrary sense.) If the aims of psychotherapy cannot be other than existential, this means for us that the aims of the psychotherapeutic attempts cannot be measured apart from concrete human existence—existence in which there occurs the living encounter of the doctor with the person who comes to consult him.

The therapeutist is certainly not a *master*, who would seek to impose his own conception of the world and, in order to do so, would rely on something only theoretically established. Quite the contrary indeed. He will be able to deliver his patient from the bonds and the blind gropings of animality (of the "Id"), only in the exact measure in which he himself has attained to a lived confession of existential values.

It is only in passing, and for this same reason, that we can remark here on how necessary it is for the psychotherapeutist himself to undergo analysis (*Eigeanalyse*, *Lehranalyse*: "study-analysis"). This analysis is not an "initiation," but rather a painful experiment which allows the psychotherapeutist to surmount, to a very modest extent, his own deceits and his own blindnesses. It would be possible to multiply indefinitely examples of this laying bare of the psychotherapeutist's soul by his own psychoanalysis. Indeed, such an analysis should be not only a course, an apprenticeship; it should provide positive aims in the direction of souls.

Among other examples of the same kind, I remember the dream of a psychotherapeutist who was psychoanalysed. He dreamed of a little hairdresser of Haifa, ugly and absurd, who saw himself wearing a halo and was convinced that he was the Messiah. The analysis of this dream showed that the subject was still at a degree of interior development far short of his ideal of being a healer and a "redeemer."

The aim of psychotherapy is not simply to "analyse," to dissociate. All the respect due to personal peculiarities and the laws of individuation having been taken into account, the aim of psychotherapy is also and above all to "transcend" whatever is dark and instinctive in the psychic organism in order to attain to value and to enlightenment. The choice is put before us always and in every domain of life. Either we are concerned with leading our lives according to positive values of existence; or we are prepared to allow our lives to be determined by a narrowness of view, by a deficiency or a total absence of these same values, and this is simply to lead being towards non-being.

In order to become expert at making existential values come to fruition, one must certainly begin by having a clear insight into oneself. This is the first aspect of psychotherapy, and it is an aspect of capital importance from the technical point of view. But it is undoubtedly an aspect which is still negative. It was, to some extent, greatly exaggerated by classical psychotherapy, especially by Freudian psychoanalysis. We call it *"therapy of the unmasking"* (*aufdeckende Therapie*), and we demand emphatically from every psychotherapeutist that he should know it fully and accurately. Were he to refuse to do so, he would be condemned to remain for ever an amateur, a sorcerer's apprentice.

But he would be a much more dangerous sorcerer's apprentice still, if he did not succeed in using the materials drawn from the quagmire originating in the demoniacal regions of the human soul, and if he did not apply himself to the constructive task of psychotherapy, a task which we call "existential synthesis."

These two aspects—the "analytical unmasking" and the "existential synthesis"—should be present in all psychotherapy, even in the very shortest. Without analysis, without penetration into the "sub-soil" of personality, the synthesis would remain an abstraction instead of becoming a lived truth. But, on the other hand, without the spiritual growth of the person, in accordance with a scale of values, it would be impossible to obtain anything more than a good functioning of the "libido," even in the best cases. This spiritual maturity will not be the fruit of sermons, nor the fruit of a more or less constricting education which attempts to impose our own norms of existence on others. This spiritual maturity can be achieved only by a change of level, by raising these concrete existential problems to a higher plane.

Analysis itself shows us that our instinctive tendencies are carefully dissembled in so far as they are dangerous; but it also shows us that spiritual problems are repressed and smothered because a solution to these problems would constitute a menace to our animality. And since the *Lustprinzip* (pleasure) is chosen as the line of conduct, sometimes anything may happen in a strictly Freudian psychoanalysis where, in particular, an attempt is made to avoid all pain, all malaise, in short all that could menace our *animality*, as the result of a decision taken at the level of spiritual problems. Now, in general, this decision to be taken is in no way a hedonistic decision. It brings neither enjoyment nor pleasure, and the passions must often be wounded at their very roots as a result of it. Often, too, man is exposed to a searing laceration.

Thus, psychological analysis (understood in its widest sense) reveals relations which are co-ordinated according to the determinist causal principle, and, from that fact, it attains to partial knowledge. When these results have been acquired, we must go on to recompose an organic whole, and we must do this by the help of synthesis. The meaning of existence is *one*; it cannot be broken up or dissociated by analysis. And it is in order to avoid philosophical *quid-pro-quos* and psychological errors that we shall not speak here of an "analysis of existence."[1] But we shall go on to commend both *psychological analysis* and *existential synthesis*.

Conclusion

We have seen, therefore, that the method of psychotherapy is paradoxical and dualist. Though it has something of biological exactitude, it is nevertheless constructive only through the mind. As we said at the beginning of this article, the exact sciences would like to answer all the enigmas, to resolve all the problems of existence. This is a pretension which cannot be accepted, since these answers cannot be found in measurable objectivity. They can come only from lived truth. Up to the present, psychotherapy was too often hybrid. It frequently sought to substitute the rational and the biological for the ontological and the existential. The task of those who know the nature of the human soul, is to liberate "depth-psychology" from its superstitions, to exorcize psychotherapy.

DOCTEUR IGOR CARUSO
Assistant à l'Institut de Médecine Pastorale
de Vienne

[1] As L. Binswanger does in Switzerland (*Daseinanalyse*) and V. Frankl in Austria (*Existenzanalyse*).

FOURTH STUDY

PSYCHASTHENIA

EDITOR'S FOREWORD

A STUDY of vocation problems and of those which arise later in the religious or sacerdotal life in those subjects who suffer from one or more of the syndromes which the writers of the following papers classify under the general heading of Psychasthenia, must prove not merely interesting but of considerable practical importance to those charged with the duty of taking decisions which relate to such cases. Bishops, seminary Rectors and religious superiors as well as all spiritual directors are continually faced with these problems and a general knowledge of their etiology and prognosis must be of use to them. These articles both enunciate the problem and indicate in a general way what may and what should be done in order to solve it.

The prudent selection of subjects and their subsequent direction and spiritual formation is of evident importance. Here we would like to emphasize that no "inner" attraction to the priesthood or the religious life constitutes in itself a call thereto. In fact, a strong and even persistent attraction is quite compatible with the complete absence of any vocation to that form of life which is the object of the attraction. The reality or certainty of a vocation is to be found in the bishop's or other superior's call to the priesthood and/or to the religious life as the case may be. These are gravely bound in conscience to call only those who are suitable and whose lives give evidence of a right intention and stable moral character which promise that the subject will stand up to the trials of and persevere in his calling. This "idoneitas," or suitability, is a positive not a negative quality. A person who suffers from moral, intellectual or physical defect incompatible with the duties of the state he seeks to enter, has no vocation to that state, no matter what "call" he may believe himself to experience. The same applies to those whose near relatives have a claim to financial assistance from them, or where their special experience is required to continue a family business which is necessary to their maintenance. Obviously then, suitability is a relative term once a certain level has been reached. The physical health and constitution demanded in a missioner in the tropics differs considerably from that required of a prospective Carthusian attached to a house in Northern Europe. Those who aspire to enter clerical institutes or those devoted primarily to teaching must possess the intellectual gifts required for the satisfactory performance of such works. The more enclosed and contemplative Orders, particularly those with a closely knit community life require subjects who possess a more placid cheerful disposition than those who will be able to find an outlet for excessive "nervous" energy in an active apostolate, and so on. It can never be too strongly urged that only suitable applicants be accepted. The failures do too much harm to the Church and to themselves to permit any other policy. Successive popes, notably St. Pius X and Pius XI, have declared in no unmistakable terms that quality, not quantity, must be sought and that one must not be led by fear of "empty novitiates," into taking unsuitable subjects, for God will not leave His Church without the priests and religious necessary to carry on His work. St. Philip Neri used to say that with ten good priests he would conquer the world for Christ. St. Ignatius Loyola, who founded the Jesuits, said: "If I could wish for a longer life, it would be to see to it that ever more prudence be used in choosing candidates for the religious life."

Actually the acceptance of unsuitable subjects defeats the aims of those who seek numbers at the expense of quality, since the presence of misfits in the ranks of the secular clergy or in the religious life often repels other more suitable entrants. Neither diocesan seminaries nor religious houses are intended to be homes of rest for persons who are mentally or otherwise unfit, or who seek to escape the difficulties they cannot cope with in the world. As our authors show in these conferences, such people do seek admission in disproportionate numbers and it is their endeavour to indicate how the unsuitable may be weeded out from those whose temperamental or other defects do not render their admission imprudent. We must also bear in mind that it is not right to assume that those who cannot resist temptation in the world will be able to do so in religion. The difficulties of such a one may differ in form, but they will not necessarily be any less, or even more easily resisted. Grace is available in each case, but in both the co-operation of the person concerned is required.

That the cure of some psychological disorders is possible is evident from these discussions and though doctors trained in our schools of Pharmacology will not be prepared to accept every therapeutic measure, such as extracts of brain tissue, employed by our French confrères, we do accept the principle that the physical organism must be made to function at its highest level for the individual concerned before other procedures are considered. We may take occasion to say that grave harm can result to one of these patients if he should be so unfortunate as to fall into the hands of a practitioner not fully trained in the science of Medicine. It is not difficult to acquire a certain technical jargon in matters of this sort and to conceal even from oneself the need of a complete and repeated physical investigation of the case.

We could quote disastrous results that followed on the "treatment" given by non-medical or inadequately trained medical practitioners in these cases and we are convinced that in no other department of human affairs is a little knowledge so dangerous.

PREFACE TO THE FRENCH EDITION

THOUGH studied by Pierre Janet, psychasthenia continues to be a form of neurosis which is not yet properly understood because it is difficult to define. On the occasion of certain study courses, organized for the Rectors of major seminaries, some doctors were invited to present the result of their observations on this subject. It will therefore be understood why psychasthenia is regarded, in this *cahier*, principally but *not exclusively* from the angle of its relationship with the priestly and religious vocation.

But is not psychasthenia, first and foremost, a constitutional state on which certain accidental elements are grafted? This is the question for which Dr. Barbier sets out to provide an answer, taking into account, moreover, that on this point the frontiers between psychogenesis and organogenesis, as yet ill defined, are being constantly rectified.

PSYCHASTHENIA AND VOCATION

In his study: "Psychopathologie et Direction," published in 1930, Père de Sinéty said that psychasthenics "constitute the major part of the psychopaths living outside of mental homes." This observation is borne out by that made by the psychiatrists who, on their side, meet a great number of these patients in their consultations.

And when they are ecclesiastics or religious who come to consult the doctors about minor psychic troubles, one is very often astonished at the discovery that many of these patients are afflicted with psychasthenia. Of course, a careful selection is made among applicants for entry into seminaries and noviciates, and those who are clearly afflicted with serious troubles or with grave blemishes of character are not accepted. Nevertheless, the high incidence of psychasthenic cases among the clergy and among members of Religious Orders, has led certain psychiatrists to say that "psychasthenia is a disease of ecclesiastics." Indeed, fifty observations taken at random among these patients—priests, religious and nuns—have given us a total of twenty eight cases of psychasthenia, or 56 per cent. This shows the important place taken by problems connected with psychasthenia.

Ought not the attention of the Spiritual Directors of major seminaries and the attention of Novice-masters be aroused by such observations? Should they not urge superiors to examine candidates for the priesthood or for the Religious Life, from this point of view? The reason for this more frequent incidence of psychasthenia must be sought within the framework of our Institutes. Is not the candidate with psychasthenia easily attracted by the Religious Life? Or rather, does not the formation which the seminarist or the novice receives, contain, in certain cases, serious elements of psychic inebriation?

This question is all the more important because psychasthenia does not reveal itself in well-defined structures and behaviour-patterns at a cursory examination. On the contrary, it is a "polymorphic" disease. A psychasthenic comes to consult the doctor because of a quasi-inability to make physical efforts; another comes on account of a whole series of troubles, which appear to be organic but which elude the doctor's diagnosis; yet another will complain of a great difficulty in fixing his attention, with the result that he is unable to study properly. Sometimes they are difficulties of a sexual order, and even real perversions—sadism or masochism. But it is principally on account of scruples, obsessions, doubts, a lack of self-confidence, or troubles due to chronic indecision, that the psychasthenic will decide to consult the doctor. In some extreme cases, ideas of suicide or even attempts at suicide, are what will bring the psychasthenic to the consulting room.

The forms in which psychasthenia expresses itself are so diverse that it requires a certain practical experience to discover their origin at a glance; and therefore in our exposé, we shall follow this plan—

We shall first attempt to define psychasthenia and to classify its most prevailing forms.

Then we shall see how psychasthenia makes its appearance, and develops.

Then we must attempt to answer the question: why this high incidence of psychasthenia among priests and religious?

Finally, we shall end by discussing the conclusion which can be reached from a medical point of view when dealing with the question of the vocation of a psychasthenic, leaving aside the therapeutic aspect.

What is psychasthenia?

The term "psychasthenia" was coined by Pierre Janet, whose works on this question still remain the most important contribution in this field. Etymologically, psychasthenia signifies: "lack of psychic energy." But in practice, the definition must be extended, because asthenia is not limited to the psyche. If the troubles ascertained do not correspond to any known organic lesion, they almost exclusively develop in hereditarily predisposed soil. We are dealing, therefore, with a *disease of the body and of the mind*, that is, with a "condition" which is permanent rather than subject to variation. There are, of course, many degrees from the simple tendency which affects only the personality, to the serious, progressive form which can lead even to suicide.

We shall attempt to outline the characteristics of the psychasthenic by studying him successively on the physiological, the intellectual, and the characterological planes.

Physiologically

The psychasthenic is often a person of more than average height, thin, slack, and gaunt. His walk is slow, like his manner of speaking. His expression is lifeless and tortured with tics. But sometimes that lifelessness will suddenly disappear; the unfocussed look will suddenly sharpen, he will speak rapidly and become excessively talkative; but quite as suddenly, everything will slacken to its characteristic vacuity and indecision.

The psychasthenic suffers from debility. The somewhat flaccid pliancy of his carriage tends to ligamentary hyperplasia, and to a general lowering of muscular tonicity. He makes use of every support he can find, and accumulates a whole arsenal of every type of body belt, straps, girdles, etc. . . . The stripping of these patients is a nightmare to a busy doctor. It is an endless task, as the psychasthenic pauses over each appliance to explain its why and its wherefore, and to direct the doctor's attention to a fresh symptom of a fresh complaint.

These are the kenaesthopaths, who are aware of all their organs. They run the whole gamut of false organic diseases: false ulcers, false angina pectoris, false tuberculosis.

But this must not deceive us into classing such patients among the *malades imaginaires*; they are certainly delicate and they really suffer.

The psychasthenic is *always tired*. He rises late, and usually maintains that he is more tired than when he went to bed. He soon looks for a chair, as though by instinct, and even forms the habit of having siestas during the day, or of spending more or less prolonged periods on a settee.

On closer examination, he sometimes shows all the symptoms of orthostatic disease, that is to say, different phenomena induced by standing, as for example orthostatic albuminury (the appearance of albumen in the standing position only), or again, orthostatic hypotension.

Everything which concerns his health is of intense interest to the psychasthenic, and this is the first sign of the egocentricity which we shall find at every stage of our account.

Intellectually

In its extreme forms, psychasthenia ends by having a profound repercussion of the judgment and intelligence of the patient, but this is an exceptional case. Psychasthenia does not usually affect the patient's intelligence, and it must therefore be dissociated from intellectual ability. There were geniuses who were psychasthenics; and there are psychasthenics who are mentally deficient.

It follows from this, that certain highly intelligent psychasthenics succeed in compensating for their deficiency in effort by limiting the normal period of their intellectual work or of their social and professional activities. But here again, these moments of vigour are short-lived, even if the psychasthenics are completely taken up with what they are doing; and it is this characteristic which enables them to be distinguished from the lazy and the listless with whom they are sometimes confused. We are dealing with an accumulator which discharges quickly, and whose time of recharging is longer than its time of production.

Another characteristic on the intellectual plane, is that the psych-asthenic tires very quickly. It is with difficulty that he can concentrate for any length of time, and if he persists in the effort, headaches compel him to cease. His work will often be sketchy and fragmentary, and his reasoning will fall short. The danger that awaits him, and which few psychasthenics escape, is that a *mental automatism* will usually take the place of creative effort.

Consequently, the psychasthenic constantly discovers that his thought processes are controlled by association of ideas which irrelevantly succeed one another. He is scarcely able to resist that association. Conversation with him quickly becomes a succession of associations, and ranges over a myriad of subjects.

Frequently, an idea imposes itself, and engulfs the whole field of consciousness. In that idea we discover the origin of the scruple, the phobia, the obsession, which, as we shall show later on, is a component of the psychopathology of the psychasthenic.

This automatism is an obligatory solution during the phases of repose, and soon becomes a torment to the patient. By diminishing effort, routine brings him some solace, but it also causes him to despair.

In practice, the psychasthenic is in danger of sinking into automatism; and, if he is a priest, into vague functionism.

Characterologically

The gamut of characterological manifestations is very extensive: self-diffidence, uncertainty, hesitation, scruples, obsessions are the principal form most usually met. But the one characteristic common to all these manifestations, is that they are egocentric.

Without being a schizoid, the psychasthenic is an introvert. He has an exaggerated and, in most cases, painfully intense interest in all that concerns himself.

In dealing with questions which involve neither his person nor his responsibility, he sees clearly and reasons correctly, though at times with slight pessimism; but as soon as these problems take on a personal character, the pathological overtones make their appearance.

He is interested in his neighbour to the extent to which he finds his own infirmities in him; because the psychasthenic looks for external support, and also needs friends, whom he often harasses by seeking from each the answer to the problem which, for the moment, obsesses him. Passing from one to another, perpetually begging advice, he becomes a little more calm only if all the answers tally; otherwise, he becomes a prey to fresh anguish.

In psychoanalytical terms, therefore, it can be said that the friendship of the psychasthenic is of a *captative kind*: even when he is very generous, the psychasthenic seeks rather to obtain than to give. Hence the frequently passionate and exclusive quality of his affection, which, moreover, will often be fundamentally free from any trace of disturbance or equivocation. The question may be rightly asked: is not psychasthenia due to a fixation of the "libido," the oblative stage never having been reached? Or rather, does not psychasthenia introduce a constitutional limitation to full emotional development? The importance of this double aspect, on the therapeutic plane, will soon be obvious.

Human support is not sufficient, however, for the psychasthenic. He searches all the texts and all the rules in his endeavour to justify himself. But when, in his reading, he comes on a comforting passage, he finds that the very next paragraph contains an idea or a directive which he immediately construes into matter for unrest and scruples.

A glance at the books on his shelves reveals the same preoccupation. The mere titles are eloquent: "Self-Mastery"; "How to Get On"; "How to Make Friends"; "The Diseases of Energy."

However, even all these supports are not sufficient for him. He must, in addition, have social systems in which external discipline is severe and serves as a prop to his weakness.

We must now turn our attention more closely to the form in which the priest most frequently meets with psychasthenia: the scrupulous. In general, every confessor will have little difficulty in distinguishing between the pathological scruple and praiseworthy delicacy of conscience. Now, in the case of the psychasthenic, the scruple has something of the artificial, the factitious, about it: there is more concern about form than about matter, about the act than about the intention. Such a psychasthenic will endlessly begin the same prayer, will hesitate for whole minutes before pronouncing the words of Consecration, will accuse himself of having administered invalid Sacraments because he has not sufficiently articulated the essential words. Another will have scruples of a sexual order, which will lay greater stress on the fact of having had, or of not having had, such and such an impure contact, than on real chastity of thought. And yet another will indulge in erotic day-dreams which do not occasion any scruple, but will be obsessed by the idea that he has perhaps been guilty of an immodest gesture during his toilet.

It is an interesting fact that one does not meet with pathological scruples in connection with faults of pride or lack of charity. Such scruples always concern fears connected with a ritual act or with a material fault.

A host of minor symptoms will confirm, moreover, the pathological character of the scruple. Thus, the psychasthenic is never sure of what he has done; he several times reopens a letter which he is about to post; he is never sure that he has posted letters; or again, he goes back several times to make sure he has closed the doors or turned off the gas. If he is buying anything, he hesitates and is unable to make a decision; he returns several times to the same shop, or immediately returns what he has bought a few moments earlier. Unable to make a decision about the least of his actions, he must always seek the advice of another person.

It is not surprising, therefore, that the psychasthenic usually suffers from an *inferiority complex*—of which, indeed, his friends are more aware than he is! Consequently, because of his diffidence, he quickly allows himself to be influenced by any and every friend or acquaintance. He is easily led into good or into evil, because his own will-power disappears before the opinions expressed to him by others.

But from self-diffidence he usually passes on to doubt those around him; because, though he is highly susceptible to suggestions at certain times, he shows obsessional stubbornness at other times. This stubbornness is all the more ridiculous because it is exerted about trifles. Thus divided in the very depths of his will, the psychasthenic ends up at last in total inaction, abandoning himself to short-sighted policies. He no longer reacts in any situation; a deep disgust for himself and for others finally colours his whole existence, and sometimes drives him to suicide.

Another characteristic trait of the psychology of the psychasthenic is *fear*—pathological fear in all its forms. It is the commonplace and unjustified fear of burglars or of any kind of aggression—a panic fear which can drive him to flight or to destruction. On the religious plane, this fear becomes an unjustified terror of divine justice, with the ideas of damnation and of unworthiness. The psychasthenic regards the eternal fire of Hell as created specially for him, and as being his inevitable destiny. In other cases, it is the idea of guilt, with its attendant ideas of self-accusation and pardon, which seizes on the psychasthenic.

A kind of dualism is often discovered in the psychasthenic. It takes the form of an opposition between the lassitude of individual action, and facts which witness to real heroism when he participates in a collective action in which he feels himself to be supported by the social milieu. This holds good also for his spiritual life: when he feels himself buttressed by a community, he is capable of a really ascetic life; but if left to himself, he is in danger of falling into the worst excesses.

Finally, we must describe the last and most specifically pathological aspects of psychasthenia: that of *obsession*.

Obsessional neurosis can take on an endless variety of forms, because anything can become an obsession. But it is in connection with sex that obsession most frequently shows itself.

In different observations, whatever their precise purpose, the same egocentric characteristic will emerge which marks the whole psychology of psychasthenics. Sometimes the obsession can take on the appearance of an altruistic preoccupation; it is nothing of the sort, and a more attentive examination quickly reveals the egocentricity of which this apparent altruism is simply the cloak. If the psychasthenic is afraid of spreading contagion, of causing damage to others, or of not having done all that he could to prevent an accident, an analysis of the reason for this obsession quickly reveals its real ground: he is afraid of his personal *responsibility*, and he wishes to safeguard his own tranquillity.

In connection with obsessions, fears can be uncovered which are scarcely credible: fear of casting lots, fear of killing, fear of aborting pregnant women, etc. . . .

If the obsession remains localized in the domain of thought, the patient will suffer extremely; but if it takes the form of actions, it becomes very serious indeed, because it then becomes *impulsive obsession* which can lead to the worst extremes.

Certain sexual perversions are, moreover, simply a form of obsession. All cases of inveterate masturbation are not due to psychasthenia, as they may be the acts of a victim of habit who is no longer able to resist temptation; but some are certainly characteristic of psychasthenia. There is a form of masturbation which is ordinarily accompanied by sadistic or masochistic phantasies; and sadism and masochism are indeed the usual perversions of the psychasthenic. It is interesting to analyse them, because the mechanisms from which they proceed are quickly brought to light. They are compensatory or self-punitive mechanisms. As to homosexuality, which is not unusual in the psychasthenic, it is often found to be coloured by sado-masochism. For completeness, we should mention fetishism. It naturally accompanies obsessional neurosis in many cases.

We must notice, however, that psychasthenia does not necessarily imply sexual perversions. The eroticism of the psychasthenic will, of course, be more or less coloured by perversion; but, on the one hand, the patient may remain completely unaware of the perversion, and on the other, all perverts are not psychasthenics.

How does Psychasthenia appear and develop?

The first question which arises in this connection, concerns the constitutional or acquired character of psychasthenia. Its interest is not simply theoretical, but it is better to reserve consideration of it until the end of this study. Since we are considering the whole matter here from the standpoint of vocation, it is useful to ask ourselves *whether it is possible to foresee in the child the emergence of a future psychasthenic.*

The existence of first scruples can be discovered during the period of preparation for First Communion and on the occasion of the Confessions which follow. It is about this age, indeed, that the first symptoms of psychasthenia make their appearance.

About the same time, other indications are equally furnished by the manner in which school studies are pursued. It becomes clear that the results have no relation to the real intelligence of the pupil. His teachers notice that he is very slow and that he quickly gets tired, and they enter in his school report: "seems incapable of any kind of sustained effort." Moreover, the school year is disrupted by periods of rest, necessitated by vaguely defined illnesses.

At the age of puberty, sexual problems make their appearance, and quickly become matters for disquiet, for scruples, and even for anxiety. Instead of being the normal prelude to adult life, the emergence of sexuality fills the psychasthenic with fear. What he fears is not merely the sexual problem, but much more *the presentiment that he must relinquish the supports of his adolescence and lay hold on life.* Hence his equivocal, and even ambivalent, attitude towards sexual experience: he fears it, and he delights in it. He closely pursues a whole series of scruples, but he also imagines unknown attractions. If, unfortunately, he learns something of the theories of elementary Freudianism, or if some of his companions poke fun at his excessive reserve, he will consider that his doubts and his hesitations proceed simply from stupid sexual repression. He then throws himself easily into adventures which merely lead to an increase of scruples and to self-disgust.

The unconsciously dreaded time comes when a choice of career must be made. This coincides conveniently with the time when one is called up for military service—a very happy period usually for the psychasthenic. He becomes part of a fixed system and is supported by group behaviour. Moreover, if he gains even one stripe, his duties and his uniform cause him to discover a self-assurance which he thought he completely lacked.

Strengthened by this experience, he attempts to find a profession whose structure and discipline will preserve this self-assurance. He remains, however, very impressionable, and therefore allows himself to be guided, often unconsciously guided, in this choice. According to whether his ideal is lofty or more mundane, he will be attracted spontaneously to one of two vocations: the Priesthood or the Civil Service.

If his choice is the former, he will enter a seminary or a noviciate, and for the first few months he will be sustained by sincere enthusiasm and real generosity; but after that, the usual psychasthenic symptoms will begin to make their appearance. These will take the form of scruples, of difficulties in intellectual effort, or of a certain physical lassitude.

Later, usually after a period of very intense scruples, the struggle becomes still more painful because the time for making final decisions has come. A certain number of psychasthenic priests and religious persevere in their choice, but at the price of superhuman efforts. There is nothing to mark them as being out of the ordinary; but those who really know them admire the daily heroism of their lives.

On the other hand, there are psychasthenics whose life is marked by successive capitulations, by great decadence, and by incidents for which they are to a great extent not accountable, but which greatly affect the reputation of the clergy.

The life of the majority of psychasthenics is mediocre, painful, and of course very meritorious; but it certainly falls short of the demands of certain active apostolates.

This evolution is never regular, but occurs in successive waves, at least in the early stages. At certain times, the psychasthenia is even considerably lightened. But little by little, the periods of euphoria become more and more rare, and finally disappear altogether.

In connection with this evolution by successive spurts, we should note that certain periodic psychoses are of a psychasthenic type and show an obsessional character during the depressive phases. But they must be recognized as such, because both prognosis and treatment will be very different from those of pure psychasthenia.

Frequency of psychasthenia among priests and religious

It is already clear from what has been said, that the ecclesiastical state offers a choice refuge for the psychasthenic. The psychasthenic seeks a framework within which he feels secure. If he is possessed by a profound spiritual ideal and by a steady enthusiasm, he will see in the form of religious life the surest guarantees for the balance of his adult life. Moreover, certain vocations among psychasthenics are authentic calls from God. Are they to be rejected *a priori*? Certainly not. A profound examination should make it possible to lead certain psychasthenics to better things. We shall see shortly how this discrimination among psychasthenics is to be made.

This need to feel himself "epauletted" and incorporated in a system, explains why the psychasthenic tends more towards the Regular than towards the Secular Clergy. On the whole, he will accommodate himself better to the form of community life than to that of an isolated apostolate. But what a burden this sometimes places on the whole religious community.

Another reason why the psychasthenic readily turns to the idea of an ecclesiastical vocation, is that he is troubled by religious scruples. These scruples urge him to seek a state which will give him a maximum certainty in conduct and a guarantee of his eternal salvation.

Since he is also very impressionable, the psychasthenic will easily come under the ascendency of some person in his environment. Great precaution must be taken, therefore, against the indiscreet conduct of a mother who has always dreamed of having a son a priest; or that of a director of conscience who has mistaken the pathological disquiet of his penitent for a supernatural call. One often meets with priests and religious who are definitely established in their chosen life simply because they have always had someone at hand to urge them on whenever they have hesitated before a decision. This raises the serious problem of whether they were really free when they committed themselves finally to the life of priest or religious. This same problem arises with even greater frequency, moreover, in the case of lay people who have received the Sacrament of matrimony.

We end by indicating two types of vocations proper to the psychasthenic. Firstly, there is the *refuge vocation*, when the subject, seized by panic when faced with the responsibilities of life, hurries away from the world because he fears the world, not because he has received a special call to a higher life. Secondly, there is what may be called the *super-compensatory vocation*, in which the psychasthenic, conscious of his inferiority and of the inadequacy of his equipment for the battle of life, seeks authority and assurance through the wearing of a uniform or through the discharge of some function. The second type is usually discovered only by analysis, and may be perfectly compatible with a sincere and fruitful religious vocation; but failure is almost certain in the first type.

It cannot, therefore, be said that the ecclesiastical life favours the growth and development of psychasthenia. It is not the religious life which creates the psychasthenic, because the person was already a psychasthenic before becoming a priest or religious. Nevertheless, we must make this reservation. If he is ill-directed or ill-counselled, the psychasthenic finds in the religious life all the conditions that favour his psychic condition. On the contrary, in the ordinary life of a layman, the demands of life, of his job, of his family, compel the psychasthenic to combat and constantly overcome his weakness.

How to deal with a vocation when it concerns a psychasthenic

Here we reach the most delicate question of all, whose answer must come, in the final analysis, from the President of the Seminary or from the Master of Novices. In every religious vocation or vocation to the priesthood, the essential element is always the supernatural call. In itself, that call is sufficient to weaken certain opinions expressed by a psychiatrist.

Indeed, when the doctor is called upon to use his medical science in a domain like that of religious vocation or vocation to the priesthood, his role has not always been perfectly understood. Some directors are inclined to demand a perfectly clear answer from him in a domain where the data is far from being purely human. Others become annoyed when the psychiatrist consulted advises against the acceptance of a candidate for seminary or noviciate. The position is quite otherwise: in such circumstances, the doctor is simply an *expert*, called in to give his opinion on a very definite point. The full responsibility for the final answer rests, therefore, with the spiritual director or with the superior, who is the only judge in this domain. A helpful parallel that immediately suggests itself is the industrial doctor in our modern factories. The industrial doctor knows the work demanded of the employee, but he also knows the rights possessed by that employee as a man; he must know, therefore, how to safeguard the rights and interests of the individual, while at the same time he bears in mind the general good of the business concern. It is in this perspective that we envisage the advice which follows.

It will be unanimously agreed that every psychasthenic candidate who is really neurotic, that is to say who is a progressive case and not just showing a tendency towards neurosis, should be eliminated. This is so in the case of the subject afflicted with an obsession which is impulsive and which is in danger of driving him to actions beyond his control.

Similarly, the hypochondriacal psychasthenic with notions of suicide, will be rejected.

In the case of a psychasthenic with a sexual perversion, the degree of the disease must first of all be established. There are certainly cases of people whose conduct, in spite of the perverse phantasms which poison their whole life, is absolutely above reproach.

However, in the interests of the subject himself, should he be advised to aspire to the priesthood? His duties as a priest will entail the obligation of hearing the confessions and receiving the confidences of others; and it may well be feared that this will have the effect of causing new scruples and fresh obsessions to arise. They are strong enough to bear their own burdens; but can they bear those of others?

The doctor is very cautious in his prognosis when he is dealing with a psychasthenic masturbator.

As to the other cases, they are nearly all types which demand frank discussion between the doctor and the spiritual director, and a searching comparison of their points of view.

When the matter concerns an Order or Congregation whose members are called to an apostolic life, and still more when it concerns the secular Clergy, the majority of *refuge vocations*, in which the psychasthenic will seek more than he will give, must be eliminated.

Some directors will doubtless argue that there are cases where the vocation may be a genuine one; and in such cases, the spirit of charity should take precedence over the interests of the group. When these circumstances exist, the Superior or his delegate can alone decide the matter and take responsibility for the acceptance of such a subject.

In *orientating* a vocation, when we are dealing with minor forms of psychasthenia, it is essential to give special attention to the subject's intelligence. *The more mediocre the intelligence, the greater must be the caution exercised.* The intelligent psychasthenic may be able to achieve a full flowering of his personality through intellectual work. If the framework of the religious life sustains him sufficiently, he will preserve his self-confidence, thanks to his successes on the literary, philosophic or scientific planes. Provided he is not subjected to an imperious time-table as a teacher and to an excessive nervous strain in maintaining good order among his pupils, a studious life will provide him with opportunities of rest and of work, which will be compatible with his psychic and physical deficiencies.

He is sufficiently intelligent to grasp fully the deep sources of his disease, and, with the helpful advice of an intelligent director or of a friend with psychiatric knowledge, *he will be able to make his own stand successfully against a number of obsessions and of scruples.*

It is equally important to decide with what *type* of psychasthenia one is dealing. The *scrupulous psychasthenic* should not be given the apostolate of a spiritual director or confessor, because there is a danger that he will infect others with his scruples or become an indiscreet questioner. Of course, experience proves that, in certain cases, these psychasthenics preserve their critical sense and are capable of directing their penitents intelligently and fruitfully. When dealing with problems which are not immediately their own, they therefore preserve their autonomy; but great prudence must nevertheless be exercised even when dealing with cases which experience seems to except from the general rule.

In the case of the *intellectual psychasthenic* who is in danger of becoming discouraged when faced with prolonged studies, care must be taken not to direct him to Orders or Congregations specially consecrated to the intellectual apostolate, or in which the formation demands aptitude for study.

Finally, there is the *physiological psychasthenic*, who is easily tired, often "in bad form," and craves longer periods of rest than of activity. To such a one, only episodic activities, such as preaching, lectures and the like, should be entrusted, because these demand single efforts limited in duration.

When speaking of this orientation of the psychasthenic, something must also be said about his formation in the noviciate or the seminary, and in the course of the studies he may be called upon to pursue before he undertakes his apostolate. A primary mistake to be avoided would consist in dispensing him too liberally from the exterior regulations and the requirements of the Rule. The novice-master or seminary director, when he meets with a subject who complains of being tired and who otherwise gives proof of good will and of spiritual generosity, will be inclined to dispense him from material obligations and often to leave to his own initiative the better organization of his external life. Charity towards the sick, and the daily experience of what happens when such young people meet with the least nervous or psychic resistance, cause the novice-master or the director to take up an understanding attitude. But the result is usually disastrous for the psychasthenics themselves. The exterior prop of which they were in need is taken away from them by this kind of act of their superiors, and they are imprudently set free from the imperious obligations of a rule which gives them an atmosphere of security. Left to themselves, incapable of meeting their own personal demands, they fall little by little into anarchy. They must not be left to their own devices. The novice-master or director should discuss with them the regulation or the discipline of their lives, and come to some arrangement with them which will take the form of firm directives and will demand fidelity on precise points. An easily wearied novice, for example, should not be allowed to rest at will; the matter should be discussed with him, and a definite time for extra rest should be fixed, to which the subject must faithfully conform.

The spiritual directives given with a view to orientating these individuals, should aim at interior discipline. An authority which is supple and friendly but also firm, concrete and exacting, is necessary for such subjects more than for others, during the period of formation for the priesthood. If the novice or the seminarian is sufficiently intelligent and generous, he will thus learn to direct himself, never to the point of having a complete autonomy, but with the minimum of external aid. In every case, it must be remembered that the psychasthenic remains, at certain times, more of a burden than a help to the

community. Fraternal charity can alone give to certain lives the joy
of participation in a common work.

* * *

To conclude this very incomplete account, we shall attempt to give
some elements of *prognosis*. But in order to make clear the reasons for
this judgment about the future of the psychasthenic, it is necessary to
deal briefly with the concept of psychasthenia—the concept which is
at the very basis of this work.

In our opinion, psychasthenia is above all a *constitutional condition* on
which certain *accidental elements* are grafted. The prognosis will flow
from the source which can be traced to these two origins.

The constitutional condition is the *organo-genetic* basis, which is
scarcely amenable to treatment. The accidental elements form the
psycho-genetic superstructures on which the action of the doctor can be
more efficacious.

How can these two origins be disclosed?

There are two points which favour the predominance of the constitutional element. The first is *heredity*. Is there a psychasthenic
heredity in the subject under examination? In the course of an examination, it may be discovered that he has among his ancestors a scrupulous
father, an obsessed mother, an aunt or a brother or a sister who has
given clear proof of being psychasthenic. Other manifestations of
mental unbalance must also be discovered among ancestors: dementia,
manic-depressive psychosis, epilepsy. These investigations enable the
doctor to discover in the subject a certain mental weakness whose
manifestations will be very variable. He must then consider the
multiplicity of manifestations, because the psychasthenic in whom the
constitutional element dominates, rarely presents a single precise
manifestation like those we have described. If, as a general rule, the
subject comes to consult the doctor about a particular manifestation,
a somewhat searching investigation and analysis quickly reveals more
or less pronounced manifestations of the usual series of troubles connected with this malady. Even when the obsession seems to be isolated,
it is quickly discovered that very little is needed to start another.
Frequently, moreover, obsession is found to succeed obsession in the
course of the treatment; one has scarcely decided that the first obsession
has been uprooted, when another immediately takes its place.

The existence of a mild constitutional basis will, on the other hand,
be deduced from the *isolated* character of such or such a symptom:
a precise fear limited to a certain set of circumstances; temporary
obsessions, always of an identical kind; scruples confined to such or
such a fault, etc. . . . When the psychasthenic manifestation is clearly

of a limited kind, it may be hoped that there is question simply of a superstructure which a well-conducted analysis will succeed in reducing almost completely. But it must be remembered that such cases are exceptions to the rule that, when a person is examined who is apparently suffering from a very localized trouble, many psychasthenic manifestations are discovered.

This fact provides us with an answer to certain superiors and spiritual directors who are suspicious about the unfavourable opinions expressed by a psychiatrist when dealing with a candidate for the religious life. "I sent this postulant or this novice to a doctor to be cured of such and such an obsession; and—what do you think?—the doctor has discovered many other pathological manifestations! Is not this a professional deformation on the doctor's part?" asks the superior. Things are quite otherwise, unfortunately, and the appeal to the doctor on a definite point has alone made possible the discovery of more serious troubles, hidden until then.

Of course, one must also be on guard, when dealing with a psychasthenic, against a badly conducted analysis which will give rise to complexes where there were none. Psychoanalysis is certainly valuable in dealing with obsessional neurosis, but it must be conducted with prudence when it deals with a subject excessively given to introspection and self-analysis.

These reflections are meant to draw attention to the fact that the prognosis should not be based merely on the *intensity* of the troubles, but also and perhaps especially on their *diffusion* and their *multiplicity*.

Moreover, experience shows that many psychasthenics, even when they appear to be seriously affected, are nevertheless capable of doing good work. They themselves usually ask simply to be well directed; and if they are so directed, they can lead a productive life, both personally and socially. Everything depends on whether the superior is a good psychologist, for it is he who must orientate the subject in conformity with his positive qualities, and, by giving him the type of work calculated to be most usefully performed by him, make fruitful a life which is very often a painful burden for the psychasthenic.

DOCTEUR ECK
Médecin-Assistant
des Hôpitaux de Paris

REV. PÈRE CH. LARÈRE
Aumônier-Directeur
de la Conférence Laënnec

THE TREATMENT OF PSYCHASTHENIA

To raise the therapeutic problem of psychasthenia is, in the majority of cases, to raise *the therapeutic problem of a constitution* with its physical and psychic characteristics, and the problem of its complications.

It is not within our present scope to deal with the symptomatology of psychasthenia. It is sufficient for our purpose to state simply that, in certain cases, it reveals itself especially by physical symptoms, while in other cases it does so essentially by psychic symptoms, and again in other cases by a varying mixture of both. We shall therefore be concerned at one time with a medicamentous therapy, and again with both, without prejudice to a subsequent mental hygiene.

1. *Physical therapy*

A number of medicaments can be used against the asthenia of the psychasthenic. When the arterial tension is low, surrenal extracts should be tried, for they are often very successful; but even when examination shows the arterial tension to be normal, these extracts should also be used. Hyper-emotivity, frequently found in association with psychasthenia, falsifies the results by creating a temporary hypertension.

Arsenic in the form of cacodylate of soda, for example, and administered in strong doses, can increase the tonicity of these patients. We ourselves readily give alternate daily injections of cacodylate and of surrenal extracts.

One may also have recourse to cerebral extracts, alone or in conjunction with glycero-phosphates, administered either by injections or *per os*; or again, to thyroid extracts in much more concentrated doses than the classic doses which are too cautious and therefore useless. Care should be taken to work up gradually to these increased doses; and one must exercise particular care when dealing with hyperemotive subjects whose emotive symptoms would be in danger of being exaggerated.

Kola and phosphoric acid can be effectively used as supporting treatment. For some years past, cortical stimulants, such as orthedrine and maxiton, have also been used, and they undoubtedly increase mental agility: ideas come freely, and words and gestures come freely to fit them. However, there is a danger that reactions of depression may set in, either because in certain cases organic reactions in a positive direction involve compensatory negative reaction—a commonplace observation in physiology; or because the medicament has made possible an apparently normal cerebral functioning, but as the result of energy which the central nervous system was not even called upon to furnish. The asthenia of the psychasthenic is, indeed, an *asthenia of exhaustion*. The psychasthenic lacks stamina, and it is in his case particularly that cortical stimulants run the risk of entailing "doping," in the pejorative sense of the word. Once a certain stage of exhaustion has been reached, which shows itself in a tendency to great physical and intellectual fatigue, the use of these products demands a full fund of reserve strength and inevitably creates a state of collapse.

All stimulants, those of which we have spoken and other thyroid extracts, and ephedrine, strychnine and caffeine, should be used with great precautions when administered to a psychasthenic subject, and only when a considerable amount of reserve energy has been built up. They should be kept available for certain short periods, the examination period if so desired, and after having "fed" the nervous system—a point on which we lay great emphasis.

The treatment of a psychasthenic—for example, during the course of a scholastic year—ought to be commenced a little after the beginning of the third term. At first, alternate injections of cortico-surrenal and cerebral extracts could be administered; for supporting treatment *per os*, recourse can be had to phosphoric acid or to glycero-phosphates, alone or in conjunction with kola or with surrenal extracts; finally, for a short period, or even on certain specified days, cortical stimulants can be administered to assist ideation.

The state of tension so frequent with the psychasthenic, the minor anxiety-states or phobias, the tendency to insomnia, the digestive spasms, the post-prandial somnolence, will be relieved by neuro-vegetative therapeutic treatments or by mild sedatives. The psychasthenic is often vagotonic; according to the case, therefore, the different neuro-vegetative medicaments—belladonna, pilocarpine, eserine, etc. —will be used, either alone or in association with gardenal, codeine or light sedatives such as valerian, ballota, passiflora. . . . These different medicaments can be obtained either on prescription or in the form of specialities, of which there are many.

2. *Mental hygiene*

In dealing with the psychasthenic, mental hygiene has at least as great a therapeutic or prophylactic significance as medicamentous treatment.

As we have already indicated, the psychasthenic is quickly exhausted and needs to rest. He is often capable of efforts which are very strenuous but short, for he has no staying power.

The psychasthenic must, therefore, have periods of short-term work and many periods of rest.

The psychasthenic always finds it difficult to concentrate for any length of time, either because of weariness, or of obsessional tendencies, or often because of a mixture of both. The stage of weariness is reached more quickly by the psychasthenic than by others, and this is soon followed by complete exhaustion because the psychasthenic, being conscientious and even pathologically conscientious, makes repeated efforts to concentrate his ceaselessly wandering mind on his task. This struggle prostrates him, and he is quickly reduced to a state of real nervous exasperation. Exhaustion, in the case of the psychasthenic and as distinct from that of a balanced person, is much more a question of bad quality of work than of quantity, even though the latter aspect may be far from negligible.

If it is feasible, therefore, the psychasthenic will benefit by dividing his morning and his afternoon in two, and by interrupting his habitual occupations if they are burdensome. This interruption must certainly not take the form of inaction, on pain of leaving the brain to act in a void or become gripped by some obsessive idea. Sunday—and, if possible, Thursday—should be "days off" for him; and, especially if he is intellectual, quarterly vacations and the long Summer vacation are indispensable to him. *The psychasthenic must sleep a lot;* he feels the necessity for this, and even after a good night's rest, he wakes up feeling tired. But if he has had his quota of sleep, he must be made to rise at the time agreed upon; otherwise, it will be found that he "lazes" interminably, and thereby makes it more difficult for himself to get started—a task which is difficult enough already.

His meals should be rich in energy content, especially in sugar content; but they should be relatively moderate, in order to exclude post-prandial drowsiness. There must be few intoxicants.

Hydrotherapy may be useful, having a calming effect in the evening and a rousing effect in the morning.

3. *Psychic therapy*

Two types of method are used in this connection. The first type aims at psychic re-education by a daily, progressive course of real gymnastics, the Vittoz Method for example; the second confines itself to the subconscious plane, and uses psychoanalysis or therapy inspired by analysis. Moreover, a distinction should be made between psychasthenia and its complications. The Vittoz Method is directed against both, and this is logical since it aims at modifying the psychological ground of psychasthenia; while psychoanalysis is more concerned with the complications—with obsessions and phobias essentially, but also with scruples.

Vittoz considered that psychic disequilibrium is due to "faulty links" between the conscious and the unconscious brain, but without this being due to any organic lesion. "Cerebral control" is the central point of his theory, and by this term he means "a faculty for achieving equilibrium between the conscious and the unconscious brain." The normal man exercises this faculty without an effort of will, but this is not so in the case of the psychasthenic. The latter exercises insufficient or unstable control; in general, his reasoning and his judgments are balanced, but, to the extent to which he is obsessed, he is dominated by ideas which he knows are absurd but to which he must nevertheless give assent. This gives rise to a certain malaise occasioned by his conviction that some of his ideas are escaping the control of reason; and this in turn gives rise to doubt, engendering indecision of action which, again in its turn, leads to insanity. Indecision, lack of certitude, hesitation, obsessions arise from a lack of real consciousness at the moment of acting. The brain exercises simultaneously its double role of rejecter and receiver, and this leads to difficulty in fixing the attention, and, secondarily, to a weakening of the power of memory.

The Vittoz Method aims at achieving control of acts and control of ideas by a system of gymnastics which could be called "ortho-psychic."

To achieve control of his actions, the subject is required to give himself entirely to what he is doing, the brain being purely receptive. In other words, the subject must feel the act but not weigh and consider it. He thus engages in sensorial exercises, in conscious acts: "true consciousness excludes all incertitude." From these conscious acts, he passes on to voluntary acts in which the will must play a leading part. In the morning, for example, the psychasthenic "wishes" to rise, despite his feelings of fatigue.

If it is not properly applied, this technique may cause in the subject the very state of tension which it is the whole aim to avoid. "A common error with all beginners is to make an excessive effort to make the act a conscious one. . . . On the contrary, indeed, the controlled act should engender a feeling of rest, because the brain should be occupied with one idea and one sensation only—that of the act to be posited." The outcome should be full consciousness in the act, a clear idea corresponding to the act, and a feeling that the act is willed.

Control of ideas demands that the idea should be consented to, that one can concentrate on the idea, and that the idea should be submitted to the will.

It is very difficult to concentrate on an idea, and here again beginners are in danger of wishing to go ahead too rapidly. The concentration exercises are at first confined to the straight line; they are then extended to more or less complicated geometric forms, to letters, to short passages, and to passages evoking a state of soul.

But the process is not confined to the establishing of conscious ideas; when the time is ripe for doing so, the subject must also be able to dismiss these ideas. This is the purpose of the "obliteration exercises" in the course of which there is a progressive effacing of what had been created—for example, of the previously established straight line.

The Vittoz Method also aims at training the will. Vittoz holds that will is never lacking in any person, but the ability to use it and the method of doing so are defective. An effort of will demands a certain number of physiological conditions, especially a condition of respiratory repletion, for exactly the same reason as a physical effort requires them. Psychological conditions are also demanded: the knowledge of what one wishes, the possibility of what one wishes, and sincerity of will. The subject is educated to really will more and more complex acts, by specially impressing on him the distinction to be made between desire, intention, and will.

But psychasthenic complications are encountered, and from that moment it is difficult to follow Vittoz who is not versed in the processes of the unconscious as determined by Freud. This results in a serious lacuna, because the Vittoz Method confines itself to the bases of psychasthenia, and it is really only by a secondary modification of those bases that it can deal with the complications.

"The tree," says Lassègue, "falls in the direction to which it has always leant." To apply this to our context: when the diagnosis of a subject's constitution has been made, it is possible to foresee in what direction he will fall; in other words, to foresee the complications of his constitution. The psychasthenic will fall into obsession. When psychasthenia is found in association with hyperemotivity, and this association is of frequent occurrence, an anxiety obsession makes its appearance which is nothing less than a phobia, pathological scruple being itself certainly nothing less than the phobia of moral fault, of sin.

But we may ask ourselves what makes the tree fall. It can be due to physical or intellectual over-exertion, to certain moments of physiological disequilibrium at puberty or menopause, to psychological or moral shocks. We are dealing, therefore, with various pretexts which reveal a latent disequilibrium. Among the psychological shocks, for example, there are some which may be perfectly conscious—the death of a parent, for example; but others may arise from unconscious mechanisms and may constitute what is commonly called "the psychoanalytic complex."

When dealing with one who suffers from an obsession or a phobia, it is always well to sift carefully his psychism, either by the method of simple conversation with the psychiatrist or by using a whole series of already classic procedures: the Rorschach Test (where the subject gives a free interpretation of what ideas or phantasies a scattering of ink-blots suggests to him, thereby revealing *personality traits*); the Thematic Appreciation Test or Murray Test, association tests, dream analyses. These result in the revelation of serious subjacent perturbations, affecting retardations, infantile fixations, sexual disturbances, etc. . . . Frequently, the phobia takes on the character of a phobia of impurity. There can be no question of curing such states of soul without having recourse to procedures inspired by analysis.

We consider it necessary, therefore, according to the needs of the case, to use a combination of the different therapeutic methods we have mentioned. These methods do not exclude one another since, by definition, each concerns a different aspect of the personality, physical and psychical, conscious and unconscious.

It is important from the outset to remove all anxiety. This is done most expeditiously by explaining his disease, at least in a sketchy fashion, to the subject, by showing him as clearly as possible the part played by morbidity in the creation of his symptoms, at the same time arousing in him a proper sense of responsibility. When this has been done, the treatment, properly so called, can begin. Care must be taken at first not to demand too strenuous efforts from the subject in suppressing the symptom; for this would result in the creation of serious anxiety states, thereby greatly retarding the cure. It is only after "psychological cleansing" that one can demand strenuous efforts of will on the part of the subject, directed against the symptom itself.

With all the caution required when one ventures a comparison, the psychological condition of a patient afflicted with neuroses—obsessional neuroses, for example—might be likened to a vehicle driven by a motor. While the motor (i.e. the psychological complex) is running, the vehicle moves, the brakes (i.e. the will) are not effective—or if they are used to the full, "the motor stalls." Thus, one meets with certain subjects who, in their violent efforts of will to suppress their obsessions, provoke even loss of consciousness. When the motor has been stopped, the complex removed, then the use of the brake will be effective, and will prevent any further manifestations of these symptoms—the accumulated momentum—which, in the last analysis, is the result of sheer force of habit.

We regard these principles as fundamental, both in the course of therapeusis and of spiritual direction. If they are ignored, impossible demands will be made on the subject. Care must be taken not to strengthen the idea that his will is ineffectual; not to increase his feelings of inferiority; not to obtain a pseudo-cure by some drastic method which entails the appearance of another symptom, more discreet perhaps in its external manifestations but also decidedly more harmful to mental and moral life.

DOCTEUR P. LE MOAL

THE EMOTIVE CONSTITUTION

EMOTION is something which is common to all men; but emotivity is a tendency which exists only in certain people. We shall prove that, at least in many cases, a special *constitution* is the basis of this emotivity.

The existence of such a constitution is implicitly recognized by the majority of authors who, directly or indirectly, deal with the problem of emotivity. But, if a thorough examination is made, it emerges that these authors offer no proof of the existence of such a constitution; at most, they point out that their subjects show other signs of emotivity in addition to the specialized visceral emotivity peculiar to them. Thus, they describe the vasomotor troubles and sudorific troubles encountered in their subjects; sometimes they go a step further by recognizing that their subjects possess a special psychology, are timid, repressed, reveal pathological tendencies, are asthenic, hepatic, arthritic —all of which leads inevitably to the idea of temperament.

A temperament may be *acquired*; and, when we speak of *constitution*, we bring in the idea of an already existing condition which is either congenital or so precocious that it makes itself felt through an entire life. We aim at showing that this is so with the majority of those who are emotive; we shall first make the classic analysis of the somatic and psychological symptoms which characterize the emotive temperament and which lead to the diagnosis of *emotivity*; we shall then go on to show that it is possible to discover a *constitution* as basis for this temperament, and to present a simple indication by which a diagnosis of this constitution may be immediately reached. We shall thus distinguish real cases of *constitutional emotivity*—emotivity which is often hereditary and family—from cases of *acquired emotivity*.

1. *The emotive temperament*

Both in cases of constitutional and of acquired emotivity, the condition is often recognized at a single glance and from a general impression. However, it is useful to analyse the elements which make possible this ready diagnosis.

(a) *The emotive eye:* In the first place, I attach importance to the "emotive eye," or rather, to the glance of the emotive person, because it introduces into the impression which it conveys, an element of mimicry. The emotive person has a *humid* look, which cannot be called shining because this latter is better applied to the prominent eyes of the sufferer from Basedow's disease. There is something sweet and attractive about that look which reminds one of the fidelity in the eyes of a dog; and this is one of the reasons which determine a favourable attitude and a current of sympathy towards the emotive patient.

(*b*) *Emotive blushing.* At least in the early stages of his life, the emotive person blushes easily, and this adds to his charm provided it is limited to that and does not take on the exaggerated form of pudic erythema or of tears. Indeed, this facility in blushing varies, and is more characteristic of freshly coloured blond persons than it is of those whose colour is darker.

(*c*) *Vasomotor troubles of the extremities* are another immediate symptom, and the handshake of the emotive is easily recognized. The hands of the emotive are somewhat cold but of a rose or violet hue, and this can readily develop in winter even to the extent of Reynaud's syndrome, and more frequently still, to chilblains. Even in summer, the emotive person's fingers are somewhat puffed and discoloured.

The sudoral troubles of the hand are yet more uniform: the hand is damp, even in winter; it tarnishes the tissues which it touches, and for that reason the emotive person is barred from certain professions.

The association of this perspiring with these thermic troubles, renders the hands of the emotive person somewhat disagreeable to touch, and in extreme cases gives the painful impression that one is touching a toad.

The same symptoms—hypothermia, cyanosis, sudation—are found at foot level and are often continued the whole length of the lower members in the form of violet-coloured patches on the legs, and often on the knees as well. But it must be remembered that these same vasomotor troubles of the legs are also characteristic of certain cases of dyamenorrhea in girls.

(*d*) *Axillary sudation* is also a good sign of the emotive temperament. We are not referring to the ordinary perspiration normal to summer, but to the tendency which emotive persons have to perspire in the cold during the medical examination, and, it would seem, in consequence of such examination. Even when such patients are stripped, and even when the cold weather is scarcely mitigated in our inadequately heated surgeries, a trickle of perspiration can be traced along the thoracic wall; and, if our patient is placed on the examination table, he will leave the trace of his presence there on both sides.

These four symptoms: the "doggy" eye, pudic erythema, the "toad" hand, and axillary sudation—have the advantage of presenting a brief objective syndrome which is beyond question and which does not need interpretation.

At every stage of the visceral examination, other symptoms emerge to strengthen this group of indications.

(e) *The heart* is erratic: rapid at first, up to 100–110, it falls pretty quickly to a normal beat, and, if a prone examination is continued for some time, it is often seen to slacken to 60.

(f) *The tension* is normal or low; and in establishing it, we are furnished with a real functional test of the sympathetic system. For this, it is necessary to have recourse to the auscultatory method, and to study with some attention the different zones of the auscultatory curve.

We must recall that, if one listens with a binaural stethoscope to the humeral artery above the brassart of the sphygmomanometer while gradually lessening the pressure in the brassart, the passage to the maximum pressure will be recorded by little dull sounds marking each pulsation; then more or less intense gasps will follow; finally, towards the minimum pressure, the ear notes, at each pulsation, a decided *drum beat*. The arterial *tones* of this third zone are the result of the vibrations of the arterial wall and are the aural indications of that vibration.

In the thesis I put forward in 1921, and repeated in several works since then, I have shown that these parietal tones were in proportion to the *sympathetic tonus* of the person examined. There is a sense in which it can be said that the sympathetic system is *the stretcher of the arterial drum*: if the tones registered towards the point of minimum pressure, and of an undoubtedly arterial nature, are shrill and almost painful to the ear, it can be said that the artery is, at the moment of examination, in a hypertonic condition. If these tones are *absent*, and the minimum pressure difficult to attain, arterial hypotonus can be diagnosed.

What happens in the case of an emotive person? Most often, the tones are *weak*, below those which one hears in the case of a normal subject. In all cases, they are *of short duration*, and, if the examination is continued, they weaken quickly with successive examinations: their *sympathetic system does not hold the charge*. More rarely, *varying tones* are found in the same patient during successive examinations, as if there were present a real *dystonus* of the sympathetic system; and there are subjects whose emotivity readily shows itself, through different organs, by alternate manifestations of spasms and inhibitions.

This little book was the occasion of my returning to this very simple point of semeiology, which I consider to be the best of clinical tests for sympathetic investigation—all the better for being more simple than the oculocardiac reflex.

(g) The oculocardiac reflex must be dealt with here, even though I do not impose it, for my part, on emotive patients.

I do not use it in my examinations for several reasons: it is disagreeable and sometimes ill-supported, and I have already said that I had many reasons for seeing my patients developing lipothymies or syncopes.

It is less easily endured by the emotive person than by the normal, and it sometimes sets up remote reactions in him, in the genital sphere. On several occasions, I have seen these reactions cause injurious affective manifestations.

It is difficult to read, and help is demanded if it is to be registered correctly.

Finally, in particular with the emotive person because of his sympathetic disequilibrium, this oculocardiac reflex yields *discordant* results. Depending on whether it coincides with a phase of hyper- or of hypo-sympathicotonus, it will yield an acceleration or a relaxation, and greater account must be taken of the consequences of the phenomenon observed during a longer period than in the case of subjects with normal sympathetic reactions.

I give these indications simply with a view to showing how difficult it will be, when dealing with emotivity, to take account of an oculocardiac reflex which one has not performed oneself. The works that have been published on this symptom in war tachycardiacs are to be read in the light of these indications. It will be understood why some speak of negative oculocardiac reflex, while others speak of inconstant results.

(*h*) *The urine* of an emotive person is usually pale, plentiful and alkaline. The precipitation of phosphates in the alkaline solution sometimes makes it milky in appearance, and this causes anxiety to the patient.

But it frequently happens that this examination cannot be carried out, because the patient does not succeed in urinating while in the surgery. This is to be attributed to emotivity, and can often be remedied by the stratagem, so well known to mothers, of turning on a tap; or better still, by shutting the patient behind a closed door to conquer his sphincteric spasm. For it is dangerous to allow the emotive person to rest in a failure, and permit him to leave without a complete examination. The following day, he will be convinced that the key to the diagnosis lies precisely in that very part of the examination which has been omitted, and that the whole business must be begun again from the start.

(*i*) *The examination of reflexes*, usually of rotular reflexes, also throws light on emotivity. But there are two possibilities here. Sometimes the manner in which the subject concentrates on the examination, really inhibits the reflex, and this contingency must be countered by little stratagems for distracting his attention. Again, it can be countered by causing the patient to kneel and testing his achillian reflexes;

the latter are for the most part readily accessible, because the emotive person inhibits them less than he does the rotular reflexes which he remembers as having been sought by previous examiners. One can then return to the rotular reflexes which will be found to be readily accessible. Sometimes, on the other hand, the reflexes are very lively, very ready and very pronounced; but one must not be in a hurry to tell the patient that he is "a nervous case." Often he will know this only too well, and will fear that he is being too easily dismissed by an easy diagnosis against which, in many cases, he already rebels. He has a great desire to explain, in terms of *physical symptoms*, the real illnesses he feels.

(*j*) *The psychodiagnosis*. So far, I have taken into account only *objective* elements; but we have touched, in passing, on many points which furnished considerable insight into the temperament of the emotive patient.

His timidity, his self-diffidence, his tendency towards minutiae, have led him to prepare in advance *a written statement*. This sometimes takes the form of a letter of several pages, posted beforehand: again, an *a* to *z* account in which everything is reviewed; or yet again, some scattered notes devoid of order, which the patient clings to and will not let you have. Another symptom is emotive stammering, which differs from ordinary stammering but which is still sufficient to thwart the questioning.

The answers to this questioning are, most frequently, a revelation either of the classic troubles of major emotivity, or a manifestation of visceral troubles which have already been brought to the notice of other practitioners, and whose "functional" character, to use the classic term, we can divine.

Psychoanalysis will not be necessary in order to direct the questioning towards some of the answers which confirm the habitual psychological reactions of many emotive patients, and which define their timidity or their fear of responsibility or their shrinking from vital steps which demand energy and self-confidence here and now—as is the case with marriage or the choice of a profession.

But this inhibiting emotion is the outer form; and if we meet it with disproportionate frequency in our questioning of patients, the reason lies in the fact that it is such emotive patients who frequent medical surgeries.

On the other hand, the influence of emotivity sometimes reveals itself in the depths of the mind, as the influence of that creative emotivity which drives the artist and the poet. It is also the influence which inspires devotion to causes or people. True, the mere indication of a profession may be an indication of emotivity. If, very often and to the detriment of the person involved, the choice of this profession is a matter of pure chance, it frequently happens that the subject has been led, almost unconsciously, into this or that professional activity by his affective tendencies and his emotions. And this, as we shall see later, comprises two currents which appear to be mutually opposed: the first is a tendency to *fall back* on solutions whose keynote is the security of a stable profession, the security of a retreat; while the second is a tendency to *press forward* to a profession demanding devotion, self-oblation, and the service of an ideal. While not going so far as to see in this the idea of inevitable determinism, we find here the two major divergent tendencies which we meet with at every stage of our investigation into emotional reactions.

It must not be supposed, however, that all is as simple as this pattern would seem to imply; and that, when dealing with each person, a complete group of indications exists which allows a firm diagnosis to be established immediately. If an absolute indication of "the emotive temperament" existed, the listing of a great number of indications would be unnecessary. The search for such-or-such signs, however, enables us in practice to reach, in a few moments and without excessive hair-splitting, a firm conclusion—at least about subjects who have not been too modified by life, since emotion, or emotivity, increases or decreases with the majority of us according to the extent of the exercise. Professional life is one of the principal causes of this modification. In principle, it can be said that the professional habit kills or disciplines emotion; and it is this which prevents those who have made a false start by choosing a career ill-adapted to their emotive reactions, from suffering excessively. Behind the professional mask, therefore, we must sometimes seek the forgotten temperamental basis, and this is by no means among the least of the difficulties in the path of this attempt at psychodiagnosis.

All this semeiology of the emotive temperament is especially valid for the first half of life, because the sympathetic system gradually loses its freshness of reaction, and successive deposits of visceral pathology cover with their sediment the emotive visceral manifestations. There remain, however, some traces, which must not be confused with the signs of senile pathological pseudo-emotivity.

2. *The emotive constitution*

A final step remains to be taken. Can it be said that there exists a real constitution as basis for the emotive temperament? I maintain that, with the majority of major emotives, there *is* such a constitution; and I hope that my demonstration of this fact will carry conviction, because it will introduce a new factor into the discussion.

It was by mere chance that, in 1921, during the systematic examination by arterial auscultation, I became interested in the connection between sympathetic dystonies and emotivity. I was aided in this by several years of hospital practice as assistant in the neurological clinic of Dr. Bériel. Besides organic cases, we received at least an equal number of "functional" ones, and these latter were confided to me.

While dealing with these patients, I noticed that a small vertebral malformation occurred with striking frequency. It took the form of an anomaly of the spinal apophyses, in a region which coincides with the union of the dorsal column and the lumbar column. Ordinarily, these spinal apophyses are characterized by a single tuberous formation; but, in these cases, I frequently noticed that 2, 3 or 4 successive vertebrae presented a double tuberous formation with median fissures.

In the most pronounced cases, I distinctly remarked a suspicion of *spina bifida*.

At other times, it was simply a case of two bifidal apophyses, equal in size, on each side of the median fissure; or one of the tuberous formations was less developed, and it appeared as if the spinal apophyse had received, on one side, a blow from a hammer.

Finally, I noticed, always in the same region, a definite *absence of protrusion* of the spinal apophyses from two or three successive vertebrae, as if a blow from a hammer had crushed or levelled the apophyses at those points; and this resulted in a curious disappearance in this segment of the median backbone. I then noticed a real protrusion of the dorsal vertebrae immediately above, the spinal apophyse of which jutted out on the next vertebrae; in certain extreme cases, there have been traces of the swelling proper to Pott's disease. I have called this third type of anomaly the dorso-lumbar *flattening*, because the appearance is that of an abrasion of the normal dorsal sculpture through an error of judgment on the part of the sculptor.

Of these three types: true oval fissure, longitudinal fissure on two or three vertebrae, and the flattening of two or three successive apophyses—I consider that the last two are minor variations of the first and have the same practical significance.

In 1928, at the *Congrès pour l'Avancement des Sciences* of Lyon, I published a first note dealing solely with the objective discovery of these anomalies, and indicating that I always encountered them in patients who presented symptoms of neuro-vegetative dystony.

Several objections were then raised. How was it that an anomaly which I had declared to be frequent, had never been noticed before? In the course of 25 years, I have shown it to generations of students or of confrères, and have made them feel it; and I believe that not one

of those who had any professional contact with me during this quarter
of a century cast any doubt on the frequency of this indication or the
ease with which it can be investigated. Often, when the back is
slightly bent, the median fissure between the bifidal apophyses is
immediately visible to the eye; or it is possible, by drawing one's
finger along the backbone, to trace quite easily the bifidity, the
"flattening." In the case of stout people, it is hardly necessary to exert
any pressure, in order to feel the apophyses quite distinctly.

The objection was also put to me that this was not a question of
real bone anomaly, but of tendinous or fibrous formations. I found no
difficulty in discovering, among the skeletons in the osteological
laboratory, fine examples of dorso-lumbar bifidities; and for fifteen
years, I have had on my hospital desk one of these spinal columns
where the bifidity of two apophyses is particularly clear.

Moreover, a reference to the osteological treatises—Hovelacque, for
instance—shows that, in this dorso-lumbar region, the spinal apophyses
diverge, in 35 per cent of cases, from the classic description. My pupil,
Marion, examined 1,011 subjects from the districts of the Rhône, the
Lozère, and the Allier, and found that in the case of 33 per cent of
them, the dorso-lumbar apophyses are not clearly traceable by simple
palpation.

But such cases, it has been objected, may be explained as a mere
commonplace anomaly: the vertebrae which connect two successive
segments of the spinal column are *transitional* vertebrae whose form is
less fixed than that of the others. This is so for the fifth lumbar, and
even for the first sacral. I countered this by saying that such objections
are scarcely in accord with those that deny the existence of bifidal
spinal apophyses, since for them their incidence becomes, on the contrary, a mere commonplace. I do not regard the objection as a valid
one. Bifidity is the property neither of dorsal spinal apophyses nor of
lumbar spinal apophyses, and there is therefore neither dorsalization
nor lumbalization of a vertebra involved here. However, I admit the
fact that we are in *an intermediate region*, in order to recall that it is in
another intermediate region, the lumbo-sacral, that we most often
find the *spina bifida occulta*, which are clearly reminiscent of the dorso-
lumbar bifidal apophyses. The first join with the upper vertebra in
the shape of an inverted V; the next two are split longitudinally; the
last takes the form of a V open towards the top. Do not all these
combine to give the impression of an *oval gap* which has closed but
slowly and, as it were, reluctantly?

What is the proportion of those who bear this vertebral anomaly? The
thesis of my pupil Tignel, based on several thousand examinations,
concludes to 20–25 per cent, varying according to how strictly one

interprets less typical cases. I will accept the figure 20 per cent, eliminating, as a measure of objectivity, the doubtful cases, and retaining only those about which all observers are in ready agreement.

Twenty is a high percentage of anomalies of this vertebral sector, it will be said to me. In answer, it can be pointed out that, during the 1939–40 war, when the aptitude for military service of subjects with vertebral anomalies came under discussion, a great number of those seeking exemption produced radiographies showing "lumbo-sacral malformation." So much so, indeed, that my friend Novel and I carried out systematic researches on some radiographies from a urological clinic. These researches showed us that more than half of these radiographies, carried out as investigations of the urinary organ, could have been registered as lumbo-sacral anomalies. The vertebral schema of the classic kind is therefore subject to frequent variations.

But is it necessary to include, in a pathogenesis, a symptom which is found in 20 per cent of the subjects?

Let us say from the outset that there is no question here of "pathogenesis," since emotion and even emotivity, is not a disease. And if we take into consideration that the *emotive temperament* is of great frequency (at least one-third of humanity), we cannot discover a *constitutional* symptom behind that temperament, unless we have established that this symptom is found in a considerable proportion of that 30 per cent of emotive subjects.

Bifidity of the apophyses in the dorso-lumbar sector makes a relatively late appearance: except in slight and questionable form, it is rarely discovered in the baby or the young child. It is only in adolescence that the double tuberosity and the median fissure which it forms, become clearly palpable and visible. This might be referred to jocosely as "the second vertebral dentition"; and I do not regard its late appearance as contradicting the idea of a slight *congenital* malformation, any more than an hereditary character can be denied to Hutchinson's teeth.

Moreover, this hereditary character of our vertebral anomaly appears very clearly in family statistics; it is almost the rule that the vertebral anomaly is found among *ancestors* and *descendants*, and I have met with families where I have established it in four successive generations. Similarly, in many families, it is exceptional not to find the anomaly present in several of the children, once it has been discovered in one of them. This hereditary and family character is, I think, the most convincing argument against the hypothesis of an ordinary, accidental malformation. It is also a great argument in favour of my theory that this minor symptom is to be put under the heading of *constitution*.

But what is the connection between vertebral anomaly and the emotive constitution, and what proofs can be put forward for this connection?

I shall not put forward, as the primary argument, that such a connection is a fact of observation. I am slow to do so, precisely because the logical connection between these two parallel facts was not apparent to me at first glance. It took a considerable time before I accepted the idea of an interdependence between these two parallel phenomena.

Then, I noticed so often the existence of well-developed bifidal apophyses in major emotive persons, that I began to connect the two facts; and my systematic observation has shown a coexistence of these two facts that is too frequent to be explained by the ordinary law of series.

By systematically examining the spinal column of all my patients, I established that the presence of bifidal apophyses *revealed* emotive temperaments which age or professional reserve would otherwise have masked, and which would have been put on the defensive if questioned.

It remained to conclude to the relationship between emotivity and vertebral bifidity. The connection established earlier between bifidity and the *spina bifida* can serve, I think, as a demonstration; not that there is any question of comparing this minor anomaly with the tragedy of complete *spina bifida*, with exteriorization of its meningocele. There is not even question of a dehiscence of the posterior vertebral arc, as is *spina bifida occulta*.

Finally, many dissections of typical cases have not revealed to me, under the bifidal vertebral arc, those adhesions or those meningeal malformations, which are anyhow not constant, but which are supposed to play a part in the functional troubles of this *spina bifida*, and which have guided the surgeon's hand in the treatment of these troubles.

Our comparison is not, therefore, a mere analogy. When we recall that it is classic to regard *spina bifida* of L5 or of S1 as an anatomical substratum sufficient to explain serious troubles of the *pelvic sympathetic system*, how can we deny that manifest vertebral bifidity of one or of several dorso-lumbar vertebrae can explain dystonic troubles of *the major sympathetic system*, which, embryologically, begins in this sector and then spreads throughout the whole organism.

What is the exact relationship between bone anomaly and sympathetic dystony? My dissections do not allow me to conclude to the presence of a fraenum or a meningeal cicatrix playing the role of an irritant. The probable explanation is more simple: the formation of the nervous system and the closing of the mesenchymatous arcs which protect it, are parallel phenomena in the course of embryological development, and the possibility of a slight dysembryoplasia, localized in one sector, can be entertained. When this sector is the lumbo-sacral segment, the dysembryoplasia is very frequently accompanied by troubles of the sympathetic system and of the pelvic parasympathetic system. If it occurs higher up, on the end of the dorsal column or the first lumbar vertebrae, it is associated with a slight malformation of the *"major sympathetic,"* and the troubles which result from this are the substratum of *the emotive constitution,* often hereditary or family.

Bifidal apophyses and professional statistics

If our readers are not persuaded by proofs which, in a matter like this cannot be regarded as absolute but seem to be convincing, we offer them an experiment on the professional plane.

If it is true that the presence of bifidal apophyses implies as consequence the idea of *emotivity*; if, moreover, it is correct to say that the emotive temperament conditions, for many of us, directly or indirectly, our choice of profession—then statistics based on the different professions should reveal very variable proportions of bifidal apophyses, the latter being discovered with greater frequency in proportion to the attraction which the profession is regarded as having for emotive persons.

We have endeavoured to draw up these statistics in as objective a manner as possible, so as to give the lie to those who throw discredit on such a method of discussion. No one, whatever the extent of his critical spirit, can improve on what we have done.

Our investigations began with the medical students in our immediate entourage. Our profession has always been one of those which is entered upon freely through a desire to render social service and through a sense of vocation; only those who can experience true emotion, in the broad sense of the word, will enter the medical profession. It was an easy matter for us to prove that bifidal apophyses were much more frequent with them than with "the man in the street," and reached or exceeded 50 per cent of a class of students.

The proportion was even greater still in the domain of religious vocations, where it reached or exceeded two-thirds of the subjects, varying a little according to the Religious Orders and their recruitment. I do not think that this statement should scandalize any person. Its religious justification can be found, by analogy, if one reads attentively the parable of the sower who sees the seed scattered on the whole field, but springing up and bearing fruit only in certain types of soil.

Indeed, it is of the first importance to notice, in these statistics based on the religious life, the *active role* of emotion, which urges towards devotion and self-renunciation. Certainly the huge majority of religious are involved, thereby furnishing the most splendid example one could give of the noble role played by emotion.

To these, I think, we must also add the cases where the *inhibiting* character of emotion makes itself felt by making the emotive person avoid more adventurous careers and leading him to seek, in the cloister or in the religious habit, a position in some sort sheltered.

Finally, there is the recruitment for a third type of vocations—the third order; here, while not suppressing the merit of such recruitment, we maintain that, in some cases, the *human role* of the spiritual director must be a factor. The attraction which the emotive person exercises naturally leads the spiritual director to take an interest in him, through a desire to lead him towards an ideal, because he finds in him an intuitive understanding which other temperaments lack. The emotive person is very malleable, and allows himself to be led more easily than others; and hence the risk that he will lend himself in too pliable a fashion to this direction. While not wishing to step outside our province, we think that spiritual directors must be put on their guard against the danger such a penitent may run of engaging himself too far in this way of life.

I ask pardon for having drawn up statistics on so noble and so complex a subject as Religious Vocation. Recalling what I have said on several occasions about the liberty which creative emotion always leaves with us, and about the aid which it gives us in our aspirations towards every high ideal, I would have it carefully understood that these statistics do not imply a materialistic determinism in this matter. They merely show us that, in the ways which lead an élite to this greatest of all vocations, emotion is found at every stage, either as the dominant motive of complete self-oblation, or as a very human factor in this decision.

Without seeking to establish the proportion of these three currents —and the first is surely the most dominant by far—it can be readily understood that a great number of persons emotive by temperament or by constitution must be included, on the whole, in the statistics; and it can be seen what indications superiors of Religious Orders can deduce from such statistics, in order that they may be able to use to the best advantage the emotive qualities of their subjects, and prevent the development of faults in them—a development which is sometimes favoured by the conditions in which they live.

*   *   *

In statistics of the professions, a special place can be assigned to members of the teaching profession. Emotive subjects are encountered in great numbers from the elementary teachers to the University professors.

In professions such as Law and Medicine, where the orientation towards instructing develops somewhat late, it can be said that it is the emotive qualities which mark out the emotive person for these functions. Loving his profession, giving himself wholeheartedly to it, eager to help his young confrères in their first efforts, the emotive person is very naturally led to become a lecturer, a painstaking coach, the chief of a clinic—stages which lead him to hospital posts or, when no obstacle bars his way, to university posts.

Similarly, many vocations of secondary schoolteachers are born of an enthusiasm which logically makes the best pupils the masters of the next generation. The same ardour and the same ideal inspires many vocations among elementary teachers. But the security of holding a government post, the prospect of a fully planned life, regular holidays, and assured pension, are not without their attraction for other types of emotive persons, and we would be over-optimistic were we to minimize their influence in attracting such types towards teaching careers.

However that may be, the arduous intellectual life of teaching careers, the moral isolation in which the teacher, like the country priest, often lives, brings emotive teachers in great numbers to our consulting rooms. More easily fatigued by the rigours of a school term than their non-emotive colleagues, they come to us towards the end of the second term, for little nervous ailments which these intellectuals analyze a little too closely. They are psychasthenics in the most exact etymological sense of the word.

* * *

Other professions are also recruited, in great numbers, from among emotive persons, and they are sometimes professions where one least expects to meet them. They are numerous, for instance, among civil servants and police officers. I do not believe that, in these cases, the desire to preserve this interior peace is an ideal seed of vocation which yields many vocations where devoted service is the keynote. It is more logical to suppose that many emotives have sought a position of regular peace and of assured pension, as represented by the uniform. They remain emotives; and this perhaps explains why, when their ordinarily pacific role becomes more active, they often undergo impulsive reactions which arise from this emotivity. In the course of recent years, we have noticed how frequently guardians of the peace come to our various consulting rooms, each with his functional malady, and each seeking, unconsciously, to evade a task which has become more difficult than he had reckoned.

DOCTEUR JEAN BARBIER
Médecin des Hôpitaux de Lyon

FIFTH STUDY

PAIN

EDITOR'S FOREWORD

THE problem of human suffering is one which exercises all of us, especially in this modern world, when the elimination of distance, as an insulating factor shielding us from the knowledge of the extent of human misery, has allowed the instruments of news distribution to bring the facts to our notice and harrow us with their details. To those who do not possess the knowledge born to us of our Faith there is no solution to the problem, and its apparent solution or alleviation in one direction often seems to determine its extension in another.

We ought to be quite clear between the age-old but, often, forgotten distinction between pain and suffering, because these terms are by no means synonymous. In this connection it is, perhaps, of interest to note that a lobotomy can abolish the patient's suffering but leave his pain untouched. Pain is, of course, an objective sensation which in its simpler forms seems to be designed as a protective mechanism both at the time of its onset and, as a pattern in the sensory memory, to determine a future adaptation to similar circumstances. It has also a protective function in disease, securing rest, etc., for a diseased or injured organ or limb until the natural mechanism of healing has had time to complete its work. However sharp, impelling, or evident pain may be and whatever reflexes it may set in motion, whether for intrinsic or extrinsic defence, it remains an experience at the animal level, and in animals can achieve no higher recognition. Animals, therefore, do not suffer. In the human, pain can be recognized *consciously* and interpreted as a deviation from other sensory phenomena that affect our minds disagreeably. Our subjective recognition of it may affect its unpleasantness and we can, so to speak, learn to put up with it, and even to suppress its manifestation or the reflexes that it sets in motion. We can also take steps to interfere with its production and, by the inhibition of certain drugs, to depress the conductivity of the affected nerves, or to remove the source of the stimulus to the periphery of the nerve. It is our recognition of the objective pain as something distressing and unpleasing, which we call suffering; and this suffering is a mental process not different in kind from that which can follow the consideration of an abstract idea not directly dependent on a present sensory stimulus. Our power of abstracting from the sensory impressions we receive and of forming a judgment in their regard both raises us above the level of the animal and gives us the power of suffering. We can suffer too from such abstractions as, the recognition of the ingratitude of our children, or of our own ingratitude to God, and we can acquire virtue and merit through suffering in proportion as we practise patience, forbearance, resignation, etc., at first on the natural level and then at the supernatural level, accepting our sufferings as permitted by God for our betterment and finally suffering, as is our privilege, in union with the redemptive sufferings of Christ, with whom we die in the security of unity and Christian hope. Even in the natural order it is recognized that sufferings properly borne, refine and ennoble the sufferer; whilst at the supernatural level, suffering is an occasion of great merit which endures beyond the boundaries of Time. For this reason as for the reason that we have a right to use whatever opportunity is given us of dying consciously, to achieve contrition for our sins, to seek the forgiveness of God before it is too late; in a word, to die in the dispositions which will best secure us our eternal happiness, no one has the right to conceal from us the knowledge that we are dying whilst we still have sufficient consciousness to profit by the knowledge. Nor has anyone the right to imperil our salvation by judging that we are so good that we need no such time to prepare for our eternal life beyond the grave, for no one knows the conscience of another. When all this has been said and safeguarded, we accept that there will be cases, indeed many cases, where it is our duty to alleviate the pain which the sufferer cannot, or is unwilling, to endure. To this end we may give him whatever doses of a suitable drug are necessary to relieve his pain, even though the minimum required may *incidentally* render him unconscious and perhaps shorten his life, *provided that* he is told of his condition and that this effect will follow the exhibition of the necessary dosage *and* that he consents to this procedure. If, however, one knows that the patient is a man of evil life and has not repented; say, for example, a lapsed Catholic who has not received the Sacraments, then it cannot be permitted that he be put beyond the possibility of repentance. In these cases we remember that a man's eternal salvation is of more importance than any temporal ease, for "what doth it profit a man if he gain the whole world and suffer the loss of his own soul." Such then is the Catholic position and it is one which until comparatively recently was also that of the medical profession; it is one that takes into consideration the greater good of the man himself.

THE PHYSIOLOGY OF PAIN

AMONG the innumerable messages which come to us from the external world or from our own bodies, and by means of which the brain is able to elicit various sensations, there exists a special class indissolubly linked with pathology. The peculiarity of this class is that it provides an indication that a dangerous disturbance is threatening the integrity of our body. While always experienced as *disagreeable*, it centres principally on our affectivity, sets up important reflex reactions and, to the utmost of its power, acts the role of a protector by causing the sensation of pain.

Despite its many varieties, pain is *one*. We are reluctant, however, to admit this fact. We prefer to make a distinction between a *more objective pain* which warns us that certain contacts we make with the external world are harmful to us (e.g. compression, burning), and which we accept because we recognize that it plays a protective role entirely beneficial to us; and, on the other hand, a *more subjective internal pain* accompanying our attacks of migraine and neuralgia which seems to bring nothing but meaningless discomfort and which we would gladly do without.

When the *psychophysiologist* places pain among the normal functions of an harmonious organism, he is thinking of the first type of pain, which is more easily accessible to experimentation; but in doing so, he comes into conflict with the *doctor* who, suspicious of this "laboratory pain," regards real "disease-pain" with its abominable and useless sufferings, as disharmony of the most obvious kind (Leriche). However, as we shall see, there is *a nervous system of pain* with its receptors, its nerves and its centres, and it is the stimulation of this system, whether in *ordinary life* or in *disease*, which is responsible for the "pain-signal" and for the "disease-pain." Fundamentally, these two differ only in their *duration* and in the *intensity* of the organic reactions.

Moreover, pain has nothing special about it. Do not the admirable sympathetic and endocrine autoregulations of normal physiology lead to the most terrible disorders of Reilly's sympathetic irritation or Selye's diseases of adaptation?

Painful sensibilities

(a) Cutaneous pain

It has long been recognized that all excessive stimulation, of whatever kind, is a source of pain; it was evident, for example, that there is a connection between the glaring light or the piercing sound and the pain felt in the visual or auditory senses, which depend on the sensitivity of the iris or the tympanum. But it was not until 1894 that the idea of *a nervous system of pain* with its own receptors, was put forward by V. Frey. He showed that, on the skin, pain occurred neither at the level of the points of touch, nor at the level of the points of heat or of cold, but when special points, the points of *piercing*, were stimulated. This specific localization of the pain-receptors is confirmed by the fact that it is possible to dissociate the cutaneous sensations. Novocaine, for example, suppresses sensations of pain while leaving intact the sensation of touch; the arrest of circulation in a limb suspends at first all sensation of touch, and then every stimulation becomes painful. During regeneration after skin-graftings or after the section of a sensory nerve, it is the sense of pain which first re-asserts itself in the form of an intensely painful sensation, diffused and not localized.

As H. Piéron has shown, no *single* cutaneous sensation of pain exists, but rather a *wealth* of varieties. To the sensation of *piercing*, which is caused objectively by the pointed nature of an object, we must add that of *pinching* and that of *burning*, whether due to excessive thermic action or to a chemical. Thus, while tickling is connected with touch, itching appears as the initial form of stimulation by burning.

It has been possible to carry out precise laboratory studies on these different types of pain. It has been established, for instance, that there is nothing in common between the pain from a burn and thermic sensation; the pain appears at a fixed temperature—above 45°C and below 10°C. Moreover, the *degree of reaction-time* (Piéron) and that of the *speed of nervous influx* (Zotterman), have proved that different nerve fibres are involved. Touch depends on large, rapid fibres (40 m/sec); piercing depends on smaller and slower fibres (16 m/sec); pinching depends on fibres which are still smaller and slower; and finally, burning is due to the functioning of non-myelinated fibres with a speed of 2 to 5 m/sec. Similarly, *electric stimulation* of the skin can give rise to three different kinds of sensation, for which Bourguignon has established different chronaxies: 0·4 to 0·7 mill./sec for the shock; 2 to 3·5 for the tingling (analogous to piercing); and 4 to 7 for the burning sensation—all of which confirms the diversity of the receptors and the greater slowness of the burning.

The nerve fibres of the different cutaneous sensitivities have also *different courses*, whether at the periphery or in the medullary cord, and this makes other types of dissociation possible experimentally or in pathology. Instead of following, like the fibres of touch, the course of the ordinary sense fibres, the delicate fibres of burning often follow the sympathetic nerves and the perivascular plexus—with the result that the section of the ordinary sensory nerves may fail to suppress all feeling of pain. Since there is nothing to distinguish these fibres from the sympathetic fibres, we may regard the sensation of burning as a sympathetic sensitivity. We know, however, that the different position of the tactile fibres and of the pain fibres explains the loss of the sense of pain in a victim of syringomyelia. This makes possible the suppression of pain by the section of the corresponding bundles (cordotomy).

In the case of piercing and pinching, the *mechanical stimulus* can sufficiently explain the excitation of the nerve fibres; but in the case of burning, we are concerned with a *chemical excitation*, either by an aggressive substance or by analogous substances liberated in the tissues through respiratory difficulties in the injured cells. Finally, the appearance of the *cutaneous wound* provides the transition between the *pain-signal* and the *disease-pain*: the same fibres are excited in the same way, but the factors of excitation become more and more complex, the aggravating factor being the disturbances of the circulation. Moreover, cutaneous pains can also have an internal origin, resulting from a chemical internal disturbance (urticaria, etc.) or from vasomotor disturbance.

Our diverse sensitivities serve not only for the genesis of sensations in the brain, but also concur in the different organic reflex autoregulations—for example that of muscular tonus at the level of the centres of the cerebellum; and in a similar fashion, the same influxes which will give the sensation of pain will be the sources of different reflexes especially on the vasomotor plane. An excitation which is too weak to be perceived as pain, may act nevertheless on the reflex plane. Thus a vasomotor disturbance is a cause of pain; but since pain provokes vasomotor modifications, a vicious circle can be created which makes it almost impossible to recognize its true origin.[1]

(b) Internal pain

There are also free sensory endings at the level of our different organs or tissues, and these originate reflex messages which contribute to harmonious functioning. And just as the cutaneous pain-fibres do not convey a conscious message except when they are sufficiently stimulated, those of the other tissues or viscera do not register in the consciousness except through an abnormal stimulation which causes pain. The only way in which this latter stimulation differs from that of the

[1] The happy effect of a sympathetic section does not necessarily prove the suppression of a sensory path. It may be due to a shrinking of a group of the vasoconstrictive fibres which acts, not only on the circulation, but on the cutaneous sensibility itself.

skin is that we cannot easily verify the cause of the pain because of the absence of a normal sensitivity analogous to that of touch. We find it difficult to localize the pain. But whether we are dealing with voluntary muscles (cramps), articulation, bones, viscera, or vessels, the causes of excitation are the same as at the level of the skin: they are *mechanical causes*, such as the violent contraction of cramps and of the different types of colic, the pains of pregnancy, the intercranial hypertension which causes chronic cephalalgia, the distension of the bladder, the torsion accompanying ovarian cysts, the compression caused by tumours . . .; or they are *chemical causes*, such as burns of the stomach, disturbances of the circulation which release harmful substances, microbic inflammations, etc. Vessels and serous tissues are especially sensitive. Usually conducted by delicate sense fibres (similar to those of cutaneous burning[1] along the plexi and sympathetic nerves), the messages of pain all meet in the posterior roots of the rachidian nerves (or the sensitive root of the cranial nerves) and end in the spinal pain-bundle.

It is peculiar to *visceral pains* that they can be perceived at *skin level*. To each of the viscera, there is a corresponding cutaneous zone, and Head has established that it is the zone corresponding to the same medullary segment. It has been supposed that there is a possible illusion here: that the brain would relate the pain, not to the viscus with which it is unfamiliar, but to the skin from which it is in the habit of receiving messages. But as the pain is suppressed by numbing the skin, we must rather hold that there exists a real cutaneous suffering of reflex origin (analogous to the contractions of the muscles of the abdominal wall).

(c) Nerve pains

When an abnormal mechanical or chemical excitation bears on any point of the path of the fibres of pain sensitivity, the result will be a pain which the brain relates to the peripheral zone from whence the nerve comes. This is the origin of the neuralgic pains of nerve compressions, of the stumps of amputated limbs—the pain can be felt in the amputated limb itself as though it were still intact—as well as of the visceral pains caused by excitation of the sympathetic ganglia.

Here we distinguish between *two types of pain* according to whether we are dealing with *irritations of the ordinary sense fibres* of relational life, such as those of piercing; or with irritations of the *delicate sympathetic fibres*. The first are acute, shooting, and precisely located; and they

---

[1] The messages of mechanical origin are perhaps conducted by tougher and more rapid fibres, similar to the cutaneous fibres of piercing.

can be relieved by section of the sensory nerve. The second are terrible, dull, localized, continuous burnings, and they can be relieved in most cases only by operations on the sympathetic. At the level of the receptors, the simple nervous excitation is quickly succeeded by an irritation in which the nerve fibres are no longer normal. In many cases of neuralgia, the attack of pain comes from a nerve which is sick and which can then suffer *without external cause*, especially if its vacularization is not normal. This explains why vasomotor troubles play a major role in the pains of persons who have undergone an amputation, and in causalgia.

Let us now consider the case of rheumatic pains. They arise from an autoexcitation of a sick nerve which becomes much more sensitive to external stimuli, and suffers, in consequence, from excitants which would normally not elicit pain (hyperalgesia—especially to cold).

Here the same chemical factors are certainly operative as in the other types of pain. As distinct from what normally occurs, it can therefore be envisaged that all the types of nerve fibres which are afflicted with neuritis, are able to originate messages of pain, either of their own accord or through the intermediary of the sympathetic fibres which accompany them.

The pain centres

It can be dogmatically stated that *pain makes its appearance when certain intense, abnormal physical or chemical conditions activate, in any part of the body, relatively delicate, slow and non-specialized sensory fibres.* At skin level, the pain is, moreover, linked with the activation of fibres which are more rapid, more discriminative, and more specialized as responding to piercing. But in order that there may be pain, it is not enough that the alarm message should go out; this message must be received and must become *conscious sensation.* Doubtless we know nothing about how a train of electric nerve pulsations can give rise to a specific sensation; but we do know what must be understood by pain centres.

Formerly, there was a tendency to relate the manifestations of consciousness and of the psychism solely to the cerebral cortex; but to-day we know what importance must be attributed to the centres of the thalamic region which fulfil at once a *regulative role* and a *role of co-ordination.* This is particularly clear in what concerns pain. The experiments of Cannon and Bard have conclusively shown that the ablation of the hemispheres not only fails to suppress, but even increases, the objective reactions of pain: cries, rage, the tendency to bite, and reactions due to generalized sympathetic excitation (dilatation of the pupils, etc.). There is no doubt that integration at the thalamic level enables us to explain, not only the reactions of pain, but even— as regards the sensation—the fact that excitation of the cerebral cortex is not painful and that extensive ablations are without effect on the pain, while irritation of the thalamus in the *thalamic syndrome* causes terrible pain. Moreover, operations at this level prove efficacious, thus testifying to an essential role played by the thalamus.

Without entering into details, it seems that a crude (protopathic) pain sensitivity may be attributed to the thalamus—a sensitivity which would be increased by the absence of the cerebrum; but, as Piéron put it: "There is no remembrance or record of this experiment which is not integrated in the personality, which cannot engender any conditioning capable of influencing subsequent conduct."

Thus, *pain does not reach real human consciousness except at the level of the cerebral cortex*. It is there that it takes on a discriminating value, the message taking its rightful place at the level of the sense localizations of the parietal lobe, where it is referred to its place in the mental image of our body. It is here that it becomes truly personal and subjective, by becoming integrated in the whole normal or pathological personality.

Whether at the periphery or at the level of the thalamus, the reaction to pain depends on the condition of the nerve and the condition of the centre, with the result that the same stimulus will not be equally painful always and for everybody. An irritated nerve becomes sensitive to every excitation; and an irritated thalamus can register pain at every excitation, even tactile. Thus, in the case of facial neuralgia, it appears that the pain centre is gradually charged between the crises; and then the moment comes when the least excitation causes intense pain out of all proportion to the intensity of that excitation. On the other hand, a much stronger excitation after the crisis will not elicit pain. But we have also descriptions of congenital analgesias which seem to be connected with an agenesia of the thalamic nuclei.

There are subjects who consciously succeed in mastering to the full their reactions to pain; while others react excessively, though they are often unconscious that they are doing so, this excess being due to their particular characters. We know, too, that in psychosurgery the severing of the pre-frontal lobe from its base can, through its effect on the character, modify completely the sensitivity to pain. Of course, the sensitivity is affected only indirectly: it is hypersensitivity of psychic origin which disappears, so that a pain which seemed insupportable now becomes endurable. But the best example of the influence of the cerebrum on pain, is provided by hysteria, where, side by side with hyperalgesias, there may be insensitive zones, in conditions where the possibility of pretence cannot be entertained.[1]

An emotionally disagreeable memory may, to some extent, be deliberately forgotten as a consequence of cortical inhibition; and similarly, one often finds, in connection with certain affective troubles, that there is a deliberate inhibition of the pain sensitivity of a bodily zone. On the other hand, intense pains without organic cause are, in the case of certain subjects, real hallucinations of pain.[2] Is not the same phenomenon found in ecstasy?

Furthermore, Pavlov has shown that, by associating a painful excitation with a pleasing dish of food, the dog came to experience pleasure from the painful excitation alone. We have here a physiological explanation of masochistic reactions. By educative conditioning in the course of infancy, all moral affectivity is constructed on elementary affectivity, at the cerebral level. The organic reactions of pain can therefore be provoked apart from all painful message, by the mere recollection of a memory or of a sensory message which in itself is not painful but which evokes a memory of pain.

While the cerebrum is thus able to modify the sensation of pain, the latter can in its turn disturb the whole cerebral functioning by impeding all other activity. Both experimentally and clinically, pain can be at the root of neuroses, and we know that insupportable pain can lead to suicide. Normal organic functioning adapts itself in accordance with alarm-messages of pain registering in the centres of the base of the skull; but if the message is prolonged, this incessant stimulation—a veritable electric shock—becomes incompatible with the harmonious play of the important regulative centres of relational life, of cerebral functioning, and of the sympathetic equilibrium situated in this region. Like all excessive emotion, pain, whether physical or moral, then throws the body into a state of *stress*, and the sympathetic irritation or the humoral disturbances which result from this, can provoke functional troubles, and lesions at the level of many differing organs. *The body, suffering because it is sick, ends by being still more sick as a result of its suffering; and hence, in its own interests, it must have the power to oppose excessive suffering.*

But this extreme condition is possible only because there exists a *nervous system of pain*—a special sensitivity of the nerves and the centres to primitive actions. The physiology of commonplace and useful cutaneous pain holds in germ, therefore, the secret of the most cruel

[1] A subject with great self-control can imitate hysterical insensibility, but this is not so in the case of hysterics.
[2] There is also the elective analgesia of demented people who sit on fire, but leap if they are pierced; and the agnosia of pain where the patient can no longer react.

sufferings. "Pain," writes Laborit, "seems to us to be the expression of the struggle to re-establish a lost equilibrium, when aggression has provoked a disequilibrium exceeding the commonplace and everyday oscillation to which we are accustomed. The absence of pain can point either to equilibrium . . . or to the abandonment of all resistance. . . . A person under shock does not suffer. As long as he is suffering, he is struggling. . . . The more the individual is free, the more he must suffer."

DR. PAUL CHAUCHARD
Directeur-adjoint à l'École pratique des Hautes Études

SPECIFIC, PHYSICAL, AND PSYCHIC EFFECTS OF ANALGESIC MEDICATIONS

THE ancient adage of Medicine, though in our days it seems to have been rubbed smooth through over-repetition, is still as true as it was in the days of Hippocrates: "Sometimes to heal, often to alleviate, always to comfort."

To lessen or to suppress pain caused by morbid processes remains one of the most definite and clear aims of the doctor. This already implies as a corollary that medications designed to deliver patients from the pains which afflict, torment, and obsess them, are as old as Medicine itself. Of course, we are no longer beholden to Nepenthe—"that wonderful powder which routs sorrow, appeases anger and banishes all evils into oblivion"—or to the "Memphian Stone" which the Greeks and the Romans used to produce local anaesthesia; but do we not still use opium, henbane, and hemlock, whose virtues were known to our fathers?

Moreover, if the doctors of former times used empirical methods in their experiments on pain, let us confess that the principle on which we take our stand is not very different. Furthermore, is there any unanimity amongst us as to the meaning of that word "pain" which we use every day? Undoubtedly the phenomenon called "pain" comprises a positive, objective element which our measuring and controlling apparatus reveals to us; but this element is not the most important. What gives to pain its specific aspect, and what makes it so difficult to describe, are the psychological factors which accompany it. Just as it is impossible to convey in words the taste of a fruit or the odour of a perfume, similarly it is impossible to convey a clear impression of what pain is like, if one's listener has not yet experienced pain.

Since it is a psychological condition, an emotion, it is quite clear that pain is infinitely more difficult to describe than are many other physiological phenomena.

Pain varies in its *ensemble* and takes a special form with each individual; and hence its analysis reveals a very personal sensitivity in each patient to the remedies and palliatives proposed for it.

This already affords a glimpse of the considerable role played by the mental condition in the development and the intensity of painful phenomena. It shows how difficult it can be to reach the psycho-physiological mechanisms which bring into action the agents known as analgesias.

In the first place, let us observe, with René Leriche, that we must distinguish between "physiological pain" which produces the majority of agents known as "nociceptives"—pain whose underlying nervous dispositions are familiar to us; and "disease-pain." There can be no question that both of these correspond to a disturbance of the central nervous system; but we wish to place a special emphasis on the great importance of the psychic factor in "disease-pain."

The medicamentous agents which prevent pain

(a) General anaesthetics

Since their analysis would carry us somewhat beyond the limits of this article, we shall not delay over the study of those substances which eliminate sensitivity to pain, and which are called anaesthetics as distinct from medicaments which have for their object the extinction of spontaneous painful phenomena. However, we must take some account of them, since the mechanism of their action, more simple than that of analgesias, can throw light on the mode of action of true analgesias. It emerges from the studies of which they have been the object, that all these substances have one characteristic in common: the capacity to penetrate the cystoplasm of the elements of the nervous system, or rather to be absorbed by these elements. Though the discussion of this point still continues, it seems very probable that general anaesthetics—those which permit the performance of serious surgical operations—are endowed, not so much with a specific chemical constitution, as with physical qualities whose presence is proved by their solubility in lipoids and their tardy dissolution in water. As our colleague, H. Busquet, has so excellently put it: "The narcotic power increases in proportion to the relationship between the solubility in lipoids and the solubility in water; or, in other words, as the coefficient of difference between the lipoids and the water." (Law of Meyer-Overton.)

Although it seems difficult to state with absolute certainty what are the elements of the central nervous system which have absorbed the general anaesthetics in question, it can nevertheless be said that they fix on the encephalon, and especially on the cerebral convolutions.

Indeed, it is possible to follow—we ourselves have done so—the path of the anaesthetic in the cerebro-spinal system of subjects prepared for a serious operation. Before the functions of the spinal cord have been suspended, the patient has already completely lost consciousness; and moreover, with sulphuric ether and with nitrous oxide, among other anaesthetic agents, the spinal reactions indicate a surprising amplification which is attested by the exaggeration of deep reflexes, the clonus of the knee, and the extension of the big toe (Babinski's test). We are not unaware, of course, that the School of Pick and Molitor has maintained that barbiturates have the property of fixing themselves regularly on the thalamencephalon—the centre which is most sensitive to the regulative influence of deep sleep and of awakening. But this conception has had to be revised.

(b) Local anaesthetics

If the general anaesthetics act in the manner we have described, what is the conduct of the local anaesthetics so frequently used by doctors and surgeons? Take, for example, cocaine—the alkaloid extract of *Erythroxylon Coca*. As distinct from the action of general anaesthetics, this substance produces a stimulation of the cerebral cortex and convulsions, while the direct impregnation of a peripheral nerve, or of the sympathetic, sets up a blockage of the conducting fibres of painful stimuli, and consequently an anaesthesia of a determined area of the body. Now, it must be remarked that if cocaine, or its substitute substances which are much easier to handle in practice, blocks in the first place the passage of pain in the afferent nerves, it also suspends at the same time the motor function, such as the elementary sensitivity to touch, to pressure, etc. The electivity of cocaine and of its derivatives, is therefore merely relative.

As to the constitutional mechanism of their action, it is very probable that the alkaloid fixes itself by absorption on the axoplasma and the conductive neurofibrils, thus suspending their functioning for a time which is all the shorter by reason of the fact that the circulation of the injected areas is more active.

In this connection, it is interesting to notice that, while cocaine narrows the calibre of the vessels, novocaine, on the other hand, induces a vaso-dilatation which is, on the whole, propitious to the diffusion and the reabsorption of the anaesthetic.

* * *

True analgesias

The substances with which I deal here are the answer to the imperious need on the part of the doctor to allay the pains caused by any kind of pathological process. But in order to apply a proper medication, one must form some idea of the origin of the "disease-pain" in any particular case; for it is quite clear that the treatment cannot be exactly the same for migraine, for angina pectoris, for facial neuralgia, and for sciatic pains. Now, what are the data which can clarify our hypotheses relative to the mechanism of pain in diseases, if not—first and foremost —the very manner in which the remedies act? In the final analysis, one always comes back to the necessity for careful and prudently directed experimentation.

By a paradox often met with in medical matters, it is the manner in which the medication acts which provides us with an Ariadne's thread to the discovery of the mechanism which is causing the pain.

(a) The visceralgias

Contrary to an opinion which was once current, the viscera do not respond directly with pain to traumatizing agents; their envelope (pleura, peritoneum, pericardium, meninges) is alone receptive of pain. On the other hand, the distensions of their cavities or the enforced contraction of their walls, is manifested by pains which are among the most difficult to endure.

But, as Mackenzie has shown in an especially penetrating analysis, it is not in the viscera that the pain is situated but in the thoracic or abdominal walls which receive the pain. Thus MacBurney's point does not correspond to the seat of the appendix, any more than the pain irradiated by angina pectoris corresponds to the position of the coronaries, or the scapular point to the gall-bladder. This observation must inevitably give rise, in the minds of doctors, to the idea that, since really experienced pain corresponds to a parietal irradiation, the proper course to take in order to suppress or lessen visceralgias is to treat, not the affected organ itself, but the area of its physical projection.

Starting from this principle, M. Lemaire of Louvain envisaged a new method, the basis of which is the blockage of the parietal nerves—a blockage easily effected through intra-dermic injections of novocaine. The success of this method was considerable.

But soon it was observed that it was not so much the quality of the injected liquid as its quantity which was important. The introduction of distilled water into the cutaneous dermatome corresponding to the injured part of the viscera, was found to be as effective as any analgesic solution.

It is no longer possible, therefore, to accept the thesis defended by Lemaire—namely, that the solution of cocaine, thanks to its neuro-tropic action, impregnates the rachidian ganglion, thereby suppressing feelings of pain. In reality, what the injection of any liquid whatever, apart from acid solutions, produces in the tissues is an action of *inhibition* or of *extinction* of the "reflex" stimulations coming from the wounded part of the viscera, rather than a directly anaesthetic effect. If further proof is needed for the existence of this mechanism, we need only refer to the imaginary pain felt by a person who has had a limb amputated: an injection of the healthy limb immediately kills the impression in the other limb imagined as still attached to the body.

Is there any need to point out that the frequently healthy effects of revulsion can be explained as due to a similar mode of action?

(b) Algias of vascular origin

If visceral pains are the expression either of distension or of spasmodic contraction of the wounded organ, can the same be asserted for the ramifications of the vascular system?

The pains which accompany the obliteration of vessels, arteries or veins, or which are the outward sign of their spasm, were known of old; but formerly Medicine had but poor means at its disposal to combat them, whereas to-day we possess a whole gamut of vaso-dilatators and vaso-constrictors.

I shall not delay here over the question of the efficacy of methods for dealing with cases of peripheral arterial spasm—methods which are current to-day; because I would thereby run the risk of trespassing into the domain of surgery. I shall deal only with two examples of very current observation: angina pectoris and migraine.

Not very long ago, the most reputable specialists attributed angina to a sudden dilatation of the aorta; but to-day it is established that real angina is traceable to a myocardiac isthemia, temporary or permanent according to the condition of the spasm or the obliteration of the coronary arteries. The best proof that one can offer for this is the immediate efficacy of coronary vaso-dilatators, and especially of Trinitrin.

And it is by a similar mechanism that the injections of novocaine in the stellate ganglion—which were so fashionable—achieved their effect; the same being true of periaortic injections which influence more directly the cardiac plexus.

In attacks of migraine, the vascular disorder is more complicated. Here, both the vaso-constrictive and the vaso-dilatatory medications have proved effective. How is this seeming paradox to be explained? The attack of migraine has, in fact, two opposed phases: the first is a phase of vaso-constriction; the second, which is of much longer duration, is a phase of vaso-dilatation. It is in the second phase, and in this phase only, that the current treatment by tartrate of ergotamine is of any avail.

Specific medications for pain

(a) Stupefying drugs

As we have pointed out, the "disease-pain" answers to a central process; it is really a *mental state*. That is why the medicaments which we use are effective in proportion as they act on the upper part of the nervous system. Here, it is no longer the peripheral receptors which come under the action of the drug, but the very centres of the sensations of pain. Furthermore, if the efficacy of the drugs is revealed by the cessation of the pain—such cessation being, according to Schopenhauer, the very essence of happiness—it is also reinforced by a feeling of euphoria or of diffused delight which can constitute a most pernicious attraction. The central action of drugs, and in particular of opium and its derivatives—morphine, codeine, heroin, encodal—shows sufficiently that these drugs prove very effective, not only against all pains connected with some physical adulteration, but even against tormenting, obsessive, *moral pain*, such as we observe in melancholia.

Too much has been said about the problem of what, for want of a better expression, is called moral or psychic pain. Even though many unknown factors remain, it would be conducive to a better understanding if our predecessors had limited the data of this question. Some of our *littérateurs* and doctors have submitted voluntarily to these drugs, so as to "live" the experience; and according to them, opium reveals itself in its effects as a poison of the sensibilities and of the intelligence. De Quincey, for example, writes: "Opium! dread agent of unimaginable pleasure and pain! . . . what solemn chords does its sound now strike upon my heart! what heart-quaking vibrations of sad and happy remembrance!" Here, indeed, is the very type of the drugs which soothe and stifle the anguish of despairing melancholia, and conquer the imperious death-wish which dies because it cannot die.

Opium and its derivatives are not without effect, of course, on the peripheral elements of the nervous system; but these effects are far exceeded by a cerebral influence. Can one describe with greater precision the action of opium? Yes—to some extent. Given that the drug acts, in general, on the most diverse physical pains and on moral pain whose basis is anxiety, we may legitimately suppose that opium and its alkaloids are directed, not only on the neuroses of the receptive convolutions of pain-stimuli, but also on the vegetative elements which are included in the cerebral hemispheres and are developed in the thalamencephalon. Add to this that the effects of opiates are not limited to the central nervous system, but act on the entire organism: respiration becomes deeper; dyspnoea disappears; the contractions of the heart slacken and are strengthened, because morphine is an excellent producer of cardiac tone; and finally, the peripheral circulation becomes freer because of the vaso-dilatation which the opiates effect when they are used in properly regulated doses.

We cannot be too insistent on the fact that though opium and its alkaloids are not narcotics as are the barbiturates, they prove infinitely more effective than the barbiturates against anxiety and anguish, and against moral depressions generally. Certainly the danger of opium can be very great when it is used imprudently and when morphine, heroin or eucodal is used: nervous subjects quickly acquire the habit and develop a craving for the drug. But with preparations drawn directly from the poppy juice, the danger is infinitely less, and we do not know of any case where thebatin tincture or Sydenham's laudanum (i.e. wine of opium) was used as the basis of an opiate therapy, and where toxicomania or even a simple condition of permanent craving resulted.

(b) Peripheral analgesias

We need not repeat what we have already said about cocaine and its derivatives; but we must mention here that certain plants—*belladonna, henbane, aconite, hemlock*—possess the singular property of deliberately fixing on certain elements of the peripheral nervous system.

As the word clearly indicates, belladonna (from Italian: bella-donna, i.e. fine lady) gives a remarkable and attractive sparkle to the eyes, because of the external dilatation of the pupils which is itself a consequence of the paralysis of the sphincter of the iris. On the other hand, this drug has an astonishing effect on the fibres of the pneumogastric (vagus) nerve, which it paralyses. Finally, the absorption of belladonna preparations has profound repercussions on peripheral sensitivity. The anaesthetic effect can be so profound that Gauthier de Chaubry, citing the example of a soldier under belladonna intoxication, tells how the latter, "mistaking his finger for his pipe, endeavoured to light it with a burning coal, and showed not the least sign of pain."

But of all the drugs derived from galenical preparations, it is aconite which perhaps possesses the most striking and the most elective anaesthetic properties. Indeed, even in the case of a healthy man, the injection of very minute quantities of aconitine is quickly followed by a tingling sensation and by that numbness of nose and of lips which are the indications of approaching anaesthesia.

Apart from surgical methods, there is no more effective remedy for facial neuralgia than aconite. With aconite, one can bracket hemlock, whose alkaloid, cicutine (water hemlock), exercises a remarkable analgesic action, thanks to the fixation of the drug on the peripheral nerves, and particularly on those of the lower members.[1] As with therapeutic poisons, the mode of action of the galenical products we have just dealt with is easy to understand, since, in every case, the analgesia fixes on the peripheral nerve conductors.

---

[1] One is reminded of the death of Socrates.

The poisons: cobratherapy and apicotherapy

A very ancient observation made by the biologists was that certain poisons, especially that of the *cobra-venom*, provoked a profound anaesthesia of the wounded area. It was also known, since the end of the 18th century, that repeated bee-stings have a singular power to arrest rheumatic pains—to such an extent, indeed, that professional bee-keepers escape rheumatism from the very fact that they have been frequently stung and thus immunized against it. But the possible use of this analgesic power in human therapy has scarcely ever been advocated.[1]

In 1929, experiments were carried out on subjects afflicted with inoperable neoplasias which were accompanied by irreducible pains. Without being, as has often been alleged, "spectacular," the results of these experiments were very encouraging. And as a result of the investigations carried out by Monalaesser and Tagnet, cobra-venom poison has taken its place among the therapeutic weapons against pain.

Although the chemical composition of cobra-venom is not yet fully formulated, we know that it contains a neurotoxine and a phosphodiastase. Moreover, thanks to the classic works of M. Phisalix, it is established that this neurotoxine fixes on the elements of the nervous system, and entails solution and breaking-up of the chromatic cell-substance (chromatolysis) analogous to what we ourselves have discovered as a result of the injecting of animals with poison from bees (Jean Lhermitte and Haskovec). This elective fixation on the nervous system accounts for the specific phenomena of poisoning: the regional anaesthesia which contrasts with the conservation of the motor qualities, on the one hand, and, on the other, the cardio-respiratory troubles originating in the bulbus, which are heralds of death.

With man, the hypodermic injection of cobra-venom alleviates very considerably the irreducible pains of cancer. It is a remarkable fact that these pains are alleviated only after a certain number of injections; for it would seem that, like so many other medicaments, neurotoxine acts especially as a result of cumulative doses, and that it fixes, not on the central elements, but on the peripheral structures of the sensitivity to pain. And this hypothesis agrees very well with the verified fact that, in many cases, cobra-venom entails a disintegration of the neoplastic cells.

Does the same hold good for poison from bees? Many observed facts seem to point that way. In the first place, the benefit of apicotherapy seems particularly striking in affections which involve the peripheral nervous system—all kinds of neuritis and neuralgia, arthalgias, myalgias of a rheumatic nature. In the second place, all the

---

[1] It must be noted, however, that cobra-venom has figured for a very long time in the homeopathic pharmacopoeia, in the dosage of a millionth part of a milligramme.

experiments carried out on animals by J. Lhermitte and Haskovec Junior have demonstrated that the poison fixes on the peripheral nerve fibres, and there effects profound alterations when the contact is too immediate. Here, as with cobra poison, only very weak doses can be used in therapeutic treatment. But it would be possible to enlarge on our explanations of the analgesic role of bee-poison.

As our colleague Porsin has shown, apicotherapy proves to be of sovereign worth in treating affections of the collagenous tissues, this being due to the power of diffusion with which the poison is endowed. Like hyaluronidase, bee-poison entails the surface penetration and the depth penetration of substances introduced into the organism, such that the active mechanism of the therapeutic injection of the poison can be reduced to two factors: increased diffusibility, and affinity for fixation to the nerve elements.

Finally, let us note that, like cobra-venom, the poison from bees exercises its beneficent influence in quasi-infinitesimal doses: one tenth of a milligramme in dry weight. The permanence of this drug in the homeopathic pharmacopoeia can thus be readily appreciated.

Physiotherapies

It is quite otherwise with the action of *physiotherapeutic medications*. Besides the application of medicamentous ionization, in which the continuous electric current facilitates the deep penetration of the analgesic (aconitine for example) and strengthens its effects, there is no doubt that the application of ultra-violet and infra-red rays, and the application of diathermy derived from high frequency currents, and also the application of Roentgen rays, prove of equally remarkable analgesic value with many patients.

Of course, it is very difficult to establish what takes place within the irradiated tissues, but everything points to the fact that the efficacy of these medications is due to the modifications of circulation which they provoke within the tissues. This interpretation is supported by the frequently observed fact that an irradiation which is too rapidly applied to an inflamed nerve tissue, for example in zona or in rheumatic sciatalgia, not only gives no alleviation of the pain, but even increases it.

Finally, I must add that the irradiations should always be used in prudent doses (antialgic irradiations) because of the modifications of circulation which they entail.

Psychological medications: Analgesic effects of psychic re-education and of hypnosis

We must emphasize, yet once more, that "disease pain" is, above all, a *mental state*, and that it would be contrary to the ever-living doctrine

14

of Hippocrates were we to limit our therapeutic action to chemical and physical agents, and even to mutilating surgical operations. The suffering patient is always an anxious person who dreads the return of those pains he knows so well; often, too, he is a person obsessed with his pains, who constantly ruminates about them, interpreting all their shades. What doctor has not met with pain-beset patients for whom the most powerful medications prove useless, if indeed these medications do not aggravate the disease? That is why a particular medicament yields "marvellous" results in the hands of one doctor which will prove utterly useless in the hands of another.

In this connection, we may recall the famous adage: "The manner of giving is more important than what is given." To illustrate this, perhaps I can give no better example than the terrible and stubbornly persistent pains in patients who have undergone an amputation. In cases of this kind, it is not the stump which is the seat of the pains, but the "phantom" limb—i.e. the amputated limb still regarded as intact. Now, after the most expert and seemingly perfect treatment; even after a series of operations bearing on the neuroma of amputation, the posterior roots, and the spino-thalamic bundles of the spinal cord; even after extensive ablation of the parietal perceptive zone (J. Lhermitte and Puech)—the pain continued unchanged. Now, in such cases, which are among the most hopeless, isolation and psychic re-education and even hypnosis may deliver the patient from his intense torture (Padovani and Bachet). Although it is risky to hazard an explanation of the mechanism of hypnosis in the treatments to which we refer, it can be said that everything occurs as if the suggestion acted in the manner of a *functional pre-frontal lobotomy*, by isolating the thalamic resonance from the cortical perceptive centres of pain.

* * *

This brief account of the modes of action which must be attributed, at least provisionally, to analgesic medications, makes no pretence at being exhaustive. What we have endeavoured to show is the diversity of the mechanism subtending the medications which we use every day, and how necessary it is to be prudent, in the interpretation of the so-called "miraculous" effects of such or such a drug, because what counts above all else in the treatment of "disease pain" is the suppression of anxiety and that restoration of mental calm which can be effected only in an atmosphere of submission to and perfect confidence in the doctor.

PROFESSEUR JEAN LHERMITTE
De l'Académie de Médecine

PSYCHALGIAS

THERE is a considerable number of patients who, the live-long day, complain of their ailments, cause disruption in their family circle, and are the despair of their doctor. They have made the grand medical tour of all the specialists; they have undergone the most minute examinations; and in spite of all this, their illness remains inexplicable and irremediable. Their doctor then resorts to the idea of a "psychalgia," and is happy to hand over this troublesome patient to a psychiatrist.

Here is a vivid description of such patients, given by Dupré: "They complain that they feel, in different parts of their body, abnormal sensations which are irksome and inconvenient rather than painful. . . . They are strange sensations; all the parts of the body are contracted, enlarged, flattened, swollen, withered, shrunken, displaced, modified as to form, temperature, weight, secretions, mobility or fixity. They are sustained and compressed by cramps, by corsets, by surgical belts, by hoops, etc. . . . Foreign bodies interpose themselves, gases find their way in, currents circulate, there are rustling, chatterings, crepitations."

In face of such a wealth of description and of comparison, who could help thinking of the "*malade imaginaire*"? Nevertheless, we are dealing with painful sensations which are really experienced, and which are known as *kinaestopathies*.

Before undertaking an interpretation of these psychalgias, we would like to sketch a general picture of these psychic pains by pinpointing certain special semiological characteristics and by insisting in particular on the psychological context and psychopathic behaviour of such subjects.

But we must first warn the reader that the term "psychalgia" is an ambiguous one, and is very difficult to define.

May one speak of psychic pains as meaning imaginary, unreal, non-existent pains? In reality, every pain is a psychological fact, a particular state of consciousness of an emotional kind. When a person experiences in his consciousness a sensation of pain, the pain exists and is really felt, even if its lesional cause cannot be discovered. To speak of non-existent pain is a contradiction in terms; there is pain and there is pretence of pain, but there is no other alternative.

There has sometimes been equal confusion with regard to the terms "psychalgia" and "pain of purely psychic origin." It is a mistake to equate these two, since this involves the *a priori* assumption that a pain can make its appearance without any alteration of the organic functions. There is, in reality, a very close correlation between psychic activities and organic functioning. It is, as a matter of fact, impossible to solve this great problem of the relations which exist between the *psyche* and the *soma*, to pinpoint the place of insertion of cerebral activity in conscious sensations: every pain is psychic because it is conscious, but not less frequently it reveals a disturbance in the functioning of the cerebral activity which makes the state of consciousness possible.

Psychalgias represent a particular variety of algias—an alteration of the kinaesthetic sense.[1] They are accompanied by a particular psychological condition, but they cannot be referred to any precise origin nor to any discernible organic lesion. They are also often called "functional pains."

Semiological characteristics of psychalgias

Psychalgias are generally pains of very varied but fixed topography and of very diverse, often indefinable types. They are also intractable, persistent, and inexplicable.

The *topography* is extremely variable, but in most cases it can be referred to—

Cranial areas: frontal or occipito-nuchal cephalalgia.
Cardiac areas: precordialgies, palpitations, thoracic tension.
Abdominal areas: gastro-intestinal or pelvi-genital.
Articular vertebral areas.

These patients are usually sent very soon to the specialist, with the result that the consulting-rooms of neurologists, cardiologists, gastroenterologists, gynaecologists and rheumatologists, are invaded by sufferers from psychalgia.

These pains can be extraordinarily fixed, but with an accuracy which is disconcerting because they do not correspond to any neurological or visceral schema, and are not accompanied by any objective indication for the disease to which they seem to point.

At other times, these pains are more extensive, and are difficult to track down and locate. They can move about, disappear for a time in one sector only to reappear in another, a new algia ousting the old.

---

[1] Kinaesthesia is the impression of well-being, experienced as an indistinct impression when the body is functioning normally. Intimately connected with our existence, kinaesthesia represents the sum of the excitations which arise from every part of the organism and vanish *en masse* into the subconscious. A person becomes consciously aware of its existence only when it is perturbed. Kinaesthesia then makes itself felt as pain or as pleasure.

Equally, they may wander variously here and there in an errant fashion.

Their type is also very variable, and can take the form of burns, prickings, tensions, discharges. But often these patients experience great difficulty in describing their sensations, and this explains their increasing wealth of comparisons and inexhaustible explanations. They mime their pains, explain them, interpret them, introduce explanatory interior disturbances, currents, discharges. By their own accounts, they suffer intensely, and they are obsessed by these abnormal, bizarre, and disagreeable sensations. In spite of all this, however, their general condition remains satisfactory, they have not lost their appetite, and are sleeping well. If one succeeds in distracting their attention, one discovers a relaxing, an alteration, almost a complete forgetting of this really painful obsession.

Finally, these pains are *intractable* and *inexplicable*. No organic lesion or visceral affection can be found, and this in spite of the most intensive investigations, the most complete examinations, the most minutely regulated dosages. Thus the patient wanders from consultation room to consultation room, while the list of remedies he accumulates grows longer and longer but remains completely useless.

It must be clearly understood, of course, that one cannot reach a diagnosis of psychalgia on these semiological characteristics alone: an intensive examination of the physical and psychological condition of the patient is also indispensable. Certain algias of a kinaesthetic type, apparently neuropathic, can form part of the clinical picture of a neurological syndrome, and in certain cases, they can be traced to their source in clearly localized cerebral lesions. On the other hand, however, the discovery of a slight peripheral irritation of the spine may appear an insufficient explanation for an algic syndrome which is disproportionately abnormal.

Thus, we cannot speak of psychalgia except in a psychic context where the pain merely represents a symptom which is sometimes on the second plane, and also frequently predominant and even almost exclusive.

Psychalgia and psychosis

We shall deal summarily with the matter of this section, since it concerns pains which are quite clearly recognizable as one of the manifestations of the psychopathic condition.

Hypochrondriacal delirium has been described by Baillarger as one of the typical forms of general paralysis; and it is well known how frequently kinaesthetic preoccupations are encountered in the course of senile or presenile demential conditions.

As in chronic interpretative and hallucinatory deliria, the hypochondriacal forms are frequent, in conjunction with an *ensemble* of kinaesthetic troubles, visceral pains and organic modifications.

Dementia praecox and the conflicting psychoses of schizophrenics reveal themselves, very often, by a well-known hypochondriacal complex: nosophobic preoccupations, kinaesthetic troubles with organic transformations, electric currents sent from a distance—all these reveal mental dissociation. It is well known that kinaesthetic troubles figure among the atypical conditions which mark the beginning of dementia praecox. It is important to be wary of subjective troubles of neuropathic complexion, which are reminiscent of those of the neurasthenic, described farther on, and which mark the commencement of dementia.

In the intermission period between their crises, *epileptics* frequently complain of strange visceral troubles, of pains, of kinaesthetic symptoms. Very often, such persons are dreamers and hypochondriacs.

Finally, *attacks of melancholia* offer perhaps the most typical example of pains conditioned by psychosis. In the majority of such cases, we are concerned with a pronounced occipito-nuchal cephalalgia in the midst of other symptoms of inhibition, accompanied by depression, remorse, anguish, inferiority-feelings, and moral suffering. But the kinaesthetic preoccupations, expressed by the patients in their own way, are very diverse: corrupt organs, obstructed intestines, decomposed blood, ideas of demoniacal possession, transformation and even obliteration of organs. These melancholics can undergo the most atrocious sufferings and martyrdoms, just as they can, on the other hand, inflict the most cruel wounds on themselves without feeling the least physical pain.

There are also some almost isolated algias, as cephalalgies for which no explanation can be given, and which nevertheless originate in an atypical, monosymptomatic melancholic condition, amenable to cure after some sessions of shock treatment.

The same is true of cases of melancholic kinaestopathia accompanied by cardiac, intestinal, and rheumatoid troubles; these are minor forms of cyclothymia, and sometimes the periodicity of the troubles alone makes the diagnosis possible and indicates the specific treatment.

In these different psychoses, the algia appears in clear connection with other troubles engendered by the affection. Whether we are dealing with a case of general paralysis, of arteriopathic dementia, of involution-psychosis or of melancholia, the problem of the origin of the algia is that of the very origin of the disease and of the organic or functional troubles which determine it.

Psychalgia and neurosis

At the beginning of this article, we have recalled Dupré's description of the kinaestopath—continually assailed by abnormal, bizarre, indescribable sensations; disturbed by the persistence of these impressions which are disagreeable and irksome rather than really painful.

These kinaestopaths vainly seek an explanation of their troubles, and ease from their obsessive sensations. They rush from one consulting-room to another; they submit to ceaseless examinations, to all therapeutic measures, and to the most mysterious practices of the healers. Sometimes they are filled with hope, but this hope is quickly dashed when the relief they have experienced proves short-lived; both persuasive and vigorous measures are without avail. One suspects a disturbance of the general sensibility, an hallucination originating in sensibility, an alteration of kinaesthesia.

When the physical and psychic condition of such subjects is more searchingly probed, the result is nearly always the discovery of constitutional asthenia, a basis of morbid anxiety which can be even an obsession, and sometimes too the discovery of a strain of paranoia. One very quickly recognizes the subject who is suffering from minor constitutional depressive-asthenic anxiety. He ceaselessly questions himself, and is ever on the alert for anything that can augment or justify his uneasiness. He is eloquent on the subject of his many functional troubles, which he records exhaustively in a long list of ailments and petty annoyances. These patients complain of troubles of digestion, circulation, respiration; of dizziness, giddiness, palpitations, sluggishness; or again, of impressions that the heart has stopped beating, that one of their members is dead, that there is a trickle of water in their head or spinal column. Their uneasiness can be allayed neither by reasoning nor by observation of the facts; it dominates all activity for these unfortunate people, who are constantly on guard about their food, about the number of their evacuations, about their pulse-rate, about the number of times they urinate—so that they are uneasy because they have eaten some pickles, because they have urinated three times one day and four times the next, etc. They are tired in the morning, are asthenic, aboulic, incapable of effort, exhausted by the first thing they do. Often timid, emotive, impressionable, they show a great neuro-vegetative instability, together with vaso-motor disorders, secretion-disorders, visceral spasms, and sexual inhibition.

This basis of physical asthenia and of minor anxiety characterizes Beard's neurasthenic, the constitutionally depressed person, the hyponeurotonic. The functional, kinaesthetic troubles are in direct proportion to the degree of exhaustion; strain, repeated efforts and emotional weariness bring on a recrudescence of the algias, a reappearance of the palpitations, the spasms, the illnesses, in the same way as an intercurrent disease, an infectious period, a physical traumatism. Rest, relaxation and calm bring more or less swift relief of these troubles, an improvement of tonus, and sometimes a disappearance—unfortunately very passing—of the feeling of helpless exhaustion. As soon as the patient becomes active again, lassitude and weariness reappear as harbingers to the functional cortège of uneasiness which fill the lives of these people. Of course, such patients find a source of strength in their doctor, are buoyed up after each visit to him, and are improved by taking certain medicaments. But here again, the effect is of short duration; hence the ceaseless consultations, the craving for new remedies, the tendency to exploit all the modes of treatment available from doctors, acupuncturators, homeopaths, and also from healers, radiaesthesists, bone-setters, and mesmerists. A certain amount of suggestibility, inherent in the affection itself, accounts for these temporary improvements, and makes it difficult to estimate the value of a medicamentous drug.

A more marked obsessional character is found in the psychasthenic whose trouble lies in a lack of psychic co-ordination when faced with the troubles of everyday life. The hypochondriacal preoccupations centre on one single theme or on several themes. They give rise to the habitual ceremonial of precautions, protection, complex rites; and the kinaesthetic troubles are nourished by a phobia of cancer, fear of a tumour, obsession about tuberculosis. It is usually easy to discover, behind this obsessive hypochondria, the mental psychasthenic basis described by Janet—diminution of mental synthesis, a lowering of psychological tension, a feeling of incompleteness—which turns the psychasthenic into an eternally wavering, scrupulous, meticulous, hesitant person, unsure of himself and of his actions, uneasy and perpetually checking and re-checking.

On the other hand, kinaesthetic troubles can occur in an apparently sthenic subject, and take the form of a delirious interpretation and a vengeful aggressiveness. Crabbed, tyrannical, complaining, he pesters his immediate family and his friends with his demands and his grievances; he fastens on to the doctor, imposes on him his own diagnoses, demands examinations, treatments, and operations. He poses as a victim, pursues, threatens, protests. He becomes aggressive and sometimes even murderous. More than one doctor has become the victim of a paranoical hypochondriac because he did not yield to his demands.

Hysteria presents a paradoxical behaviour-pattern: anaesthesias and analgesias are more frequent with the sufferer from hysteria than are pains.

It is usually easy to trace fundamentally atypical pains, accompanied by a whole ensemble of spectacular manifestations, to hysteria.

On the other hand, it may be a much more delicate matter to recognize such a condition when we are dealing with an algic syndrome which imitates an organic affection almost perfectly; or again, it may be no easy matter to determine the part played by hysteria in a syndrome which appears to be functional.

Dupré and Logre have emphasized the mythomanic constitution of such subjects, the considerable part played by their imaginative tendencies and their suggestibility. Besides, the idea of an initial, commencing factor—notably, of an affective shock—undoubtedly assumes considerable value. Hence the reason why one should avail of all the procedures for investigation in this research—especially narcoanalysis and amphetaminic shock, which can have, moreover, a therapeutic value.

An analogous problem often raised in practice is that of manifestations of pain and persistent subjective troubles subsequent to accidents or traumas and liable to entail medico-legal consequences or claims for compensation. Care must be taken not to reach an over-hasty diagnosis. Algic consequences make their appearance months or even years after a trauma. The post-commotional syndrome of a person who has sustained a head injury, presents one of the most typical examples of these syndromes of a functional type. The cephalalgia is here more or less diffused, variable, intermittent, sometimes considerable and really obsessive, preventing all sustained activity. It is accompanied by a whole body of subjective troubles, dizziness, giddiness, palpitations, disequilibrium, weariness after the least effort, defects of memory, and difficulty in making any intellectual effort—if not, indeed, a complete inability to make it. . . . Not infrequently, too, one finds characterological troubles, unstable humour, irritability, and an unusual nervousness which is increased by insomnia. It is a recognized fact that these diverse manifestations, which appear to be neuropathic, may correspond to cerebral, cicatricial lesions provoked by a brain-trauma—lesions which are too minute to determine objective neurological symptoms, but which the electroencephalogram and especially the gaseous encephalography can discover, and, as a final proof, can heal.

Similarly, tenacious algic sequences with a sensation of burning, of painful smarting, can persist for years after an even slight trauma of the members. The frequent importance of vasomotor and sympathetic troubles, the very course of these pains of a "causalgia" type, enable them to be connected with the reflex neuro-vegetative syndromes studied by Leriche and Froment.

However, though a considerable number of these post-traumatic algias correspond to an undoubted anatomical alteration, it must be borne in mind that these troubles are just as frequently exaggerated. It may be a question of a perfectly conscious exaggeration, a deliberate pretence, often difficult to carry out; or it may be a question of an unconscious or almost unconscious exaggeration of the pains, generally known as "sinistrosis," which has increased to some extent since the introduction of existing social legislation.

The idea of claim, of the right to compensation, of prejudice, plays an unconscious part in the development of such "interested" psychoneuroses; but this does not necessarily imply that one can question the sincerity of the claimant, since in his case it may be rather a tendency to paranoia. It is then a very delicate matter to intervene, because one must endeavour to avoid both strengthening the conviction and contesting the reality of the troubles.

If we have dealt in some detail with this problem of hysterotraumatism, the reason is that it constantly arises in connection with expert examination for the purpose of fixing the amount of the compensation to be made. Thus, not only must organic lesions be taken into account, but also subjective elements and psychological factors.

*   *   *

One could go on to add clinical picture to clinical picture, by showing the variety of psychological conditions which underlie the development of psychic algias. We must now attempt to give an *interpretation* of them.

As soon as one endeavours to give a pathogenic explanation, one necessarily subscribes to a doctrinal system which presupposes a whole body of theories with which we cannot deal in detail here.

How, then, are we to deal with these patients?

Are we to regard them as victims of their own imaginations—or, in other words, are we to regard their sufferings as non-existent merely because of the fact that no organic reason can be assigned for them? This would be to misunderstand seriously the reality of the troubles, the legitimacy of such sufferings being amply proved by the facts. We need only instance, as proof, the depressive cephalalgia which accompanies, with perfect regularity, the developed varieties of inhibitions and melancholia, and which disappears when they are cured by shock-treatment.

Are we, in accordance with certain mechanistic theories, to attribute these sufferings to an injury or derangement of the major pain-centres? We do not think that this does more than pinpoint to some extent certain mechanisms activitated by these algias; it does not provide a real explanation for psychalgias.

The development of our physio-pathological knowledge has enabled us to describe the centres of cognitive integration, as well as the centres of protopathic sensibility; and the troubles of the bodily schema, as well as those of painful hyperaesthesia. Efforts have been made to localize the thymic reactions and the affective repercussion of pain. The full importance of thalamo-cortical relations, of the relations of neuron to neuron, of association reflexes, has been demonstrated. But how are we to explain the derangement and the particular susceptibility of these cognitive and thymic centres? How are we to explain this extreme variety of kinaesthetic sensations, how interpret anxiety and anguish, if not by seeking to localize in the hypothalamus the multiple functions of consciousness itself?

It is, of course, possible to trace some troubles, apparently functional, to certain cerebral lesions. The aurakinaesthesia of an epileptic (as distinct from the psychalgias of epileptics), the subjective syndromes of those afflicted with cranial injuries, and certain pains in those who have undergone an amputation, have as their origin a causal lesion. More and more knowledge has been gained about the different types of thalamic algias and cortical algias, but this has nothing to do with psychalgias.

Is it even possible to hold that every algia is connected with an irritation of the spine—even an irritation which is very small and inaccessible to our present means of investigation? And are we to explain thus the very special characteristics of these kinaestopathies, and the considerable affective element which accompanies them?

It is a well-known fact that affective repercussions from pain vary greatly from one person to another. There are lesional organic pains which can engulf the whole field of consciousness, become obsessive and tyrannical, and, after the lesion has been cured, remain in a hypochondriacal form. It is scarcely necessary to stress *this vicious circle created by pain and anxiety*. Should we, therefore, put the blame on a special susceptibility of the centres of affectivity, or should we not rather blame an abnormal psychic constitution? Whether one or other alternative is accepted, the problem is no nearer to solution.

Should we look for a solution to psychogenetic ideas? The idea, the fear, the suggestion, create the symptom. Cancerophobia, it is said, will soon reproduce in the body of the person who suffers from it, the pains and symptoms of the cancer of which he or she lives in fear. This is an over-simplified theory which leaves out of consideration the principal problem concerning the *origin* of this fixed idea, of this phobia, of this susceptibility.

It is on these conditions that psychoanalytical theories seek to throw light. Depth-analysis should lead to the discovery of the genesis of the mental processes whose origin entirely escapes the conscious mind. It should enable the kinaesthetic syndrome to be traced to unconscious psychic conflicts, the fruits of repressions dating from infancy or the consequences of present unsatisfied urges. The diverse mechanisms of conversion, of projection, of autopunition, of regression, make their appearance, and effect a state of morbidity which is accepted as a compromise in the conflict between the Ego and the hostile functions. The anguish of the conflict externalizes itself in the body as an algia. Psychoanalysis thus reveals to us a certain number of mechanisms, but does not furnish us with the explanation.

Each person will be drawn, according to his formation, his affinities and his personal conceptions, towards one or other of these attempts at theoretical interpretation. But no one can opt to regard the algias either as pure products of the imagination or as simple neurological disturbance. It must be clearly recognized that we are incapable of explaining, not only the course, but also the pathogenesis of these algias. In most cases, psychalgias are accompanied by physical asthenia, psychic asthenia, and above all, anxiety; but it is impossible to trace precisely the relations of causality existing between these diverse components. Does the anxiety engender the asthenia and the algia? Or is the anxiety simply an emotional phenomenon, as in the case of other manifestations, all arising from the same cause, and evolving *pari passu*? Is the algia the *first effect*, but perceived as charged with such affectivity that it alters the psychic constitution? But then, how are we to explain this abnormal affective repercussion? In endeavouring to pursue this discussion, one always comes up against the question of the relations which unite the body and the mind—the problem of psychic integration in an organic stimulus, which problem is the vast field of psychosomatic medicine.

*   *   *

In these conditions, it is clearly very difficult to lay down a line of conduct.

Two conceptions should be ruled out—

That which regards the pains as non-existent and endeavours to reason with these patients. This is a clear sign of inexperience or simplicity. Mere persuasion is unavailing.

That which regards the malady as an organic lesion, and treats it as such. This is equally useless. Moreover, such an attitude only serves to confirm the subject in his convictions, and frequently entails an idea of vengeance, especially when an intervention has proved ineffective.

Therapeutic treatment will aim, therefore, at treating, not the algia in itself, but *the neurotic or psychotic ensemble*.

We possess, as a matter of fact, very few procedures which have been proved to be effective.

An attack of melancholia will yield to electric shock-treatment; but this is in reality a symptomatic treatment only, which scarcely touches the cause, since the attacks will recur. This treatment is useless for the psychalgias of hypo-neurotics and psychasthenics, whose cure is a much more delicate process.

According to the particular demands of the case, we must seek the aid of sedative drugs, of general or nerve tonics; we must endeavour to effect a deconditioning, to modify the affective atmosphere; it may be necessary to envisage recuperative psychotherapy, a liberation of emotional charges, and even sometimes a psychoanalysis. The variety of these methods shows the complexity of the cases, as also their own varying efficacy. It must be clearly recognized that the results are inconstant: with some, the success is remarkable; evanescent with others; and almost completely useless with others, again, in spite of many attempts.

We do not wish to enter here on the problem of Psychosurgery. We would like to point out, however, that altogether exceptional circumstances and a severe psychopathic clinical picture must exist to warrant our suggesting an operation whose results are known—results which are often deceptive in these psychalgias, but which are, on the other hand, favourable in cases where the pains have become obsessive.

It must be clearly recognized that, in so far as psychalgias remain mysterious, our therapeutic efforts will always be groping.

Dr. Robert Pauwels
Interne des Hôpitaux de Paris

THE SURGERY OF PAIN

THERE is scarcely any pathological condition which is not accompanied to some extent by pain; and this pain disappears as soon as the causal lesion is cured. Of course, the intensity of the pain may be such that it necessitates active therapy, but the medicamentous arsenal which we possess and which includes everything from Aspirin to opiates, is sufficiently rich and varied to alleviate the keenest pains.

But there are some cases, happily few, in which the pain becomes really the essential element of the disease, and for which it is no longer possible, because of the chronic character of this pain, to use medical therapies. The reason is that, in these cases, such therapies quickly prove insufficient, and lead to toxicomania. The diseases on which these circumstances can prevail are varied and extend from facial neuralgia—in which the pain is the only symptom of a completely unknown lesion, and the gravity of which is solely the intensity of this pain—to generalized cancerous metastases, in which the pain is merely one of the elements of an affection whose treatment is beyond the present resources of medicine.

It is for all these cases of intense and persistent pains that an effort has been made to find, in the surgery of the nerve tracts, a means of suppressing pain.

Attempts have been made in different directions. Some consist in the interruption of the sensory tracts at some point of their ascending course towards the cerebral hemispheres; others, under the influence of Leriche, attempt whenever possible "to act on the functionality of the sensory tracts through the sympathetic and the endocrines." This second method is, no doubt, infinitely more physiological than the first, but it is equally certain that it is generally less sure and less rapidly efficacious.

Before describing the different operations and listing their indications, we think it will serve a useful purpose to deal briefly with the sensory tracts and with the more discussed one of the sympathetic system.

1. *Anatomy of the sensory tracts*

The body is divided into a certain number of sensitive dermatomes. From each dermatome come neurons which, following the course of one or of several peripheral nerves, enter the spinal cord through a posterior root. Every dermatome corresponds, therefore, to a sensory rachidian root or to a sensory cranial nerve which is its homologue.

Each of these neurons which entend from the peripheral receptor to the spinal cord, is a primitive neuron or protoneuron. At its termination, a second neuron or deuteroneuron continues the connection to the Thalamus.

All the sensory neurons of the entire body end, therefore, in the Thalamus, which is the great cerebral sensory centre. From the Thalamus, fibres extend to cerebral cortex in the parietal region: these are third sensory neurons.

Every sensory influx, therefore, travels from the periphery of the body to the cerebral cortex by way of the neurons.

From the periphery—where the sensation is collected by receptors which are the sensory corpuscles—to the spinal cord, all the neurons of the same dermatome are grouped together to form the sensory root which goes into the cord. But after their penetration of the spinal cord, these neurons do not all follow the same course; with the fibres which have come from the lower and upper stages and which are also ascending towards the Thalamus, they group themselves into a certain number of specialized bundles with such or such sensory function. We can thus distinguish three different bundles corresponding to three groups of sensibility: deep sensation passing through the posterior part of the cord; the thermic and pain sensations passing through the antero-lateral, and the tactile sensation passing through the postero-lateral area of the spinal cord.

(a) *Deep sensation* uses the tract of the posterior bundle of the cord. The posterior rachidian root, in penetrating the cord, is divided into two internal and external portions. The internal portion reaches the posterior part of the cord on the same side, where it forms, with the upper and lower fibres, the bundle of Goll and the bundle of Burdach which end at the level of the nuclei of Goll and of Burdach in the Bulbus. From the nuclei of Goll and of Burdach arises the second neuron, which extends to the Thalamus. The fibres of this second neuron, in its ascending course in the cerebral trunk, quickly become interwoven with those of the opposite side, and continue with them to the point where they form the sulcus of Reil, situated in front of the fourth ventricle and of the Aquaduct of Sylvius in the protruberance. At the level of the peduncle, the right and the left halves of the sulcus of Reil separate and continue to the Thalamus on each side.

The bundles of Goll and of Burdach, and of the sulcus of Reil, are therefore formed by the fibres of the deep sensibility. It is in the Tabes that the lesion can be effected with the maximum of purity—a lesion which is clinically revealed by troubles of deep sensation with ataxia.

The fibres of tactile superficial sensibility, and, more precisely, of the epicritical sensibility—that is, of the fine and discriminate sensibility—also follow the same course as the fibres of the deep sensibility.

(b) *The thermic and pain sensibilities* follow a very different tract in the medulla. When the posterior rachidian root has penetrated the medulla, it is divided, as we have said, into two portions: the internal comprises the fibres of the deep sensibility; and the external is formed essentially of fibres whose function is the transmission of thermic and pain sensibilities.

When these fibres reach the medulla, they end by articulating themselves with the posterior grey cornu of the medulla. It is from these cells of the posterior grey cornu that the second neuron comes. The fibres of this second neuron interweave with those of the opposite side, passing across the posterior and anterior grey commissures. They then travel from the opposite side, forming a very important bundle situated in the lateral cord of the medulla: the lateral spino-thalamic bundle or posterior spino-thalamic bundle. Arrived at the Bulbus, this spino-thalamic bundle takes the course of the lateral cord; at the Protuberance it approaches the sulcus of Reil and links with it to continue the journey to the Thalamus.

In their medullary course, the fibres which constitute the spino-thalamic bundle are disposed in juxtaposed lamellae, the fibres mutually corresponding. As they reach the different stages of their course in the spinal cord, the fibres repress towards the postero-external part of the bundle those fibres which have originated lower down. And thus the fibres occupy in this bundle a position which is the more superficial according as it corresponds to a lower level of penetration into the medulla—to a lower level of the body, in other words; and they occupy a more profound position according as they correspond to a more highly situated segment.

There is no neurological affection which, as the Tabes does in relation to the posterior cords, chooses electively the spino-thalamic bundle. Syringomyelia, whose lesion is a centro-medullary cavity, entails anaesthesia to pain and to heat in a perfectly determined zone corresponding to one dermatome or several dermatomes; and this, not through lesion of the spino-thalamic bundle, but through destruction of the grey commissure—that is to say, through section of the fibres which, at a determined medullary stage, pass from the cells of the posterior cornu to the spino-thalamic bundles which they help to form.

(c) *The ducts of the tactile superficial sensation* are less precisely traced. We have seen that the epicritical sensation is regarded as taking the course of the fibres of deep sensation. The protopathic sensation—that is, the gross tactile sensation—follows a course bordering on that of the thermic and pain sensations. The fibres of the first neuron, when they penetrate the spinal cord, are also articulated with the cells of the posterior cornu. From these arise the fibres of the second neuron which interweave in order to form an anterior spino-thalamic bundle in front of the spino-thalamic bundle. In reality, the latter is infinitely less clear than the former; it is formed of short fibres which are relayed, stage by stage, to the different levels. From the Bulbus, this bundle becomes confused, in some parts, with the sulcus of Reil; in other parts, with the posterior spino-thalamic bundle. All these sensory bundles end, therefore, in the Thalamus which constitutes the grand relay of cerebral sensation.

A thalamic lesion, such as occurs through a centre of softening, gives a sensory syndrome of a very special kind, consisting of very hidden troubles of superficial sensation; much more considerable troubles of deep sensation; spontaneous pains, or rather, a painful sensation; and finally a phenomenon of hyperpathy or "over-reaction." Every sensation at the level of the hemibody is perceived with a component of pain, especially every sensation of cold; moreover, even emotion provokes a painful sensation in the injured hemibody.

But the Thalamus is far from being solely a sensory relay. In the first place, from the sensory point of view, it seems to act much more as a selective filter than as a simple relay; in the second place, anatomical studies have shown that the sensory fibres end in a limited part of the Thalamus—its postero-external nucleus—and have made clear the multiplicity of its connections with the cerebrum. It is therefore generally held to-day that the Thalamus plays a role in the majority of cerebral mechanisms.

From the Thalamus comes a third neuron which extends to the parietal cortex. But this last portion of the sensory tracts is very different from the preceding ones. Beyond the Thalamus, an excitation of the parietal cortex is no longer capable of producing a sensation of pain, any more than the destruction of this zone is capable of suppressing a painful syndrome. A parietal softening gives a syndrome which is essentially composed of troubles of deep sensation and troubles of the stereognostic sense, in association with slight hypoesthesia; but the painful sensation is in no way modified.

It is all exactly the same, therefore, as if the painful function were integrated at the level of the Thalamus.

This classic description of the sensation tracts has never been disputed as an account of the course followed by the sensory fibres. On the other hand, however, there is no unanimity about the dissociation of the sensory function in deep sensation and in the superficial sensation of touch, heat, and pain. In particular, doubt has been cast on the existence of pain as a sensation proper, having its own specialized receptors for perception and its own special conductor tracts for transmission.

There are, of course, weighty arguments in favour of the classic conception—

(1) As we have already pointed out, there is the anatomical lesion of Syringomyelia and the trouble which it entails—the suppression, in a determined area, of thermic and pain sensations, while both tactile sensibility and deep sensibility are conserved;

(2) There is also the surgical section of the spino-thalamic bundle, which we shall presently describe. It induces in the entire subjacent area the same thermic and pain sensations, with conservation of tactile sensation;

(3) Again, it has been shown through the study of chronaxies, that pain is transmitted through thicker fibres than those of the other sensations.

But, as against this there are other, no less compelling arguments—

(1) The direct touching, in the course of an operation, of a peripheral nerve or of a sensory root, always gives a sensation of pain, to the exclusion of any other tactile or thermic sensation. Must it not be admitted, therefore, that the fibres of pain are infinitely more numerous than the others?

(2) The direct excitation of the posterior cords which contain only fibres of deep sensation and of tactile epicritical sensation also causes a pain which is no other than the shooting pain of the Tabes;

(3) Cutaneous sensation is not the only one which can be affected by pain. A visual, auditory or olfactory sensation can be neutral, agreeable, disagreeable, and even painful. Now, no one has ever proposed the existence of a pain tract in the optic nerve, the acoustic nerve, or the olfactory nerve;

(4) Besides painful sensations, there are also agreeable sensations. What tracts have they? Certain sensations, agreeable in one set of circumstances, become painful in other circumstances, and this variation can be the consequence of physical elements, but can be equally the consequence of purely psychic elements. It is hard to understand what, in such circumstances, will guide the excitant precisely towards the receptor and the sensory pain-tract. Leriche puts the matter perfectly: "From the very nature of things, there is not and there cannot be an excitation which can be called painful, as long as the brain has not pronounced judgment on it. Our corpuscles of touch, our sensory end-organs, are not endowed with any quality which enables them to say in advance that a particular sensation will have an affective character, or that it already has such a character, and therefore should take its course along such or such a fibre."

However, this discussion, however important it may be, has no effect on the practical issue; and no one can deny that the section of the spino-thalamic bundle entails the disappearance of the sensation of pain in the bodily zone subjacent to the section. This is a fact in face of which it is of little practical consequence whether this Cordotomy has sectioned the bundle of the "pain sensations proper" or the bundle of an ill-defined sensation provoking pain in such or such physiological or pathological conditions.

Besides the cerebo-spinal sensory system, is there a sympathetic sensory system?

There is no doubt that perivascular sensory fibres exist. The pain entailed by the coagulation of the meningeal artery, under local anaesthetic, is a clear proof of this. But do these fibres belong to the sympathetic system or to the cerebro-spinal system? The majority of them undoubtedly belong to the cerebro-spinal system in connection with the adjoining peripheral nerves; but besides these, which are short fibres, there are long fibres which follow the entire course of the vessel and enter the spinal cord through the communicating branches. These fibres would certainly be real sympathetic fibres, having their own course; but the others could be annexed to the area of the sympathetic properly belonging to the cerebro-spinal system.

There also exists a visceral sensation arising from the vegetative system. This sensation is normally latent and unconscious, but it can become painful under the influence of a specific excitation. This sensory tract undoubtedly follows the course of the sympathetic. The majority of its fibres reach, by way of the communicating branches, the posterior rachidian ganglion which is their cell of origin, and then they reach the posterior cornu of the spinal cord by way of the posterior root. But some of the fibres seem to have their cell of origin in the sympathetic ganglia of the dorsal chain. They too reach the posterior cornu of the medulla, but without being interrupted in the posterior rachidian ganglion.

Thus, all these sensory fibres annexed to the sympathetic or properly belonging to it, reach the posterior cornu of the medulla. Their intramedullary course is disputed. Some maintain that these sensory fibres take the course of the spino-thalamic bundle; others maintain that their course is in the posterior cord; while others, again, claim that they have their own course.

2. Surgical operations against pain

The significance of operations is totally different in cerebro-spinal surgery and in the sympathetic surgery of pain.

(1) *Sympathetic surgery* seeks to correct "the vaso-motor disorder

which creates the atmosphere of pain or alters perhaps the threshold of painful phenomena" (Leriche).

Sympathetic operations can bear on all levels: peri-vascular sympathectomy with resection of the peri-arterial membrane and of the nerve fibres which it transmits; infiltration of the ganglia and of the sympathetic chain; section of the ganglia; stellectomy and thoracic ganglionectomy; section of the communicating branches; splanchnic sections, etc.

The major indication for these different operations seems to be the existence of vaso-motor troubles. These troubles constitute the essential element in the arterial pains of arthritis, ischmic gangrene, acromelalgia, and erythromelalgia. They are also found in the pains felt by certain patients who have undergone an amputation, as well as in certain forms of causalgia and of post-traumatic algias.

With these operations, we must bracket surrenalectomy, which, like sympathetic infiltrations and ganglionectomies, acts by means of a mechanism of vaso-dilatation in the case of arthritis, and in the painful spasms of sufferers from hypertension, or the endochrine operations such as parathyroidectomy and thymoparathyroidectomy in those suffering from ankylosing polyarthritis with hypercalcemia. It is possible, indeed, that the equilibrium of the calcium proportion of the blood and of the tissues is one of the conditions of the sensory order (Leriche).

These different sympathetic or endocrine operations have a number of undoubted successes to their credit. They are most effective, it seems, where there is serious vaso-motor trouble; but their action is certainly not absolutely constant or compellingly definitive.

It is possible that, in the more or less proximate future, it will become possible, through a better knowledge and a better comprehension of physiology, to treat an ever increasing number of painful syndromes by means of sympathetic, endocrine or other operations; but by acting, as these endeavour to do, in a physiological manner. It is not the least among the merits of sympathetic surgery, that it has shown this way to the treatment of pain.

(2) *Cerebro-spinal surgery* has no other purpose than the interruption of the tracts which transmit sensations of pain. The section can bear on any point, whether on the first neuron proceeding from the periphery to the medulla, or on the second neuron proceeding from the medulla to the Thalamus. On the other hand, a section of the tracts of the third thalamo-parietal neuron, or of the sensory parietal cortical centre, is absolutely useless. It appears indeed, we repeat, that the sensation of pain does not go beyond the level of the Thalamus.

However, above the first and second sensory neuron there is a zone whose section or whose destruction entails, not a disappearance of the pain, but a modification of the patient's attitude towards it. This is the frontal zone at level of which different operations of the psycho-surgical type can be performed, in certain very particular cases of intolerable pains. These interventions in no way concern the sensory tracts; they are completely different, in their very principle, from the preceding types.

Operations on the sensory tracts can be done on the first neuron or on the second neuron. The choice of where to operate will be decided, on the one hand, according to the extent of the zone of pain, and, on the other hand, with a view to respecting the essential fact that a section can be efficacious only if it affects the tracts of the pain—above the point of origin of the pain—in the ascending path towards the Thalamus.

A. Operation bearing on the First Neuron

The first neuron extends from the periphery to the posterior cornu of the spinal cord, following the path of a peripheral nerve and then of a root.

We know that every neuron is made up of a cellular body and of two extensions—one extension which is cellulipetal and dendritic; and one which is cellulifugal and cylindraxile. The cellular body of the first neuron is situated very close to the spinal cord at the level of the posterior root ganglion; the cellulipetal extension is the peripheral nerve, and the cellulifugal extension is the posterior rachidian nerve.

Operations on the first neuron can affect, therefore, either the peripheral nerves or the rachidian nerves.

Indications for *sections of the peripheral nerves* are exceptional. In the first place, they can be performed only on the sensitive nerves to the exclusion of the mixed nerves; otherwise, a paralysis of the corresponding area accompanies anaesthesia. In the second place, they are transitory: the section of a neuron in the upper part of the root ganglion is followed by a regeneration. This is observed, for example, in the alcoholic injection of the peripheral branches of the trigeminal nerve in cases of very limited neuralgia—alcoholic injections which, in such cases, are very easy to provoke and are efficacious for a period of some months.

Radicotomies do not present the same difficulties. In the rachidian canal at the level of the penetration into the spinal cord, the posterior sensitive roots are easy to separate from the anterior motor roots. Moreover, the section of a root is never followed by its regeneration.

The technique of Radicotomy is simple and perfectly well established. After having decided the precise place where the roots are to be sectioned, a Laminectomy is performed which is in respect of as many vertebrae as the roots one intends to cut. The opening of the dura mater exposes the cord and the emergence of the roots. The latter, after having been separated from the anterior roots, are sectioned in their intradural course. It is important to excite the root electrically before sectioning it; this produces a pain whose seat blends with that of the pain in question, and thus provides an assurance that the radicotomy is being done exactly at the level desired.

It is therefore a simple and efficacious operation for all pains whose origin is peripheral; but it has the following restrictions.

Radicotomy can be performed only if the painful area includes merely a small number of roots, and this is especially the case where we are dealing with a superior member or an inferior member. The section of several roots can provoke trophic troubles in the anaesthetized area. Moreover, radicotomy entails, with the disappearance of superficial sensibility, an abolition of deep sensation: that is to say, it produces a real ataxia.

For these different reasons, this operation will be confined to the peripheral syndrome of pain affecting the area of a single root, or at least of a small number of roots. A neuralgia of Arnold's nerve; cervico-brachial algia; a femoro-cutaneous neuralgia; an internal neuralgia—are all examples of indications for radicotomy.

With these radicotomies, we must link the neurotomies of the sensitive cranial nerves (V and IX) which are the homologue of the posterior nerve roots.

Neurotomy of the trigeminal nerve has one major indication: essential facial neuralgia. We are familiar with the pain which is followed by short crises—this "painful tic" whose cause is unknown and which, in the majority of cases, is recalcitrant to all medicamentous therapy.

This neurotomy should be carried out behind the Gasserian ganglion, which is the homologue of the posterior root ganglion. Neurotomies of the peripheral branches yield only passing results.

There are different techniques for this retrogasserian neurotomy.

Gasserian alcoholization by means of percutaneous injection through the foramen is, in the hands of a surgeon accustomed to performing it, a very simple operation. The results are not always certain, as are those from section; but we believe that alcoholic injection should be unhesitatingly proposed in the case of very aged and deficient subjects, for whom every operation is vitally dangerous, and also for very timid subjects.

Neurotomy through the temporal tract reaches the nerve immediately behind the Gasserian ganglion by way of the extradural tract. At this level, it is possible to dissociate, among the nerve fibres, the three contingent ones which form the three branches of the trigeminal nerve: the ophthalmic, the superior maxillary, and the inferior maxillary. It is therefore possible, when dealing with a neuralgia which bears electively on one of the three branches, to perform a partial, elective neurotomy.

Neurotomy through the posterior tract sections the nerve immediately at the point of its emergence from the protuberance, where it is not possible to dissociate the fibres of the different branches.

Neurotomy of the glosso-pharyngeal nerve is indicated in cases of essential neuralgia of this nerve. Such cases are very much rarer than neuralgia of the trigemenal nerve, but they are similarly characterized by very severe crises of pain—at the level of the amygdala and of the inner ear on the same side.

This neurotomy should also be retro-ganglionic, being performed behind the Andersch ganglion. It is carried out through the posterior tract before the penetration of the nerve into the posterior divided opening.

B. Operations bearing on the Second Neuron

The second neuron extends from the posterior cornu of the spinal cord to the Thalamus. Three types of operation can sever it: Myelotomy; Cordotomy; Thalamotomy.

(*a*) Myelotomy surgically produces a lesion of the sensory fibres characteristic of Syringomyelia. We have seen that the fibres of the second neuron, after their departure from the posterior cornu of the spinal cord, interweave with those of the opposite side, passing across the anterior and posterior grey commissures to reach the antero-lateral area of the cord on the opposite side.

A commissural median longitudinal section of the cord interrupts the fibres at the level of their interweaving with those of the opposite side. It therefore provokes a bilateral thermic anaesthesia and an anaesthesia to pain in the area corresponding to the section.

Myelotomy is technically much more difficult to carry out than Radicotomy. The site of section of the cord, after laminectomy and the opening of the dura mater, is difficult to determine. Moreover, unlike electric excitation in the case of roots, there is no process which makes it possible to verify the proper height of the section. Finally, the fibres coming from each posterior root cross the commissure at the level, not of one medullary segment only, but of two or three segments.

For all these reasons, Myelotomy is more and more infrequently used, radicotomies or cordotomies being preferred.

(*b*) *Cordotomy* consists in the section of the spino-thalamic bundle through which, as we have seen, the fibres of the thermic and pain sensations pass. It therefore entails an anaesthesia of the whole part of the collateral hemibody subjacent to the section. This means that, in connection with the zone which one wishes to anaesthetize, one carries out a dorsal, cervical, protuberantial or peduncular Cordotomy. We immediately add that protuberantial and peduncular cordotomies are rare.

Dorsal Cordotomy is performed, by preference, at the height of the third or fourth dorsal vertebra. After laminectomy and the opening of the dura mater, the serrated ligament is used in order to carry out a slight rotation of the cord on its own axis. The section is then carried out between the serrated ligament and the anterior root.

Cervical Cordotomy is performed at the height of the second vertebra by means of an almost identical technique.

Cordotomy is an excellent operation for all cases where Radicotomy is out of the question because the area of pain extends too high, thereby necessitating the section of too many roots to be practicable. It is thus, for instance, in the case of pain suffered by those who have undergone an amputation, where a dorsal Cordotomy suppresses the pain of an inferior member, while a cervical Cordotomy suppresses the pain of a superior member.

Certain surgeons prefer, in all these cases, a cervical Cordotomy to a dorsal Cordotomy, because they think that, at the level of the dorsal swelling, the pyramidal tract is in danger of being injured during Cordotomy, much more than at the level of the cervical medulla.

In every case, it is important to obtain an anaesthesia rising higher than the area of pain, because it frequently happens that the upper limit of the insensibility obtained becomes lower in the days following the operation.

Cordotomy produces an anaesthesia in the hemibody of the side opposite to the section; in a case of bilateral pain, it is possible to perform a bilateral Cordotomy. In truth, however, the latter runs the risk of entailing some sphincteric troubles, and that is why certain surgeons prefer to perform the operation at two different times and at two different levels.

There is scarcely any pain, therefore, which will not yield to a Cordotomy. The only contra-indications for the operation are: when the seat of the pain is too high, at the level of the cephalic extremity or of the first cephalic roots—in which case a protuberantial or peduncular Cordotomy can be performed; and when a pain is due to a lesion of the sensory tract at a higher level, that is to say, when there is a thalamic syndrome.

(*c*) *Thalamotomy* is the highest operation bearing on the pain tracts.

It is performed at the level of the postero-lateral nucleus of the Thalamus, in which all the sensory fibres of the body end. Above the Thalamus, it is not possible to provoke or to suppress a sensation of pain.

The operation consists in a coagulation of the postero-lateral nucleus of the Thalamus, located by means of a stereotaxic apparatus. As a matter of fact, although postero-lateral thalamotomy is a logical operation, it runs counter to indisputable clinical facts. We know, indeed, that a softening of the postero-lateral nucleus of the Thalamus gives a syndrome whose major elements are pain and hyperpathy, though it must be added that this syndrome of pain does not appear at once but only after some weeks or some months. Now, the lesion produced by Thalamotomy is not appreciably different from that resulting from a vascular accident.

For the rest, Thalamotomy is at a stage where it can still be regarded as experimental, and it is still too early to judge the efficacy of this operation.

C. Psychosurgery

Very different from the operations on the sensory tracts or centres are those which bear on the dorso-median nucleus of the Thalamus, the frontal lobe, or their connections. These are the operations of psychosurgery.

It has been remarked that certain psychopaths—who, before being leucotomized on account of their mental condition, were suffering definite organic pains—no longer complain of these pains after the operation. This fact has led, in some cases, to the practice of these operations for a purely analgesic purpose, and the results obtained have been the same.

There is certainly no question here of a suppression of pain, but of a modification in the patient's attitude towards his pain. Whereas before the operation, the patient was perpetually mournful, complaining, self-centred, thinking only of his pain and ceaselessly demanding opiates, after the operation he is calm, relaxed, cheerful, and no longer seeks sedatives. He will make a sudden grimace, put his hand to the painful area, and cry out; but very soon he will resume his conversation, without attaching any importance to this pain.

We shall not deal with the description of these operations or with their modes of action, since this has been dealt with in the *Cahier* on Psychosurgery. (English translation: *The Ethics of Brain Surgery*. The Mercier Press.) We merely recall that there are three varieties: Leucotomy, which is the most frequent; Topectomy; Thalamotomy —which bears on the dorso-median nucleus of the Thalamus, and is therefore very dissimilar to the postero-external Thalamotomy of which we have spoken above.

It is quite certain that these operations, even if they do not alter the personality to any extent—and they certainly do, as can be seen by reading the *Cahier*—are nevertheless mutilating operations and should be reserved for very special cases.

With a view to entailing less drastic alterations of the personality, it has been proposed that we should confine ourselves to the unilateral form of these operations; but for our part, we have found that only very passing results are got in these cases.

We think that the indications for this operation must depend on two conditions—

1. That we are dealing with a pain so intense that it demands strong doses of morphia. Furthermore, we must know that, in these cases, the patients think only of their pain, of the injection they are about to receive or have just received, and this to the exclusion of all other preoccupations. And—

2. That this pain cannot be assuaged by any other process, because of its seat, or its extent, or the condition of the patient.

This implies that this kind of operation does not come up for consideration except in very special cases: as for example, the terrible pains of generalized cancer, or certain particularly painful forms of the thalamic syndromes.

Finally, there is the problem of psychalgias. Here we are dealing with a category of patients who complain of insupportable pains, now in one place, now in another, and this for many years. All the examinations carried out to discover the cause of these multiple pains have always shown the patient to be quite healthy. Such patients really are psychopaths rather than sufferers; and if a psychosurgical operation is envisaged for them, it will only be as a last resort when all psychiatric therapies have failed.

DR. RAYMOND HOUDART
Assistant de neuro-chirurgie des Hôpitaux de Paris

PAINLESS CHILDBIRTH

BEFORE we deal with painless childbirth, a preliminary question must be raised as to whether it is lawful to envisage such childbirth. Should we not rather be content with the classical pattern of birth: "Thou shalt bring forth children in sorrow"?

Of course, there are still some women who look on childbirth as a physiological act which fits perfectly into the natural order of things; and such women do bring forth their children without any help. There are others who fear that their love for their children will be lessened because of the fact that they have not undergone the pains of childbirth. But for one woman who refuses to accept any diminution of pain, there are many who beseech you to lessen these sufferings as quickly as you can.

Moreover, both on the human plane and the medical plane, obstetrical analgesia is not only not prohibited, but may seem even to be imperative.

On the human plane. There are, of course, deliveries which are effected in a perfectly regular fashion, and whose ease and rapidity astonish even the woman herself. But frequently, especially with first children, there is prolonged labour, and dilatation is halted or progresses very slowly in spite of uterine contractions which appear to be strong and regular. This results in great fatigue for the mother; and this fatigue, in conjunction with increasing anxiety, cannot but make the least pain more insupportable, and runs the risk of retarding still more the birth of the child. Such women, indeed, exhausted by long hours of suffering, have no strength left to assist by their own voluntary contractions the emergence of the head, when the period of expulsion comes. A kind of vicious circle is thus created, one element of which must be eliminated. Finally, this painful delivery, which is sometimes the result of a badly endured pregnancy, is not without repercussion on the general health during convalescence and in the months which follow the birth. It is by no means rare to find women who remain exhausted and asthenic for a long time, and who dread—if indeed they do not completely refuse—another pregnancy. In these conditions, should the doctor take up a passive attitude towards such pains, seeing that such an attitude may increase the suffering of the pregnant woman who interprets this passivity as meaning that the suffering is an inevitable element of childbirth? Is not the doctor's primary role to soothe, to lessen suffering, whatever may be the causes, qualities or form of that suffering?

On the medical plane. The pains of childbirth, sometimes extremely severe pains, are not as natural as may be supposed. They often indicate an anomaly of uterine contraction, a certain hypertonicity of the uterine muscle—that is to say, an increase in the tension of muscular fibres. And this hypothesis has two dire consequences: the first consequence is that these contractions are made useless, because they no longer work towards the dilatation of the cervix, the latter rearing, as it were, by reason of a too brutal eagerness to dilate; the second consequence, deriving from the first, is the danger of causing pain to the foetus—and we shall see presently how dreadful are the results of this.

But what, then, is the pain of childbirth?

The gravid uterus contracts in an intermittent fashion, these contractions being painless though often very powerful; and this may even involve the possibility of a premature diagnosis of pregnancy. Why, therefore, are the uterine contractions of labour painful? Why is childbirth a painful physiological action?

Some authors have held that pain was designed to serve as a warning of imminent parturition. Professor Harteman of Nancy dwells on the risks run by both mother and child if the birth occurs without previous warning signs. This opinion is shared by Kreis of Tarbes, who holds that the warning provided by this pain was indispensable to our ancestors in order to prepare them for the event, since they had no means of knowing the precise date of birth.

Others have held that the pain of childbirth conditioned maternal love. It has, indeed, been demonstrated experimentally that hinds who gave birth to their fawns under an anaesthetic, refused to have anything to do with them; and from this, as well as from some human examples, some would conclude that obstetrical pain is the foundation of maternal love. But is it logical to suppose that maternal love can be in proportion to the intensity of the pains? Have any women been met with, who love their child less intensely because they have been anaesthetized? The converse, indeed, is not always true. An obstetrician has set on record the case of a woman who underwent a very painful first confinement, and who had other children later on under anaesthesia. Involuntarily and unconsciously, she nourished a kind of resentment against her first-born, the child of her pain.

It must be admitted in all honesty that we cannot furnish a valid explanation, at least on the scientific plane, of the suffering felt in the course of a confinement. But this does not prevent our studying its character, its seat, its transmission tracts, and the part played by the general psychic condition in producing it.

What is the *character* of the pains accompanying childbirth? At first, they are endurable, because they are not severe and come with intervals of about ten minutes between them. In the case of the first child, they coincide with the period when the cervix is effaced. During dilatation, the uterine contractions become more frequent—every four or five minutes—last longer—forty to fifty seconds—and grow more severe. It is these pains that one should begin to eliminate or to lessen. During the expulsion, the pains, although still severe, are endured more easily and are less felt, because the muscular effort relieves the area of pain. Finally, during the emergence of the head, the pains become extremely intense because of the considerable distension caused to the vaginal mucous membrane, the muscles, and the particularly sensitive nerve plexus.

What is *the seat of the pain*? The pain is centred in the uterine muscle —with some women, in the body itself; with others, at the level of the cervix. It may be due to a pain in the muscle itself, or more probably to a modification of the circulatory regime, to vaso-constriction, to ischemia, or yet again to a modification of the local nervous system.

The *study of the nervous tracts* which relay the uterine sensation, is more interesting; because the ideal mode of intervention would be to dissociate the sensory ducts from the motor ducts, in order to suppress the pain without modifying the uterine spasm. It emerges from the works of Professor Pigeaud of Lyon that the pre-vertebral and latero-vertebral sympathetic constitutes essentially the specific sensation tract of the pregnant uterus—the tract which transmits to the higher centres the special painful sensations which accompany the uterine spasms of labour. While the uterus remains ordinarily sensitive to injection, for instance, the anaesthetizing of the lombar sympathetic suppresses the pains of childbirth without appreciably modifying the progress of dilatation. But it is not certain that this sympathetic duct is the only one involved, and therefore the sensory tracts must continue to be regarded as very widespread and complex.

However this may be, the sense impressions are transmitted to the higher centre, at the level of a region known as the thalamus. The latter, in its turn, transmits them to the cortical area, which is the centre of a higher activity, which governs and controls all the major life-processes, and consequently the neuro-vegetative functions. This means that the condition of the cortex—or, to put it more directly, the condition of the woman's psychism—can have and does have a considerable influence in deciding the intensity of the impression of pain. We thus enter into the *psycho-somatic* domain; it will be useful, therefore, to deal briefly with some of its aspects.

In the few weeks preceding confinement, the majority of women cannot rid themselves of a certain apprehension—a legitimate and by no means imaginary apprehension, because it is often more marked in the case of women who have already borne children than it is with women in their first pregnancy.

Certain psychic influences are grafted on this psycho-somatic uneasiness: the alarmist words of mothers, mothers-in-law, and friends, as well as the not less harmfully maladroit and conflicting words of encouragement given to the expectant mother. The simple and uncomplicated delivery is, of course, not worth the bother of even mentioning; but cases full of picturesque and melodramatic detail will be lingered over, each pain and each moment of danger being savoured to the full. The result of all this is to implant *fear* in the expectant mother; and it is this fear which increases the intensity of the pain, if indeed it does not to a large extent create that intensity. And experience shows incontestably that women who are already in a state of panic, and who are therefore ill-prepared, are exposed to the most intense pains and find it most difficult to master them. The English writer, Dick Read, who has made a particular study of this aspect of confinement, maintains that fear of the confinement has become the greatest disturbing factor of neuro-muscular harmony. Through its association with "labour," the instinctive desire of maternity has been submerged in what he calls "a restless sea of pain and of danger." Pavlov, he goes on, has shown that elements which give the keenest pleasure will become the very causes of excruciating pain, if they are constantly presented in conjunction with terrifying accompanying circumstances. And he adds that it is in order to escape from the fear rather than from the suffering, that the majority of patients seek analgesia. It can be seen how this idea should be integrated in the procedure known as natural delivery or the Read Method.

Finally, the unknown quantities and the multiplicity of factors which enter into this whole question of pain, already underline the difficulty of obstetrical analgesia, all the more so as the latter must obey certain imperative conditions which we shall now examine.

What, then, are the *conditions* absolutely governing obstetrical analgesia? There are three essential conditions—

(*a*) It must not entail danger for the mother.
(*b*) It must not complicate the delivery.
(*c*) It must not adversely affect the foetus.

Another important though less imperious condition is that it should be easy to carry out and not costly.

It is quite clear that analgesia is forbidden only if the danger to the mother is thereby increased. Complications are certainly more frequent in the course of anaesthesias than in the course of analgesias; but the latter can, however, entail some incidents or accidents, especially in view of the fact that often *a substance induces relief only if it anaesthetizes*.

These accidents will take the form of—

Syncopal or asphyxial conditions;

Pulmonary complications due to the aspiration of the contents of the stomach into the bronchi;

Serious icterus, in the case of chloroform which is toxic to the hepatic cell;

Finally, death itself, especially with spinal anaesthesia.

Pregnancy seems to increase the risk of this technique, as can be seen by comparing the mortality rate of 0·5 per cent in surgical practice, with a mortality rate in obstetrical practice of 3 to 5 per cent, according to the writers on this subject. Such contingencies should always be borne in mind when one decides to use analgesia.

Neither should analgesia *complicate the delivery* by creating what Professor Le Lorier has called "an artificial dystochia." Indeed, one of the disadvantages of analgesia, especially in its generalized form, is that it hinders the motor function of the uterus by diminishing or even eliminating the uterine contractions, and by impeding the expulsive efforts of the terminal period,[1] thus entailing a great increase in the application of forceps in order to induce complete dilatation. Finally, these anaesthetics can obstruct a phenomenon which is indispensable in the course of a delivery—namely, the retraction of the uterus which enables it to effect its hemostasis and to arrest the bleeding of the placental site. This obstruction predisposes the mother to haemorrhages, the especial danger of which is well known.

The third condition, which is perhaps the most difficult to fulfil, is that the analgesia *must not adversely affect the foetus*. This presents the most serious problem, and provides the real touchstone for deciding the legitimacy of analgesia as an obstetrical technique. The child can suffer as a result of analgesia—

Either directly, through the transplacental passage of medicamentous substances (antispasmodics or anaesthetics acting through intoxication); or

Indirectly, through the anoxemic action of these anaesthetic agents. This latter is certainly the major danger.

This anoxemia registers very quickly and very decisively on the central nervous system, whose oxygen needs are proportionately the highest of the entire organism. It runs the risk of entailing more or less considerable lesions, of oedema, of congestion or of haemorrhage, with the consequent risks of suffering and even of death to the foetus

---

[1] The woman under analgesia has neither the will nor the necessary energy to contract her abdominal and perineal muscles.

in the course of labour, and above all the risk of death to the newly-born at birth. Even the newly-born who have escaped these initial accidents, pay a very heavy price later on; many neo-natal pulmonary affections, troubles met with in rearing the newly-born, character troubles, and epileptic syndromes, are caused by these microscopic lesions of the central nervous system. It emerges clearly from all this, that oxygenotherapy must be called upon to fight against this anox-emia. The ideal would be, therefore, to mix oxygen with the anaes-thetic, and this in the highest possible proportions.

Moreover, as was seen above, analgesia increases the number of the forceps, and we know how harmful the forceps can be to the cerebro-meningeal centres of the foetus. Of course, this accusation is too readily hurled by paediatrists, and must be met with a certain reserve; because a forceps, correctly applied to a head well bent on the perinaeum, makes a rapid delivery possible and saves the child from the risks of anoxemia arising from analgesia and from the period of expulsion.

The final conditions demanded of obstetrical analgesia are of a practical order. To be of any practical value a process of analgesia must be *simple*, and must not require *an over-complex instrumentation or a too-numerous personnel*, which would have the effect of limiting it to women of great wealth.

These conditions having been dealt with, we must now turn our attention to the procedures which are available.

There are two main types of obstetrical analgesia—

Those which concentrate on the feeling of pain, by lessening the sensitivity of the central origin through medicamentous inhalatory or parenteral action on the cortical regions;

Those which block the conduction of pain by acting on the sym-pathetic or para-sympathetic nervous system, thus preventing the pain from reaching the cortex.

In each group, we shall deal only with the best known techniques, and we shall end with a discussion of basic anaesthetics and of the Read Method, which is specially noted for its pathogenic conception.

Here, then, is a first group—

Chloroform is the most anciently known procedure, and perhaps the most frequently used even to-day. Used in England for the first time in 1847, it became celebrated through its administration to Queen Victoria in childbirth by Doctor Simpson—whence the name "the queen's anaesthetic." Chloroform is administered in little whiffs during each uterine spasm. Some doctors extol its merits, and prefer it to all the others; while other doctors emphatically proscribe it, because of its toxicity for the liver,[1] the possibility of sudden syncope

---

[1] Because, in order to be effective, analgesia requires a great quantity of chloroform.

through adrenaline-chloroformic discharge, and its too sluggish elimination which exposes the child to a depression of the respiratory centres.

Cyclopropane is an excellent anaesthetic, at least in theory. It acts with remarkable effectiveness and rapidity on the pain, and the cessation of sleep is equally rapid when the mask is removed. It entails no danger for the foetus, especially since it can be mixed with at least 90 per cent of oxygen. However, its use meets with a certain number of difficulties. It demands the presence of an anaesthetist at the bedside of the pregnant woman, because it can be administered only in a closed circuit, and is not without danger, since it can form an explosive mixture with the air or with the oxygen. It is also very expensive.

Nitrous Oxide, in association with oxygen in scientific proportions —35 per cent and more of oxygen—is one of the most interesting agents of obstetrical analgesia, because of the rapidity of its action. The degree of analgesia necessary to suppress or at least considerably diminish the pain of a contraction, can be obtained so rapidly that it is not necessary to begin the inhalation before the onset of the contraction; two or three deep breaths are sufficient. Its elimination is also quasi-instantaneous. Moreover, it has not a disagreeable odour, and it readily combines with other anaesthetics. Various types of apparatus have been devised which enable the woman in labour to administer the anaesthetic mixture to herself.

Trichlorethylene or Trilene is very popular at the present time, since it was brought to a satisfactory state of purity and its stability was assured. The main interest here is that it induces real analgesia even before the loss of consciousness; and this has the advantage of allowing the analgesia to be continued throughout the period of labour without eliminating the co-operation of the pregnant woman at the expulsion period. It is harmless both to mother and to child, and is cheap. It should be noted, however, that trilene must never be used in a closed circuit, because its contact with the soda lime results in the production of very toxic products.

The second group comprises—

Rachianaesthesia (Spinal anaesthesia). Exceptional indications must exist in the domain of analgesia before this process is resorted to. Its advantages are that it effects a temporary suppression of the pain (about an hour), induces a complete and rapid relaxation of the tension of the cervix and of the lower segment of the uterus, and also a perfect retraction after delivery which considerably diminishes the risk of haemorrhage. But all this must not and cannot blind us to its serious disadvantages: cephalalgias, phenomena of hypotension which can even be fatal, nervous consequences, and a mortality of 3 to 5 per cent.

There is only one indication for it, and this is the rapid termination of a pregnancy through the base duct (the Delmas method); but then we are no longer dealing with analgesia.

Infiltration of the lumbar sympathetic is, in the opinion of Professor Pigeaud of Lyon, one of the safest and most important ways of obtaining a good analgesia in the course of a delivery. A left unilateral injection of 40 to 60 cm^3 of a solution of percaine in the proportion 1 to 150, which can be conveniently carried out at the level of L2–L3, induces an efficacious anaesthetic infiltration of the pre-vertebral and latero-vertebral lumbar sympathetic. This infiltration suppresses the centripetal nervous conduction of the utero-lumbar root of the hypogastric plexus, and, without notably affecting the uterine dynamic, suppresses the pains of childbirth for a period averaging two hours. This infiltration can be repeated if necessary. We have here a very remarkable process of analgesia. The failures have only been 5 per cent of cases, and the process is perfectly harmless both for the mother and for the child.

Continuous caudal anaesthesia is an extremely attractive process which is simply the ancient epidural anaesthesia brought to perfection. Specially recommended by Hingson of Philadelphia, who is at once its promoter and its enthusiastic advocate, continuous caudal anaesthesia can be regarded as ideal. It consists in introducing through the sacral hiatus a semi-stiff trocar through which a long supple nylon catheter is pushed, the latter rising to the area of the first lumbar segment. An analgesic solution is then pushed into the peri-dural space, and this solution bathes both the medullary roots and the rami-communicacations. Thus, peripheral analgesia of the nerves of the sympathetic and parasympathetic conduction is effected.

The clinical results of this analgesia are very remarkable. The process is certainly effective, because the pains are completely suppressed while the contractions continue. The child *in utero* is not, so to speak, involved in this process, and it is notable that Hingson's results are especially favourable in cases of premature birth—a fact which constitutes a criterion of the highest value.

Unfortunately, certain technical characteristics of the process condemn its systematic and widespread use in normal deliveries. It demands specialists who are perfectly familiar with this particular technique, because its application is not easy. Apart from the risk of infection (which has sometimes led to meningitis and osteitis) and apart from a certain proportion of failures (7 per cent), there are certain conditions of the sacral hiatus which render the process impossible or dangerous.

Certain substances are also used either to strengthen or to prepare an analgesia, and these are known as basic anaesthetics. The more important ones are—

Morphine which acts on the painful contractions. Its use may be indicated especially when the contractions are too intense or when there is uterine hypertony. But the great disadvantage of morphine is that it diminishes the excitability of the respiratory centre. Its administration in the last hour of the delivery is not to be recommended, since such administration may cause the child to be born in a profoundly anoxemic and narcotized condition.

Dolosal which is an antispasmodic and a parasympathicolytic, and, like strophine, acts on the cerebral centre of the pain. It is administered through duct I.M. or I.V. in a dose of 10 cgr., repeatable 3 or 4 times in the course of the labour. It is a good basic anaesthetic.

Spasmalgine which combines pantopon, papaverine, atropine, and which is administered through duct S.C. or I.M., and even through I.V. when the action must be rapid. This product is much used to-day in obstetrics, both because of its action on the pain and its effect on the uterine contractions. This action shows itself in an acceleration of dilatation in the case of cervical spasms; and in certain cases, it shows itself in an increase of the intervals between contractions, in a regularizing of irregular contractions, in a subsidence of hypertonus, and in a neutralization of the excessive action caused by the ocytocics.

Scopolamine which suppresses consciousness of painful feelings, and at the same time effects a blockage of the parasympathetic, which blockage is particularly useful in pregnancy. But the disadvantage is that, in provoking a considerable excitation of the cortex, one actuates at the same time a quasi-immediate tendency to the production of oedemas and to a depression of the respiratory centre.

In the interests of simplification, we shall include here *curare*, which is not an anaesthetic. It paralyses the striated muscles and has no effect on the smooth muscles. It cancels to some extent the resistance which the perineal muscles offer to the expulsion of the foetal head. One can thus curtail indirectly the woman's sufferings, and diminish the risk of perineal laceration. That is the reason why we mention it here.

Finally, we cannot end this brief glance at the processes of obstetrical analgesia without dealing with a technique which originates from a completely different principle: *the Grantly Read Method*, which Professor Thoms of Newhaven in Connecticut has been using for several years. It is based on the physical and psychological preparation of pregnant women for their delivery.

The physical preparation is carried out by doctors and especially by monitresses who assemble these women and put them through a course of gymnastic movements aimed at strengthening the abdominal, lumbar, and femoral muscles, and especially at rendering supple the ligaments of the articulations of the pelvian and peri-pelvian regions. It is less a question of exercises as understood in classic gymnastics, for the emphasis is put on movements made in the ordinary course of the day, especially when doing housework.

The psychological preparation consists, first of all, in educating the women. They receive a course of instruction about pregnancy and about the delivery itself; they are taught about the mechanism of the uterine contraction, the dilatation of the cervix, and the progression of the foetus, and it is made clear to them that all these phenomena are linked with clearly defined anatomical processes. Finally, they are taught how to settle themselves most comfortably during their lying-in period, both during and apart from the uterine contractions. They are instructed how to co-operate at the moment of the expulsion of the foetus.

Read has said that in the case of a hundred women who followed the course, there were less forceps, less use of anaesthetics, less maternal and foetal morbidity, than in the case of a control group with whom a comparison was made.

It would seem that this technique is equally widespread in the U.S.S.R. where it is known as the psychoprophylactic technique.

The great merit of this method is that it shows *the importance of the psychic factor* in the preparation of women for delivery, and also demonstrates the improvement in the mechanics of expulsion achieved through physical exercises.

There is a final aspect, or more accurately a final consequence, of painless childbirth, which is not without interest and which must be indicated briefly before we go on to show how one can carry out an obstetrical analgesia. "To suppress the pain is to inhibit the motor function," wrote Professor Vignes. Now, in order to mitigate the diminution of the uterine contractions, doctors have recourse to sub-stances capable of exciting the uterus—to ocytocics, the chief of which is pituitrin; whence the frequent association of the two methods. Furthermore, certain doctors have held that the more rapid the labour, the easier it will be to induce analgesia and the less serious will be the consequences of doing so. And immediately one exceeds the strict limits of obstetrical analgesia, and one verges, insensibly but none the less really, towards the more or less explicit idea of directed medical delivery—or, as some have called it, methodically rapid delivery.

The Delalande Method combines an anaesthetic and an ocytocic, in the form of chlorokelene (25 per cent of chloroform and 75 per cent of ethylic chloride) and an ocytocic (pituitrin). The method enters in when all the conditions for a favourable and rapid completion of delivery are present: absence of disproportion: the head well bent, advanced or at least fixed; a cervix whose degree of dilatation and of suppleness is of less importance than its thinness. Two elements must vary harmoniously with each other in order to obtain a perfect result—

(*a*) Pituitrin, of which Delalande recommends a very strong dose. The dose may vary with the susceptibility of the uterine muscle, but excessive timidity already dooms the experiment to failure.

(*b*) The anaesthetic, which one then begins to administer, and which will play a role of regulator and of curb on uterine contractility. While it kills the feeling of pain in the woman, it at the same time relaxes the cervix and moderates the body.

Finally, there has been some instances recently, by Belgian authors, on the worth of intra-venous perfusions of pituitrin, which present the following advantages: the doses are weaker and more manageable; the perfusion can be arrested at will; and the effect on uterine contractions is profound.

But with this matter we have entered into a very complex domain where the legitimacy of this practice is highly debatable and a source of scandal to more orthodox doctors, because the chief victim of this therapy, however mild it may be, will always be the foetus.

How should an obstetrical analgesia be realized in practice?

We lay down at the outset, as essential principles, that an analgesia should not be contemplated except in a clinic or maternity home which provides a minimum of material guarantees; and only under the supervision and on the responsibility of a duly qualified doctor, assisted by a nurse or a midwife trained in anaesthesia. In these conditions, major complications will be avoided, or at least they can be remedied in the best conditions. It is better not to undertake an analgesia than to carry it out badly.

We shall deal only with the case of the *firstborn*, because the problem is more simple with later births where the pains are often less severe, or at all events not so long and more easily endured. Let us suppose that Trilene is used. We must recall, in the first place, the full importance of the psychological preparation before the lying-in period, and how necessary it is that the mother-to-be should reach the end of her pregnancy in excellent physical condition.

At the first onset of the pains, the woman goes to a clinic where the doctor receives and examines her in order to show that he is taking her case in hand and that she is not going to be asked to cope with it unaided. The doctor must also insist on the calm and tranquillity which should be felt by a woman in labour. She should also be put in a special room with soft light, far from bustle and noise.

During the period of the taking-up of the cervix and the beginning of dilatation, the pains are usually more endurable, and are most often diminished by dolosal, spasmalgine, or dolosal-phenergan mixture.

During this period, the woman is taught how to apply the mask correctly, how to calculate the beginning of uterine contractions; how to take large inhalations as soon as she feels a contraction, in order to hasten the analgesia; and how to cease from these inhalations as soon as the pain begins to lessen.

It is important to begin the analgesia before the onset of the major pains. The women are much more calm at this stage and more attentive to explanations which will enable them to carry out the analgesia in an effective manner; and it should be borne in mind that a period of from 15 to 30 minutes is sometimes necessary to allow the woman to familiarize herself with the apparatus. As a matter of fact, failures are always due to the fact that the analgesia was begun too late when the women were in an agitated condition.

The apparatus should be given at once to the woman, in order to give her a sense of confidence.

The apparatus should first be set at a minimal concentration in order to prevent the impression of slight suffocation which the higher regulations of the apparatus can provoke. In this way, the woman gains confidence in the method, because at the outset she experiences no discomfort. But this concentration is generally insufficient, and the strength of the anaesthetic must be increased gradually, after five to ten uterine contractions, in an endeavour to decide what is the dose which is capable of provoking an appropriate analgesia.

One must act gradually, because at least ten minutes are needed to obtain a state of saturation which will result in the beginning of the pains being deadened by the basic analgesia provoked by previous inhalations —the new inhalation acting, in fact, only as a reinforcing element.

This analgesia lasts from 3 to 5 hours, and sometimes longer. Even more than in the course of a normal delivery, it is necessary to exercise vigilance over: the mother—in order to calculate the number and the intensity of the uterine contractions; the infant—by listening to the heartbeats, and examining the amniotic fluid after the rupture of the amniotic sac.

Thus the period of complete liberation—the period of expulsion— is gradually reached.

The great advantage of Trilene is that it does not suppress consciousness, and therefore allows of expulsive efforts.

During the emergence of the head, it is recommended that the doctor himself should direct the analgesia, and continue it to the stage of slight anaesthesia.

These, then, are the medical aspects of painless childbirth. As we have seen, the whole matter is much more complex than would appear from the enthusiastic articles in periodicals giving a "popular" and incompetent account of the progress of medicine.

In conclusion, we must emphasize that the term "painless childbirth" is very equivocal. It is less a question of "putting the patient to sleep," than of mitigating certain intolerable pains. Many voices have been raised, in the name of morality and of religion, to condemn a method which is stigmatized as materialistic and anti-Christian because it seeks to suppress pain completely. A better-informed public opinion will realize that the end in view is to save the woman from suffering beyond certain limits, and to reduce the dangers of the delivery for the foetus. Such a result has been obtained only through the progress made in the knowledge of anaesthesia, and through a better understanding of the physiopathology of "labour." And this is only one aspect of the battle which the doctor is fighting against pain.

DOCTEUR MICHEL CHARTIER
Interne des Hôpitaux de Paris

ANALGESICS AND CHRISTIAN PERFECTION

Is the desire to lessen physical pain in conformity with the spirit of the Gospel?

At first glance, the question may appear somewhat disconcerting when one remembers the number of times Christ healed the sick, and when one recalls the parable of the good Samaritan which He related to His disciples as a model for their conduct.

But it is equally true that the cross stands in the centre of Christianity, and that it teaches us that there can be no salvation without shedding of blood. In imitation of the crucified Christ, the Christian should know how to endure the trials of this life, not in a spirit of stoicism but in a spirit of faith. We know that many of the saints carried this imitation to a sublime degree; not content with enduring the hardships that came their way, they sought out suffering: "either to suffer or to die," was a saying of St. Teresa of Avila.

The problem, therefore, is not merely an abstract one. If the Christian should not accept anything which lessens his sufferings; or if, at all events, he would be choosing the better course by refusing such assuagements—then why not go on to question the propriety of our attempts to lessen the sufferings of others?

What is the answer to this difficulty? Must we, once again, fling an anathema at the modern world, at science and at the assistance which science brings to suffering humanity? Must we lament over the effeminacy engendered by material civilization? Or must we, on the contrary, distrust the effort, the courage in enduring pain, the asceticism, which discards the joys of living and the glow of well-being?

The answer cannot be found in these extreme positions, because, in fact, both veer away from reality in order to devise a purely intellectual and abstract system.

As is so often the case, Christianity affirms two equally incontestable truths in this connection, and it is for us to reconcile them if we can. This is not as difficult as it might appear.

* * *

The first of these truths contains an answer to our question, and this answer stems directly from the example and the teaching of Christ— the example and the teaching of charity. We must assist one another in all our needs and sufferings. It is thus that the Church, the inheritor of the spirit of Christ, looks on this matter.

It has, perhaps, never been sufficiently emphasized that the care of the old, of abandoned children, and of the sick, begins in history with the coming of Christianity. The idea of such care was born with Christianity and developed with Christianity. The hospital—that sociological phenomenon which seems such a characteristic of our civilization; that centre of medical science and of the fight against disease—had its origin, like so many other works of mercy, in the Christian society. And, in the Middle Ages, the hospital in France was called *la Maison-Dieu*.

The disciples of Christ, therefore, very quickly recognized that the healing of the sick is one of the activities most imperiously commanded by charity.

Continuing this long tradition, Pope Pius XII said recently in this discourse to doctors (April 26th, 1952): "The grandeur of your task, gentlemen, is that it makes you to be real collaborators with God in the defending and the enriching of His creation. It is in this sense that Holy Scripture says of the doctor that 'God has created him' (Eccles. xxxviii, 1). He has created him to be the instrument of His mercy in assuaging the sufferings of his brethren. . . . The doctor is a blessing from God."

This attitude of pity is not to be interpreted, therefore, as a concession to the ideas of our time. It expresses a fundamental demand of the Christian religion. Christ is the Saviour of the whole man; He does not distinguish between this part of man which is to be saved, and this other part which is to be neglected, but He deals with the whole man in order to restore man to his primitive integrity. Of course, the salvation can become whole and entire only in the next life, but it is already begun here on earth. It begins first of all in the soul which, if the soul so wishes, is healed of its wounds and received into the friendship of God; but it also extends to the body, even though as yet in a more inchoate and incomplete fashion. And, since all man's evils are regarded as enemies by Christ, it follows that this fight against evils, this striving for liberation from them, must be affirmed constantly by Christianity and must reach to every part of human life.

Since, therefore, charity demands that we should succour disease in order to restore to the patient the use of his strength and his faculties, it cannot be forbidden to combat the effects of disease, and is not pain one of the principal of such effects? Moreover, even when it is not the result of a serious biological disorder, does not physical suffering often result in depressing the person and weakening his moral resistance? Consequently, it is always a work of defence or of reparation which is involved—a work rendered legitimate by the good at which it aims.

But this must not be read as a disruption of the very foundations of asceticism and a shattering of the Christian's spiritual energy, because here again we encounter a demand of Christianity. This is the second truth of which we spoke above: the example of the Garden of Olives and of Calvary must never be forgotten. Neither our own salvation nor that of the world can be effected unless we participate in this redemption through suffering—(i.e. through suffering in union with Christ's Passion we can participate in our own salvation and that of the world.—Editor). But if the modern doctor assuages pain more than his ancient confrères, is this really because the human condition has undergone, on the whole, a great change? Is it not true to-day, as in the era before anaesthetics, that the human condition comprises its quota of difficulties, of sufferings and of trials, which provides many opportunities for strengthening the will, for uniting oneself with the crucified Christ in a spirit of faith, if one wishes to avail of them? The assuagement of suffering which we accept for ourselves or which we bring to others will always be very limited. Consequently, it is always perfectly legitimate.

* * *

It was at the beginning of the XIXth century that, through the progress of chemistry, the decisive step was taken in the war against pain. For it was then discovered that the buccal or respiratory absorption of certain substances resulted in a lessening of physical suffering, and even, with certain doses, a complete loss of consciousness. This new medical discovery necessarily raised certain deontological problems which sometimes called for delicate solution.

If we consider not so much the nature of these chemical bodies as the use to which they can be put, we discover that they can be placed in three categories: drugs, anaesthetics and analgesics.

Drugs are used apart from all medical practice, in order to induce a euphoria or even an intoxication wherein the miseries of life can be forgotten.

Anaesthetics are used in surgical operations in order to suspend local sensitivity to pain, or in order to provide a complete loss of consciousness.

Analgesics are sedatives which lessen or even completely suppress pain, while leaving the patient conscious and master of himself.

With one exception, we shall concern ourselves exclusively in these pages with analgesics and their use. And we shall study three principal cases: painless childbirth; the risk of creating drug habits; and the succouring of the dying.

Painless childbirth

This is the exception to which we referred, for it involves an aesthesia, not an analgesia. It is the only use of anaesthetics which is questioned, and that is why we deal with it here, since no difficulty can be raised from a moral point of view with regard to the other cases, provided the dictates of prudence are respected.

It should be noted that the first use of chloroform was directed towards easing the pains of childbirth. It is a matter of history that, in 1852, Queen Victoria called in the Scots doctor, Simpson, the initiator of the method, to assist at the birth of one of her children.

Protests were, it can easily be understood, forthcoming from certain religious groups. Did not this method run directly counter to the word of God to the banished Eve: "Thou shalt bring forth children in sorrow." Moreover, the opponents of the new procedure pointed out, there is nothing pathological about the birth of a baby, apart from certain cases of malformation and complications; and therefore, in the course of this most natural of human processes, there is no reason why aids should be given which are justified only by disease or by abnormal conditions.

Furthermore, they urge, is this anaesthesia absolutely harmless to the mother and to the child? There are physical dangers for the child, and psychological and moral dangers for the mother. Does not the pain of childbirth, bravely endured, constitute an essential element of maternal feeling, in that deeper ties of affection unite the mother with the child whose birth has caused her so much pain? Recent experiments, indeed, seem to confirm these contemporary attacks on James Young Simpson, because it has been established that female animals, anaesthetized during parturition, rejected their offspring and treated them as strangers.

However, a fact that should be noticed is that the opposition to the new method was much more lively among Protestants, especially in Scotland, than among Catholics. The reason for this is probably the much greater tendency among Protestants towards a literal interpretation of the Scriptures. In the XIXth century textbooks of Moral Theology which we have been able to consult, we have not met the least allusion to this question, a fact which shows that it presented no difficulty to the moralists.

Nevertheless, a widespread attitude of suspicion persists among many Catholics. What should we think, therefore, of the arguments which we have just summarized, and which are at the root of this feeling of uneasiness? They have no real validity. Exegetes have long since pointed out that the words of God, in Genesis, constitute the declaration of a *de facto* state of affairs, rather than a command or a malediction. Furthermore, whatever interpretation one prefers, these words—"Thou shalt bring forth children in sorrow"—do not envisage exclusively the final act of childbirth, but the pregnancy as a whole. Now, in spite of all the assuagements provided by modern medicine, it is incontestable that, with the majority of women, pregnancy imposes sacrifices and sufferings of all kinds. As to the actual delivery, Dr. Chartier has pointed out in his article that there it is never, strictly speaking, painless. The most that can be hoped for is a diminution of these sufferings in so far as they are too severe. There is therefore no real objection to such assuagement, provided every care is taken that the child does not suffer as a result.

The assuagement of the dying

It is a well-known fact that euthanasia has been accepted in certain countries, especially in some parts of the United States. But in this domain, as in that of all human relations, the moral ruling still remains the old precept of the Decalogue: "Thou shalt not kill the just and the innocent." Apart from cases of legitimate defence of individuals or of societies, to provoke voluntarily and directly the death of another is always homicide, and to kill oneself either directly or through the ministrations of another person is always suicide. And both these actions are absolutely forbidden by the Moral Law.

We are not concerned here with these extreme cases, which are dealt with in another section of this book under the heading *Euthanasia*; we are concerned with aids which can be given to patients whose life is in danger and who are suffering excessively, even though sometimes these aids are emergency treatments which seem, at first sight, akin to euthanasia.

Two questions arise in this connection. Is it permissible to render a dying person completely unconscious in order to deliver him from his sufferings? And may one attempt to lessen the agony of a dying person at the risk of hastening his death?

Towards the first question, a whole school of moralists adopt a reserved or even resolutely negative attitude. The motives for this condemnation have been summarized, in the XIXth century, by a Canadian Council: "The patients would no longer have the opportunity of performing acts of piety; they would be deprived of the final merits which they could otherwise gain, and would be exposed to eternal loss." What is demanded for the Christian, therefore, as an inalienable right, is the opportunity of courageously supporting the sufferings of the final hour, of looking death in the face by consciously accepting the will of God and by uniting himself in spirit with the Passion of Christ. Death is the supreme trial, the occasion for the greatest act of faith and of love which man can make towards the Supreme Will of his Creator. Thus it is that, in the midst of its final humiliation and miseries, human nature can attain to its moment of finest grandeur. To deprive it of this power is to run counter to its real good.

Some theologians, however, while fully accepting these truths as part of the most authentic Christianity, believe that they can legitimately adopt a less rigorous attitude.

On condition that the dying person has set his worldly affairs in order, and above all that he has made an act of submission to the Divine decrees in his regard and has received the Sacraments, these theologians do not regard it as morally forbidden to render a patient unconscious if, tortured with pain, he is in danger of falling into despair and blaspheming the goodness of God.

But it must be emphatically stressed that this is completely different in every way from an attitude very often adopted, which consists in keeping the patient in complete ignorance of his condition and in rendering him unconscious in order to hide from him the proximity of death. Every Christian must repudiate such conduct.

The second problem in connection with the dying is that of the hastening of death caused by the very attempt to assuage suffering. The doctor may be dealing with a patient who is suffering intensely but whose suffering can be assuaged only with difficulty and by inducing a state of general insensibility through sedative injections—of morphine, for example. Is this euthanasia? Certainly not, because there is no intention of inducing a speedy death. The direct purpose and the immediate result of the injection is to diminish the pain. If one had at hand a means which makes this diminution possible without entailing inevitable death, one would use that means.

Consequently, if the conditions indicated are fulfilled, there is no reason why it should be unlawful to run the risk of hastening death. These conditions, once again, are: that the patient has prepared himself for death as perfectly as he can; that the sufferings he is to endure are intolerable; and that the doctor confines his doses to quantities which are absolutely necessary to induce at least a relative reduction of suffering.

The establishment of drug habits

By using certain sedatives in the treatment of persons suffering from serious diseases or recovering from an operation, does not one run the risk of creating in such persons cravings which will accompany them when they leave the hospital and which will lead to habits of toxicomania? The danger is not an imaginary one, especially in certain circumstances, as for example when the illness is protracted or when it is necessary to submit the patient to a series of successive operations entailing severe sufferings. Sometimes it will be possible to avoid this serious consequence by using sedatives which do not entail this risk, or by keeping the doses below danger-strength. But there will be cases where the effect will be inevitable, both because of the nature of the treatment that must be given and because of the patient's temperament. A grave obligation rests, therefore, on the doctor in question; he must not discharge the patient without inviting him, with all possible urgency, to undergo a course of disintoxication. Otherwise, he may be adding another toxicomaniac to the number already existing.

Anaesthesia and analgesia are great blessings, and one is therefore justified in accepting them oneself or in using them on others. But it is obvious that their use by any man who respects human values, must always be in accordance with the dictates of the virtue of prudence— a condition which is a general one for the use of all technical procedures.

REV. E. TESSON, S.J.
Professeur à la Faculté de Théologie de Paris

THE DISCOVERY OF ANAESTHETICS

THE history of anaesthetics is one of the most outstanding episodes in man's warfare on pain. Although man's preoccupation with suppressing or at least reducing physical suffering dates from the first days of his creation, it was not, however, until the XIXth century that the doctor first succeeded in inducing the first complete anaesthesia.

There were, of course, precursors whose work must not be forgotten; but it is a fact that anaesthesia has celebrated its centenary only a short time ago. We are dealing, therefore, with a science which is still very young and still in course of development.

The discovery of ether goes back to the era of the alchemists, when Raymond Lulle saw rising up from his philtres a white liquid which he called "sweet vitriol." But two centuries were to pass before Paracelsus again discovered this "white water" when he was condensing a vapour from a mixture of sulphur and alcohol. Going a step beyond his predecessor, he experimented with this mixture on chickens which, he said, "drank it willingly and then fell into a deep sleep, from which they awakened after a certain time without having suffered any ill effects from it." This observation, made in an era when science was still in its "descriptive period," was destined to be buried in the imposing pharmacopoeia collected by a disciple of Paracelsus, the apothecary Cordus.

Several centuries were to pass before medical inability to suppress pain artificially caused by the surgeon, began to trouble men's minds. Thus, in the XVIIIth century, less than a hundred years before the discovery of anaesthesia, we find the barber-surgeon Bailly of Troyes summoned before the courts for having attempted to put his patients to sleep by administering vegetable juices. Guy Patin, professor of the University of Paris and a celebrated practitioner of his day, protested against this imprudent doctor and against "this system which as yet has worked no miracle." It was thereupon forbidden, under pain of severe sanctions, to render patients insensible.

It was the discovery of a new science—Chemistry—which lifted Medicine out of this rut.

In 1773, an English pastor of Leeds, Joseph Priestley, discovered nitrous oxide, a powerful anaesthetic. In his leisure hours, this pastor liked to stroll into a neighbouring brewery, and there watch for a long time the little bubbles of air which form on the surface of a fermenting liquid. The workers were amused at this dreamer who took such a great interest in so commonplace a fact; and the chemist, Black, when consulted, dismissed the whole matter by saying that this phenomenon consisted quite simply, of "globules of fixed air." Priestly was not satisfied with such explanations; he continued his investigations and succeeded in isolating from this phenomenon a chemically pure gas—carbon dioxide gas. He resigned from his ministry in order to devote himself to science, and discovered, one after the other, sulphuric acid, hydrochloric acid, and finally, by heating iron filings damped with nitric acid, he discovered nitrous oxide.

But Priestley was not content with discovering these new substances. Already, in connection with his experiments on the production of pure oxygen, he recounts, in his book: *Essays and Observations on Different Kinds of Air*, how the idea came to him of studying the action of this gas on the body. Having observed that a flame burned more intensely under the action of this gas, he deduced that it could be usefully employed for pulmonary diseases, where the normal adduction of the air is not sufficient. He proceeded to test out the effects on himself of absorbing a certain quantity by means of a pump. He immediately experienced a feeling of a greater freedom and lightness in his chest. Who knows, he goes on to ask, whether these inhalations of vital air will not be used in the future as a luxury? "Up to the present," he says, "apart from myself only two mice have enjoyed this privilege."

Led by a spirit of deduction, Priestley revealed a new method of absorption. Is not the lung, by reason of its extensive surface, the organ which most rapidly introduces active substances into the blood stream? Furthermore, since the absorption and elimination of gas are effected through the mechanism of respiration, cannot the doctor easily control the dosage of this gas?

After having studied the effects of oxygen, Priestley was preparing to study those of nitrous oxide when he was again taken up with theological disputation and abandoned his scientific work.

However, Priestley's idea continued to germinate. "Pneumatic Medicine" began to establish itself, and recourse was had to gas in order to combat troubles of the respiratory organs—in the case of asthma, for example. But nitrous oxide continued to be regarded as a harmful gas, the first attempts at using it having often proved fatal. This disfavour served only to increase the interest taken in it by the young Humphrey Davy, then an apothecary's apprentice in Penzance. In 1798, he read Priestley's book on gases, and secretly produced the dangerous drug. One night, he decided to experiment on himself and he inhaled this famous gas; instead of dying as a result, he found himself seized with a new and strange feeling of joy which induced an uncontrollable hilarity in him. Continuing his experiments, he also discovered the anaesthetic effects of the product; but, having been surprised by his employer in one of his solitary crises of incomprehensible gaiety, he was immediately dismissed.

Humphrey Davy had, however, the good fortune to be then engaged by Dr. Beddoes, the celebrated director of the "Pneumatological Institute" of Clifton, near Bristol. This centre of "pneumatic medicine" was also a research laboratory, and Davy could at last devote himself to real research. He continued his experiments on himself, and soon extended them to his friends. Among them was the poet, Coleridge, who gave one of the first descriptions of the effects of "laughing gas" in a style far removed from that of classic observations. He described the "voluptuous sensations" and the "marvellous visions" he experienced in those "three and a half minutes" when he lived in a "world of new feelings."

From the very beginning of his experiments, Davy had noticed that the inhalation of his gas caused migraine and toothache to disappear; and he deduced logically from this that it could eliminate pain. This "laughing gas" seemed to be able to appease physical pain; was it not therefore reasonable, he argued, to recommend its use against surgical pain? Davy might have gone on to discover anaesthesia; but, caught up with other chemical researches, he gave no further thought to the medical application of his gas. Moreover, certain doctors, alarmed by the fact that the pulse of patients treated with this gas showed disquieting signs of slackening, began to throw discredit on the work of Davy. As yet, the fame of the gas was only its power to induce an intoxicating sense of well-being.

Twenty years later, one of Davy's disciples, Faraday, made a passing observation (*Journal of Art and Science*, 1818) in which he mentions the first anaesthesia. Having remarked that a mixture of ether and ordinary air, when inhaled has a similar effect to that of "laughing gas," he records the case of a man who excessively inhaled some ether and, as a result, was plunged into a lethargic condition which, with some interruptions, lasted thirty hours. But Faraday was not interested in medicine, and this recorded fact went unheeded.

Thus all the attempts towards discovering a remedy against pain, appear to have been systematically stifled at the very moment when they seemed about to succeed. This is surely due to the fact that, up to then, none of the researchers had been really in close contact with human suffering. As laboratory scientists, they carried out their researches with zeal but not with a passionate sense of mission. When other tasks called them, they abandoned their first purpose without a scruple. Only a doctor could discover, in the daily pattern of his life, the necessary incentive without which no discovery is carried to its conclusion. At least, it would seem so from a reading of history.

A young doctor of Ludlow, in England, Henry Hill Hickman, could not resign himself to the infliction of atrocious surgical pains on his patients. He was in near agreement with the definition of a surgeon as "simply a savage armed with a lancet," as John Hunter has put it. Chancing to visit Shiffnal, where Dr. Beddoes was born, he heard about "pneumatic medicine" and about the labours of Priestley, Davy, and Faraday. On his return to Ludlow, he devoted all his leisure time to the study of gases. Experimenting on animals, he induced a condition of absolute lethargy which enabled him to carry out serious ablation without the animals evincing any sign of pain.

He had then to seek approval for his method from the scientific authorities, in order to transfer his experiments to man. When he met with a hostile reception in England, Hickman turned to France and appealed to the Paris Academy of Medicine. The result was that he received a condemnation in full and due form from this learned assembly, in its session of September 29th, 1828. Returned to England, Hickman died some months later, at the age of twenty-nine.

Can it be said that this lack of interest in the assuaging of pain, shown by the medical élite of both England and France, was general? At that time, Velpeau wrote: "The idea of performing surgical operations without pain is a utopian dream which it is no longer possible for us to indulge. A cutting instrument and pain, in surgery, are two concepts which are always linked together in the minds of our patients; and we surgeons must accept this association of ideas." And Liston, in England, saw no other solution except a limitation of surgical operations. But there were other, more humane surgeons, who began to think, with Dupuytren, that "pain kills just as haemorrhage does."

It is to America that the credit goes for having provided a practical answer to all these tentative reflections. Davy's discovery of "laughing gas" had there taken its place as something with which to entertain one's friends. It was amusing, during parties, to administer a little of the gas to volunteers and watch the effects. In fact, Davy's discovery became socially popular, for this was the era of the American "ether-parties."

In the course of a party of this kind, a young doctor from the village of Jefferson in the Southern States, Dr. Cramfort Williamson Long, noticed the insensibility of his friends when they were under the influence of ether. He tells us how he remarked that they beat and pummelled one another with a violence which would normally have caused pain; but that when he later questioned them, they all said they had felt nothing. Therefore, had he not found, in what everyone regarded merely as an amusement, the remedy against pain? He broached the matter to one of his patients who was suffering from two small tumours on the nape of his neck, and this patient agreed to inhale a strong dose of ether and to submit to an operation. The exaeresis was immediately carried out without causing the least pain to the patient, and thus Long succeeded in performing the first surgical operation under anaesthesia. But he did not possess the unshakeable faith of the researcher whom nothing can daunt, or the scientific knowledge of the expert who assembles his proofs to buttress a creative intuition, or the necessary strength of character to stand up to the united opposition of his fellow-doctors. After eight operations under anaesthesia, he yielded to the force of massed opinion which branded his method as highly dangerous. All this happened in 1842.

Nevertheless, it was again during an "ether-party" in December, 1844, that a dentist called Horace Wells, aged twenty-six, made the same observation: a man under the influence of ether fumes does not feel the pain of his wounds. On the verge of being a declared bank-rupt, Wells thought that he could use this idea to inaugurate painless dental extraction, and thus replenish his coffers. But in his anxiety to make money, he did not trouble to investigate the necessary doses to be given, or the manner in which this gas should be inhaled. He gave up dentistry and became a picture-dealer.

But Wells's attempt, which received the limelight of publicity, were followed attentively by a Boston dentist, William Thomas Green Morton. This dentist took the wise precaution of submitting to the guidance of a chemist, Dr. Jackson, and thus perfected a technique which enabled him, in 1846, to perform painless extractions.

Far from being satisfied with the clientele who besieged him, Morton glimpsed the import of his process for the whole field of surgery. He quitted his dental practice and devoted himself to research. He perfected an inhaling apparatus for ether fumes, tried it out on animals and on himself until he was satisfied with it, and then proposed to Dr. Warren, chief surgeon of the General Hospital, that it should be tried out on the patients. Conquered by the assurance and the enthusiasm of the inventor, Warren agreed to attempt an operation under ether.

The operation took place before a hostile audience, on October 16th, 1846, and was a complete success. The distrust of the medical body was immediately swept away, and within a few months anaesthesia under ether became the current practice.

It only remained to find a name for the Morton process, and this was done by the poet-doctor, Oliver Wendell Holmes. In a letter to

Morton a few days after the operation, he points out that, as everyone wishes to add his contribution to the discovery, the only thing he could do would be to suggest a good name for it. He suggested "anaesthesia," which, he says, is a near synonym for "insensibility"; the adjective, he goes on, would thus be "anaesthetic," and the product employed could be called "the anaesthetizing agent."

Less than a year after the first painless operation at the Massachusetts General Hospital, an Edinburgh doctor had the idea of extending this new technique to pregnant women. James Young Simpson, chief doctor of the maternity section of Edinburgh Infirmary, had long been seeking a means of diminishing the pains of his patients; and now, with this new technique, he attempted to carry out the first painless deliveries. His attempts failed because the women were seized with very violent vomitings. Then a Liverpool pharmacist advised him to use a new product, called chloroform, which had been discovered by an American army surgeon in 1831 and whose chemical formula was later established by the French scientist, Dumas. On November 4th, 1847, Simpson carried out his first delivery under chloroform; and six days later, he presented to the Edinburgh Surgical Society a paper dealing with fifty deliveries under anaesthesia. One would have thought that Edinburgh would have welcomed this new technique of Simpson's—Edinburgh which had become a celebrated centre of surgery, thanks to Joseph Lister who had discovered the principle of antisepsis. But did not the Simpson technique clash with the literal interpretation of the Bible? This was enough to unleash violent Protestant opposition against him. This pseudo-theological dispute about a purely medical technique lasted for five years, and was then settled by Queen Victoria. In April, 1852, she called in Simpson and was delivered under anaesthesia.

The history of the discovery of anaesthetics now enters into its expansion phase. Progress was made, both in perfecting instruments and techniques, and in the use of the new product. We shall take a rapid glance at these stages, so near in time to our own day.

In 1852, James Arnott used a mixture of snow and ice in order to induce a local insensibility by means of cold. He thus carried into practice a fact previously observed by Larrey, a surgeon of the *Grande Armée*.

In 1854, Dr. Scherzer brought back cocoa-leaves with him to Europe, and the chemist Gaedicke discovered cocaine in them. Five years later, this cocaine was isolated by Nieman.

However, after a period of enthusiasm lasting some years, a certain number of accidents were recorded, arising from the use of chloroform. Medical opinion grew uneasy. Doctors reverted to ether, whose method of administration was perfected; and they began to use nitrous oxide (Klibowitsch, 1880). Then a combination of different gases was envisaged, with a view to reducing the dangers of narcosis (Billroth, 1880). Finally, 1881, Crombill of Calcutta carried out the first pre-anaesthesia with morphine—a technique which would have been extolled by Claude Bernard in 1869.

Local anaesthesia now underwent a development. Only twenty years after the discovery of cocaine, Freud, founder of psychoanalysis, studied in conjunction with Carl Koller its local action (Spring, 1889). Then Koller pursued his investigations alone at the ophthalmological clinic of Vienna, and discovered local anaesthesia. This developed. In 1885, the American Halsted discovered blockage anaesthesia; and his compatriot, Corning, discovered spinal anaesthesia. That same year, in France, Reclus practised truncular anaesthesia, and then splanchnic anaesthesia. In 1894, Carl Schleich described anaesthesia by infiltration; and, five years later, Bier and Tuffier independently discovered rachianaesthesia (spinal anaesthesia).

In 1905, Eichhorn and Braun made the synthesis of an important substitute for cocaine. This is novocaine, which produces an equivalent effect, but is less toxic. At the same time, Stephane Leclerc sought to induce artificial sleep by means of electric current, and Korf used scolamine in pre-anaesthesia for the first time.

The imagination of researchers was thus taken up with multiplying the ways in which narcotics could be administered. In 1910, the American Gwathmey used the rectal track in administering to his patients a mixture of oil and ether. Pitha administered enemata of belladonna, but this rectal narcosis attained to its full development only in 1917, when Eichholz effected the synthesis of Avertine or Rectanol.

Inhalatory narcosis was also enriched with two new products: ethylene (1923) and cyclopropane (1929).

Finally, there was the innovation provided by the use of intravenous injection which has the advantage of sending the anaesthetic directly into the blood stream and thus shortening the induction of the narcosis. There were first attempts in 1872 by Dr. Ore of Lyon, who performed fifty anaesthesias with intravenous chloral; and also the attempts of Kramkoud with hedonal, at the beginning of this century. But the real advance of intravenous anaesthesia came with the discovery of the barbiturates: veronal (in 1903), somnifere (in 1923), and above all, evipan, the quick barbiturate, whose synthesis was effected in 1932. Finally, we have to-day the more rapid and non-toxic product, sodium pentothal.

In concluding, we shall say a word about the use of a substance which seems to have a great future: curare. Known since the XVIth

century, this substance became of use only when, between 1935 and
1940, crystallized detubercurarine, dosable and easy to handle, was
extracted from it. In 1942, it was introduced into anaesthetic practice
by Griffith and Cullen.

C. L.

SIXTH STUDY

EUTHANASIA

EDITOR'S FOREWORD

ONE must recognize in the world of to-day wherein God has called us to serve the time of our probation that our non-Catholic contemporaries, who order the daily course of their lives according to the requirements of a materialistic expediency, do still experience a certain need to explain their deviations from the natural law in terms of, what is little better than, sentimentality and a recourse to unsound and unproven economic theory unguided by the light of reason and *a fortiori* that of Faith. In this they are quite well intentioned and often contrive to conceal from themselves the essential selfishness which motivates them, not the less truly because they are unaware of it. In them a faulty environment and oft-times the early development of unethical habits, apparently accepted by others of their kind, has overlain and obscured the fundamental principles of the natural law implanted by God in the heart of Man. Yet it is not completely hidden, and so they find the need to explain actions, which they realize are not ethically right, by faulty though often honest reasoning and a sentimentality which takes no cognizance of God's design for the individual human being. Nowhere is this phenomenon so evident as in the case of the apologists for birth control and euthanasia. In the articles which follow, the problem of the latter practice has been reviewed from all angles in order that its ethical relation may be made clear.

Until quite recently, that is to say, in the last ten years or so, the protagonists of euthanasia were few in number; they had no large following and their propaganda was more often whispered rather than proclaimed aloud in the market place, whilst a doctor who was known to practise it would regret that the knowledge had become public and would not be favoured by patients who held the opinion that they went to the doctor to be cured of their ailments or to have them alleviated but who had never thought of regarding him in the role of a private executioner. It would be too much to say that public opinion has changed in this regard, but it is quite certain that this practice is on the increase and that with the knowledge and connivance and in some cases the active direction of medical men of consultant or specialist rank who, a few years ago, would have imperilled their position and done violence to their consciences had they countenanced such a practice. There are not a few patients even in some of our leading hospitals who are victims of this procedure. The procedure adopted varies from the crude methods of removing the pillows from elderly people whose illness precludes adequate respiration in the horizontal posture, or the giving of evidently excessive doses of lethal drugs, to the more scientifically refined intravenous injection of insulin or the like. These cases do happen and are not infrequent in places where formerly they would have caused immediate action against the doctor concerned. Even though such practices are claimed to be merciful, "putting him out of his agony," . . . "making a bed for a case for whom we can do something useful," etc., they are quite contrary to the Common Law of England and defiant of the Law of God, who alone has the power of life and death and who has not delegated it to the medical profession. We believe that the great majority of medical men in the world, and certainly in these countries, are entirely opposed to such a practice, but there are some men in practice who do it, and to find it tolerated in good hospital practice argues a decadence in medical standards. Some such cases have been done even against the patient's expressed will, but it is equally wrong even at the patient's request, or with his consent, for no one can give another permission to do what is morally wrong in itself. We hope that there will be a new resurgence of traditional morality, based as it always has been on the law of God, among our non-Catholic brethren, and that they will set their faces steadfastly against a practice which is unethical and which can only undermine confidence in their position as the exponents and practitioners of the Healing Art. Perhaps, once a respect for the life of the living embryo or foetus had gone and it had become a part of medical teaching to divorce the natural act of marriage from its natural end or purpose, we should not be surprised to find that there are those who have an equal lack of respect for the "right to live" of the aged and the suffering. We hope that the day will never come when the aged, the incurable, the troublesomely sick will be secure of their lives only in the hands of a Catholic doctor, but such is the end term of the present fall from tradition in a noble profession. We have every sympathy with human suffering and espouse every lawful method directed towards its relief, but we Catholic doctors recognize that death is not the end of conscious existence, that as Christians we are privileged to unite our sufferings with those of Christ suffered for our redemption and that the divine purpose for mankind cannot be achieved by defying the precept, "thou shalt not kill." It becomes no man, least of all the doctor, to brand himself, or his profession, with the brand of Cain.

EDITOR

MEDICINE AND EUTHANASIA

Monsieur le Président, Messieurs,

Your Association has recently given your attention to some questions concerning Artificial Insemination—that is to say, concerning the very beginnings of life. To-day, by way of antithesis, I ask you to consider some of the difficulties which confront the doctor when he is face to face with death; and I shall deal especially with the method known as "Euthanasia" which proposes that the incurable and the dying should be given a "sweet and tranquil" death, rather than be allowed to continue on the rack of pain a life without hope of relief.

* * *

Some random examples, chosen from a thousand such, will enable me to consider this problem in its philosophical, moral, and social aspects.

One of my medical friends, a fine doctor and a man of high moral standards, was assisting at the bedside of his mother who was dying from an inoperable cancer. Her agony began, and normal doses of morphia were powerless to assuage the awful pains. The dying woman, an intelligent and keen-minded person, had always been on terms of close intimacy with her son, and she had made a pact with him about her disease. Invoking that pact, she now begged him to honour it by not prolonging her agony. My friend, who had abandoned all hope and was overwhelmed with grief at his mother's sufferings, took his syringe, increased the dose and injected it. A few minutes later, a sweet and calm sleep took the place of the pain, but her breathing weakened and ceased. She had, indeed, "ceased to suffer."

My friend, who had thus set himself up as the judge of his own mother's life, was to become, a few years later and for quite different reasons, the judge of his own life, when—with the same courage or the same presumption—he committed suicide.

What took place in that sick room, with no witnesses present, between these two persons so closely bound together by great natural affection? As a son, my friend was seized with passionate pity at the sight of the death agonies of his dear mother. As a doctor, he responded to her last appeal by an act which was efficacious but mortal, after he had diagnosed complete incurability.

263

Whatever excuse one may wish to find for such an attitude, it must be admitted that here death did not do its work *unaided*, but found at least a helper or . . . an accomplice.

In his own eyes and in the eyes of Society called upon to pronounce judgment on him, was my friend guilty of compassionate homicide or even of parricide? Did he merely violate his medical oath?—that oath which says: "No matter who demands it of me, I shall not give a lethal drug nor shall I take the initiative in suggesting its administration." On the other hand, has he not been faithful to the spirit of that same oath? For it says: "Into whatever house I shall come, I shall enter for the benefit of patients, and I shall carefully avoid all deliberate injury."

Such are the doubts to which this tragic event gives rise. I may add that, while they seem inevitable in the case of every doctor who assists at the death of relations and friends, they are none the less usual when the doctor is dealing with a dying person who is a stranger to him.

In this connection, I am reminded of the circumstances which, according to Cabanis, accompanied the death of Mirabeau.

Mirabeau, in agony and having lost completely the use of speech, asked by a sign for pen and paper, and wrote: "To sleep." When Cabanis pretended that he did not understand, Mirabeau again wrote: "As long as it was believed that opium would establish the humour, it was rightly refused; but now that there is no alternative except to turn to an unknown phenomenon, why not try that phenomenon? And may one allow one's friend to lie dying by the roadside for several days?" But Cabanis refused to consider all this; and Mirabeau again wrote: "My friend, are you not my doctor? Did you not promise to spare me the pains of a death such as this? Do you wish me to bear the regret of having given you my confidence?"

It was then that Cabanis yielded to these sufferings and these appeals, and, with the assistance of Antoine Petit, administered opium in order to alleviate Mirabeau's sufferings and to hasten his death. Were Cabanis and Petit guilty of murder? If so, could they not find some extenuating circumstances in the fact that they acted only under the compelling urge of their own compassionate friendship and on the written request of their victim, made while he was perfectly lucid?

The examples which I have just given concern euthanasia in its—so to speak—individual form only, and as the end of that relationship of compassion which unites the doctor and the agonizing. But cannot one be led to envisage collective euthanasia, in great public calamities such as epidemics or wars? One remembers how Bonaparte, in Jaffa, overcome with pity at the sight of the plague-stricken, ordered

Desgenettes to poison them. Desgenettes refused to do so, saying: "My duty is not to kill, but to *conserve*."

This famous example underlines the opposition which can exist between the ideas of a leader of prestige, amenable to a kind of collective compassion, and the ideas of a doctor who will not consent, even in such circumstances, to overstep his traditional and properly human duties. On that occasion, Desgenettes rendered a considerable service to Bonaparte, because, by refusing to carry out his order, he undoubtedly saved him from the severe censure of posterity. At all events, he did not create the spectacular precedent which would have subsequently made it possible for French legislation, under the influence of Bonaparte, to enter on such a dangerous way. For, if Bonaparte's order had been obeyed, what might we not have seen, as a result, in the "dying wards" which are periodically filled in consequence of wars, revolutions and epidemics, and where these men, thus singled out by fate, are huddled together to die in an atmosphere whose tragedy has never been so poignantly evoked as by Georges Duhamel in his *Vie des Martyrs*? What would we have seen but the transformation of these would-be places of refuge into slaughter-houses—and all this under the reassuring sign of the Red Cross? And if euthanasia had been admitted in these extraordinary conditions, would it not have been accepted inevitably into the daily routine of our hospitals, and finally into the ordinary course of private medical practice? Who can say what the remote consequences of a refusal can sometimes be?

The few facts I have just instanced show how different can be the actions of doctors in face of death.

In hastening his mother's death, my friend was certainly filled with profound pity; but, as his own suicide shows, his whole attitude seems to have been subordinated to a certain conception of life and death—a conception reminiscent of that which the ancient Stoics cultivated. Cabanis did not philosophize much in his dealings with the dying Mirabeau. In his hesitations, we sense, of course, a certain uneasiness; but in the last analysis, he was merely a sceptic, eventually accessible to compassion. In Desgenette's opposition to Bonaparte, on the other hand, we see the rigour of a doctrine which undoubtedly takes in the whole sweep of medical possibility, but which is equally conscious of the limits of that possibility.

With such examples before us, how can we fail to appreciate how great a temptation euthanasia offers to the doctor?

Has not every living person the right to a sweet and tranquil death?

Is it not the doctor's duty to give him such a death?

These questions are not merely theoretical, because they arise sooner or later for all men and daily for the doctor.

The ineluctable nature of death, which each one of us hopes will be sweet and easy, authorizes me therefore to ask you whether we should not again consider the problem of euthanasia. I would ask you to linger over it, so that we doctors may see it stripped of its doubts and its prejudices, and may ask ourselves to what extent we should demand of the legislator that he relinquish his policy of dumbness. We shall do so, of course, in the light of the most recent acquisitions of medical science, but above all under the aegis of the traditional qualities of medical humanism.

*   *   *

It seems imperative, above all else, to examine the solutions that were given for these problems by the different civilizations which, in the course of centuries, faced up to this aspect of them. It is quite clear that the desire for an easy and rapid death is, for man, an intense longing as old as man himself.

Antiquity took up a very special position in this matter, which is clearly expressed by Plato, notably in Book III of *The Republic*: "Every citizen has a duty to fulfil in every well-governed State; and no one has leisure to pass his life in diseases and in remedies. You will establish in the State, O Glaukon, a discipline and a jurisprudence such as we have in mind; and it will be confined to serving the needs of citizens who are of good bodily and mental constitution. As to those who are not physically healthy, they will be allowed to die. . . ."

Here is the essence of the mind of antiquity in this matter, because we find the same fundamental ideas, not only in Athens, but also in Sparta and beyond the frontiers of Greece, in all the civilizations which, before the advent of Christianity, succeeded one another on the shores of the Mediterranean; and even in Mesopotamia and in India.

It was this idea of the efficiency of the individual and his subordination to the collectivity, which caused the world of antiquity to ignore the liberties of the individual and to institute slavery; just as its contempt for life led it to counsel abortion and euthanasia when the interests of the State, of the City, of the clan or of the family demanded them.

Undoubtedly, some contrary philosophical currents, issuing from the Far East, seeped into Greece by way of Pythagorianism, and spread more or less secretly in the form of that mysterious Orphism which declared the fundamental impurity of certain acts. Undoubtedly, the Jewish world escaped this fatality of antiquity to a considerable extent. For all that, however, it remains none the less true that, despite these important prefigurations, the appearance of Christianity marks an epoch in the moral evolution of humanity; for the Christian faith dogmatically affirmed the eminent dignity of man, God's creature, endowed with a free and immortal soul.

The ancient principle of *Exodus*: *"Insontem et justum non occides"* inspires all Christian philosophy in its respect for life, for it was on this principle that nascent Christianity relied, from the beginning, to give *a moral basis to human justice*; and it is in the name of the same principle that Christianity spoke its condemnation, not only of *abortion*, but also of *euthanasia*. For is not the sick person this innocent, this just person, whom God protects and whom the doctor may not kill but only assist or cure? These spiritually minded ideas quickly spread, and finally influenced the whole of society in the Middle Ages.

In the Middle Ages, the Christian perspective saw human life as a mere passage to a life beyond the grave; the agony of death, however torturing, was in that perspective but a pale shadow of the sufferings of Christ's lonely death on the Cross; each man's pain, being the image of that of the Redeemer, received in this perspective a significance, a value for salvation.

In such conditions, the doctor himself can have only a limited and modest role. "Away with the idea that I can do everything," said Maimonides in the XIIth century, with that very profound Hebraic sense of the sovereignty of Yahweh and the limits imposed on man. Ambroise Paré, in a later century, added with the humility of a simple servant of God: "I tend the patient, but God alone is master of life and of death, of healing and of agony, of anguish and of serenity."

The first reactions against these conceptions date from 1516, when there appeared in Louvain a description of them in that curious essay of a new "Platonic Republic"—*Utopia* by St. Thomas More. In this book, the resurgence of the pagan current is made evident: "But if the disease be not only incurable, but also full of continual pain and anguish; then the priests and the magistrates exhort the man, seeing he is not able to do any duty of life, and by overliving his own death is noisome and irksome to other, and grievous to himself, that he will determine with himself no longer to cherish that pestilent and painful disease. And seeing his life is to him but a torment, that he will not be unwilling to die, but rather take a good hope to him, and either dispatch himself out of that painful life, as out of a prison, or a rack of torment, or else suffer himself to be rid of it by other." (Ralph Robinson translation: second amended edition, 1556.)

This text is symptomatic of the re-emergence in our modern world of the idea of efficiency, so dear to the Ancients; the sick individual—bound to the service of the City by an implacable law, but now of no further service to the City—must be no longer tolerated either by himself or by others.

In the XVIIth century, another Englishman, Francis Bacon, clearly underlined the idea of his predecessor, and invented the word "euthanasia" (easy death), precisely defined the technique and confided it, not to the *magistrate* and the *priest* as More had done, but to the *doctor*. He says that it is the function of the doctor to give health to his patients and to mitigate their pains and sufferings; and this, not only when such mitigation may lead to cure, but also when it can serve to procure a peaceful and easy death. The magistrates and the priests to whom More gave the charge of purifying the City, find that the doctor is made to replace them in exercising this redoubtable power of the Demiurge which, in the Platonic sense of the word and in order to reorganise a formless world, sends from life to death those who are physically weak or enfeebled by old age—the dead weight of the City.

This fundamental text of Bacon, in its fearsome technical precision, makes the euthanasia demanded by Nietsche after a more literary fashion in 1889, appear almost commonplace. "As for the parasites of society, those patients who find it inconvenient to live longer, who lazily vegetate, having lost the sense of the future. . . ."

We must now consider how the legislator responded to the theoretical, but imperious, demands of More, of Bacon, of Nietsche.

* * *

Until the beginning of the XXth century, Western legislations, fully penetrated with the spiritual principles of respect for the individual, did not follow the philosophers or theorizers of assisted suicide. Euthanasia remained legally premeditated or passionate homicide. But in 1903, in New York, the State Medical Association instructed its members that the life of a cancer patient whose neoplasm has relapsed, or of a tuberculous patient in the final period, or of an unfortunate paralytic, may be shortened by an easy death.

In 1906, *the first legal text concerning euthanasia* was voted at a first reading, on the proposal of Miss Ann Hill, by the Parliament of Ohio. The text laid down that any person afflicted with an incurable disease accompanied with intense pain, could demand a committee of at least four people whose business it will be to decide how opportunely to terminate this painful life.

The Parliament of Iowa, some months later, on the motion of Dr. Gregory, passed a bill extending enthanasia, not only to the incurable, but also to malformed and idiot children.

Just as we have delayed over Bacon's text—the first manifestation of euthanasia in its systematic and scientific aspect—so we must also deal in some detail with this first juridical recognition of euthanasia. This Iowa bill was not immediately ratified by Anglo-Saxon countries, because Washington repudiated in no uncertain fashion both it and the State Medical Association's recommendation. We notice that, on the one hand, the power of Demiurge—transferred, at Bacon's demand, from magistrates and priests to the qualified doctor—is here confided to a commission of four members. This accords very well with the general evolution of democracy which confers on a supposed infallible number the power which is regarded as suspect when in the hands of the qualified man. Moreover, and above all, we would like to point out emphatically that in these texts there is a sudden passage from individual euthanasia to pluri-euthanasia applied to other categories of the weak. This is evident from the very outset of the juridical recognition of euthanasia, *and is most disturbing*. European Parliaments, on the other hand, have resisted this idea of an organized and legal Nirvana. In 1913, the Reichstag, like Washington, rejected euthanasia; and in December, 1936, the House of Lords rejected it by 35 votes against to 14 in favour.

We shall now consider the position of French legislation as regards euthanasia.

In France, article 295 of the new *Code Pénal* stigmatizes as a murderer every voluntary author of a homicide, whoever he may be; but article 518 leaves it in the hands of jury to weigh and consider the facts, and to bring in a verdict of acquittal or a verdict hedged about with extenuating circumstances. In a word, article 295 condemns euthanasia in principle, without naming it; but article 518 makes it possible for jurisprudence to modify considerably what may appear to be over-rigorous in any concrete case.

In application of this, we recall that, on November 5th, 1929, Richard Corbett, who had shot his mother after having watched her writhing in agony for a week, appeared before a jury at Var on a charge of murder; and that four years later, a certain Mme. Uniska appeared before the *Cour d'assises* for having supplied poison to her husband when he was in the agonies of cancer. They were both acquitted; but the fact that they had to stand their trials, is ample evidence of the distrustful attitude taken up by French Law towards euthanasia.

Previous to this, the *Cour de Cassation* had concluded in a verdict given (*arrêt le Floch*, Nov. 16th, 1927), that "the protection assured by the Law to all persons constitutes a public guarantee; and hence, the consent of the victim to an action which is homicidal, cannot legalize that act."

On the other hand, we observe that, since 1922, the Penal Code of the U.S.S.R. declares legal any homicide committed from motives of pity and compassion and at the request of the victim.

The conclusion that emerges from this rapid glance at the mind of the legislator in this matter, seems to point to the existence of two contradictory currents, and makes it clear that the legal fate of euthanasia depends on the role assigned to the individual in a given society.

To the extent to which this society is impregnated with materialism, the idea of collective efficiency dominates, as it did with the Ancients; the value of the person as an individual is almost nil, and euthanasia tends to take its place in the juridical system under the mask of compassion.

On the other hand, to the extent to which this society preserves spiritual values, the idea of efficiency yields to the respect due to the human person, *qua* person, whether he is weak or strong, dying or healthy; and euthanasia never receives legal recognition because the legislator rejects it in principle.

* * *

We have dealt with these philosophical and juridical considerations, and we must now consider euthanasia in its properly medical aspect.

In order to permit the legislator to solve his doubts and his distrust, some doctors have proposed a kind of compromise between the feeling of compassion which they have for those in agony, and their patent fear lest the practice of euthanasia should lead to unacceptable abuses. In a word, not daring through compassion to forbid it entirely, they endeavour to set clear-cut limits to its admissibility, and with this in mind they surround it with such a wealth of precautions that one can only compare such doctors to men who, desiring to preserve a forest from being burned out, fearfully and dejectedly decide to take the fire's part. They make it clear, of course, that they admit only euthanasia for those in agony, and this they qualify as to time, as to the subject undergoing it, and above all as to its indications, which should be palpable and indisputable for every doctor who is normally instructed and in good faith.

In order that this euthanasia may be legally applicable, they laid down a whole series of conditions.

The patient must have reached the last stage of his disease, and must be a prey to sufferings which are at once intolerable, incessant and incurable. Euthanasia would thus be limited to *a very brief period* of the disease.

Moreover, the patient must himself have expressed clearly his desire to see an end put to this final suffering, and, consequently, he must have been still free to convey such a wish to his doctor. Euthanasia would thus be limited to the *conscious and consenting* patient.

The doctor must have established the diagnosis of agony and the fatal prognosis, in consultation with the medico-legist and the specialist. Euthanasia would thus be outside the competence of *any group of three unqualified persons.*

This decision would be effective only within the framework of a series of diseases expressly and exclusively indicated in the law.

Finally, the technical processes to be used would be expressly and exclusively enumerated.

Thus, this medical aid—which is similar *in appearance only*, to the care which one normally gives to the last hours; but which, as we shall see, is quite dissimilar *by its very nature*—would be an assistance given as seldom as is practically possible.

In these conditions of extreme limitation, it could be expressed according to a legal formula analogous to that used in the decree of July 29th, 1939, article 87, concerning therapeutic abortion. For example, it could run like this—

"When a patient afflicted with a disease which the present data of science declares to be incurable, will suffer from intolerable and incessant pains, the doctor, at the express desire of the patient, must call into consultation a medico-legist and a medical specialist in the disease in question, and these three, after examination and discussion, shall attest in writing that the patient's condition legally warrants euthanasia. A copy of the consultation shall be sent to the family; the other two copies shall be kept by the two doctors."

This text would allow the doctor to effect euthanasia in certain circumstances, just as the maternity doctor has the right, since the decree of 1939, to effect in certain circumstances the therapeutic termination of pregnancy. Does it seem a right and proper thing that such an addition should be made in order to complete article 518 of the *Code Pénal*, which up to now has been silent in this matter?

Before you give an answer to this important question, I would like to make a few remarks on this matter and commend them to your consideration.

Under pain of hypocrisy, we must emphasize the very special character of this new action which is proposed to the doctor and which clearly exceeds by its very nature, the curative task to which the doctor is bound by our traditions and our Code of Deontology. The Code says, in effect, that the practice of medicine is a ministry (art. 10) and that "the first task of the doctor must be to preserve human life, even when he is mitigating pain" (art. 23).

There is surely a manifest difference of *nature* between a doctor who conceals from the dying patient, when possible, the incurable nature of his disease, watches by his bedside, prescribes the analgesia which soothes the pains and the cardiac tonic which strengthens the heart, and who seeks and ceaselessly seeks other medications when the ones he is using prove ineffectual; and, on the other hand, a doctor who surrenders in the fight against pain, ceases to tend the patient, and not only allows death to take its course, but also informs the patient that death is at hand in order that he may have the right to hasten it by *deliberately* administering, for example, the analgesic, not in a therapeutic, but in a mortal dose.

This latter attitude is assuredly not that of a *panseur*, of whom Ambroise Paré wrote: It is not that of a healer, of a soldier engaged in the unequal but truceless fight against pain. It is that of a judge delivering the death-sentence; of a judge who will carry out that sentence himself.

It is of little consequence whether the doctor, in making this decision, does so alone or in consultation with two—or with ten—of his confrères. In either case, he thereby performs an action which is not *medical* in the commonly accepted sense of the word. It is also quite clear that to accord such prerogatives to the doctor—prerogatives which, moreover, he does not claim—is to give him a kind of sovereignty over life and death. Now such an idea runs counter to ordinary morality, and its consequences are fraught with danger to public order.

Binding, an eminent German lawyer, felt this perfectly when, in 1920, he studied euthanasia and defined it as "licence to destroy lives which are not worth living." Even in this very extensive form, he considered that it is licit and that it needs no juridical justification.

Intuitively rather than expressly, he nevertheless realized that the doctor is exceeding his normal role, and he tries to meet this difficulty by mustering arguments which are certainly very specious. Who is the murderer in euthanasia? he asks. Is it the doctor? No—it is the patient, because it is he who kills. *The doctor merely substitutes one cause of death for another*, this cause having the advantage of taking quicker action. Just as the doctor has the right to prefer one therapy to another, similarly he has the right to substitute a painless death for a painful one. He does not kill; he merely directs death towards a better exit. The doctor, according to Binding, has not only the right to practise euthanasia, but the duty to do so; because, since the alleviation of physical suffering is certainly his role, euthanasia is part of the *care* which he *owes* to his patient. The proof, he adds, that the doctor who practises euthanasia is not legally a murderer, is the fact that the codes have nothing to say on this matter.

It seems quite possible to us that the codes have other reasons for being silent; and that these reasons arise from the extreme complexity of the problem on the purely medical plane, apart from all philosophical and religious considerations.

Speaking as a practitioner, I earnestly beseech you not to allow yourselves to be deluded by this apparent certainty of incurability which seems to be the result of the final consultation proposed, in all good faith, with a view to protecting the patient. If we are prudent, we shall doubtless ask ourselves of what *order* is the faith which can be given to this concordance of men of good will, in the conjectural and uncertain domain of disease; and we shall endeavour to analyze it.

Since euthanasia can be medically justified only by the fact of incurability, it follows that this fact must be established with absolute certainty. Now, such certainty demands: firstly, that a precise diagnosis of the disease in question must be reached; and secondly, that a clear prognosis must be established as to the evolution of the pathological process. It must be recognized that, in practice, neither the diagnosis nor the prognosis is always certain.

If, as happens in the majority of cases, the doctors, by conscientiously using all the clinical and scientific acquisitions of modern Medicine, reach a diagnosis with strong presumption of certainty, it remains none the less true that the prognosis is often unpredictable, not only as to the final outcome of the morbid process, but above all as to its duration.

It will be objected that the consultation of several doctors may clear up many doubts. This is true only to the extent to which consultation among several doctors serves to correct the errors of one another; but the addition of several uncertainties cannot result in the absolute certainty which is rigorously demanded for euthanasia. There are many instances of errors in diagnosis, committed both by technically and morally unassailable doctors, and by groups of doctors who have simultaneously or separately examined the same patient. Errors of prognosis, in the same conditions, are more numerous still.

I shall take two significant examples.

A man of 68 was ejected from his automobile and had his head wedged between a heap of stones and his upset vehicle. Rescued unconscious, with the signs of a fracture of the cranial base, he was skilfully tended by four doctors who used every means to rouse him from his coma. Despite active medication, his breathing became irregular and slackened, his pulse weakened and became irregular, and the death rattle began. With such signs of death before them, the doctors made no further effort. However, they then decided to endeavour to keep the dying man alive for another few minutes so that a relative of his could arrive in time. They began to give him a random number of injections of ether and caffeine. To the astonishment of all, the heart resumed its beating, breathing returned, and the injured man emerged from the coma. He has since enjoyed excellent health.

A young woman, afflicted with a puerperal infection, was tended by two specialists who gave her every care, in consultation with two local doctors and a chief of the gynaecological clinic. All agreed that nothing could be done for her; all medications had been unsuccessfully tried, and the last agony began. One of the three doctors who remained by her bedside decided to make a final attempt, but the other two refused to co-operate with him in doing so, on the grounds that it would be of no avail. Her death, they argued, could not be prevented. And yet, the final medication was completely successful and the patient made a perfect recovery.

In either of these cases, euthanasia would have been certainly criminal, had it been envisaged. In the light of these medical facts, therefore, we must surely admit that, in many cases, there is no infallible criterion which enables the doctor to pass from conjecture to certainty, in all domains but especially in that of incurability. Medical conjecture most frequently entails, in practice, a probability which is sufficient to warrant our taking action, for medical laws have, of course, their constants; but such conjecture rarely leads to that mathematical certitude, if we may so put it, which is demanded to justify euthanasia.

In spite of all this, however, suppose for a moment that you do us the doubtful honour of blindly following the indications we have suggested within the very limited field of euthanasia of those in agony. Some of you, filled with enthusiasm for the method and sensitive of the misery of our human condition, may well go on to ask: If the doctor can establish an infallible prognosis of incurability in a given case, why limit the beneficent action of euthanasia to patients who are conscious of their agony? Why not extend it to the incurable patient who is unconscious? To the paralytic who is a burden to his family? To the idiot who is a burden on the rates? To the mentally defective and the degenerate who figure so largely among delinquents? To the person who is a *lusus naturae*? To the deaf-and-dumb and to the blind, when no institution has enabled them to adapt themselves to social life? etc. . . .

The doctor himself is at first hesitant and uneasy because of the confidence that is put in him; but he will yield to the arguments drawn now from social efficiency, now from science, now from compassion, and he will come to demand, in his turn, that the legal indications for euthanasia should be more and more extended.

Further, we have seen in recent years where this medical sovereignty has led in other domains—in the domain of racialism, of eugenics, of experimentation—when it is backed by a systematic or imprudent legislation. In 1935, Karl Brandt and Gerard Wagner gave the première of their film: *I Accuse*, during a Nazi festival. This film, which showed the truly lamentable condition of sick and incurable children, made a strong plea in favour of their suppression, pure and simple, by the implementing of a "euthanasia programme" euphemistically called *Todesgnade* ("The boon of death").

On Hitler's personal order, this programme was carried into effect methodically and consistently. A precisely worded questionnaire, which aimed at establishing "the right to death," carried the name of the patient, his age and his disease. One doctor, between November 14th and December 1st, 1940—i.e. in 15 days—completed 2,109 of these questionnaires. The method used to secure death was more simple and, it was said, more natural. The method was starvation.

The reaction of the Churches and of the Bishops—particularly the Bishops of Limburg and of Munich—was one of intense opposition. They gave full formal condemnation to this "Diktat which established the sovereignty of Medicine in defiance of human rights."

But bear in mind that this wholesale experiment in euthanasia, stigmatized by the Nuremberg Courts which also honoured those who opposed it, was perhaps comprised by implication in the first American legal ratification of 1906. The German experimentation went far beyond the limits of the American intentions; nevertheless, it merely followed and developed what was germinally contained in that 1906 legal decision. For on what grounds are we to prohibit the doctor from passing along those dangerous roads which lead from euthanasia of the agonizing to euthanasia of the incurable, and from individual euthanasia to collective euthanasia? Again, why limit penal euthanasia to major criminals? Why not extend it to the host of delinquents regarded as abnormal? Finally, why not pass on to euthanasia of certain racial groups, in the name of some ideology?

Thus we see that although this legal formulation which we were putting forward with quite an open mind, is very restricted, it contains an explosive power whose dangers can scarcely be measured. From the moment when one ceases to respect the ultimate value of each individual life, is not one inevitably drawn on to the slope which leads to contempt for all human life?

In conclusion, I may add that it rests with the prudence or the rashness of the legislators to ascribe or to refuse to doctors a role which frightens the doctors themselves, and which the majority of doctors refuse to consider because it is contrary to their ancestral tradition and because they will not usurp a right which is not theirs.

For some doctors, moved by generous pity, legal euthanasia is the final gift of compassion to the agonizing; but for many others who are more prudent, even if less learned, euthanasia is to be branded as a pact with Hell—an attitude which they take up because they are more concerned with guarding the values of humanism than with exposing those values to danger.

The problem is to decide between these two attitudes.

PROFESSEUR L. PORTES
de l'Académie de Médecine

EUTHANASIA

MEN seldom contemplate calmly the problem of death. The anguish which accompanies its contemplation is increased because of the traditional belief that death is painful.

Quiconque meurt, meurt à douleur (whoever dies, dies in pain), wrote François Villon. This idea is strengthened by the idea, no less firmly ingrained in the human mind, that the moments preceding death are a time of real combat.

This idea of a painful combat is so widespread that some people wish to avoid its terrors through a quick death, which they imagine to be painless, while at the same time they are not quite certain that they will really escape these terrors. Some, in an attempt to anticipate any omission in their regard on the part of Providence, even admit the possibility of dying without pain, and—a much more serious matter—the possibility of putting an end to sufferings by self-imposed death.

Since *the idea of suffering* is one of the terrifying elements of death, let us attempt to appreciate its importance before we consider attempting to suppress it.

We must first of all distinguish between pain and suffering. Suffering is a psychic or moral condition which is not always accompanied by organic pain. The converse, on the other hand, does not hold because pain is always accompanied by suffering. One frequently hears patients who are suffering greatly demand death; what they desire is the suppression both of physical pain and of moral suffering. But can we be sure that the conscious personality—what Le Dantec calls the consciousness of co-ordination—is intact at the precise moment when the patient accepts death? It seems reasonable to admit that, under the action of a serious auto- or hetero-intoxication, the consciousness of the dying becomes clouded or completely darkened, while at the same time the sufferings of death are considerably diminished.

However, it is not always so, because sometimes the kinaesthetic sensation of death increases the awful cruelty of the physical pains. The patient is conscious of his pains, and he is also conscious of his approaching end. The psychological aspect of such a death is so complex that it is very difficult to grasp the full extent of its terror. This reaches its acme when the patient must endure the anguish of "living his own death"—which is the case with a person whose physical torments seem to go on and on. "Human nature," wrote Goethe, "has its limits. One can endure pleasure, pain and suffering

277

up to a certain point beyond which one inevitably succumbs." This
lapse occurs when the instinct of life and of conservation has lost all
its potentiality.

Two possibilities result from this. Consciousness is completely
clouded, and the patient does not experience the horror of sinking into
death; or consciousness persists, and the patient, keenly experiencing
the imperious and awful approach of death, demands that we should
take some steps to shorten his suffering.

This feeling of pain, indissolubly linked with death, is instinctive by
nature. Bacon said that "no man is capable of fully enjoying life if he
has not cultivated the habit of thinking serenely on death." Indeed, it
is man who imputes to death the last sufferings of disease. But disease
has nothing in common with that which ends it: disease belongs to
life and not to death.

Disease belongs to nature, or to life; agony, even though it seems
proper to death, is entirely in the hands of man, and what is dreaded
is the terrible struggle of the end, and especially the supreme, the
terrible second of the yielding of life to death. "It is not the arrival
of death which strikes terror," writes Maeterlinck, "but the departure
of life. It is not on death but on life that we must act. It is not death
which attacks life; it is life which injuriously resists death."

This means that man must be educated in the art of living. We must
accustom ourselves to look death in the face, seeing it for what it is,
stripped of its funeral trappings and the terrors with which the imagination has clothed it; for it is as veiled in such trappings and such
terrors that we usually regard the face of death. But this is not the real
face of death; for the truth is that death descends among men in order
to dismiss a life or to change the form of a life. It is still far off when
the terrible struggle begins which we endeavour to prolong as much
as possible.

Though philosophical speculation can sometimes lead men astray,
there is one guiding principle which stands first and foremost: the
sacred character of human life and the indispensable limitation of our
rights over it. The question: Have we the right to kill in order to
put an end to pain?—can receive an affirmative answer only at the
price of a diminution of the value of human life, and results from
literary licence, blind humanitarianism, glorified individualism, general
indulgence, and a weakening of spiritual structure. It is as the result
of a general lowering of courage and of morality that the socio-
philosophical dogma, known as euthanasia, has come to exist.

What is euthanasia?

Littré defines it as "good death, death which is easy and painless."
Euthanasia is the act of giving a painless death to those suffering from

an incurable disease, when the prognosis is fatal and when the patients are tortured by intolerable and persistent physical pains which cannot be lessened by any known therapeutic means.

Euthanasia can be practised either in *a state of perfect health* or *during the course of a disease*.

When it is practised in the case of a person enjoying good health, euthanasia is merely agreeable suicide. It is the graceful death of Seneca, of Petronius, of that nonogenarian who, according to Valerius Maximus, "while enjoying perfect health of mind and of body, justified his decision by the fear of having to endure the reverse of a fortune until then favourable to him, because he had held on to life too long." An agreeable type of suicide, therefore, in which is found a mixture of sentiments of weakness and of enjoyment. In the case of the poor, the usual method is gas, which is supposed to be soothing and easy; again, there is hanging, which is also supposed to have easy elements. Both of these ideas may be due simply to pre-conceived notions about such deaths.

The euthanasia with which we are especially concerned here, is that which is practised on the patient at any stage of the development of his disease. For the suffering person, it signifies the right to an easy death scientifically induced.

Euthanasia, which can be practised by the patient himself, or by the doctor who organizes it, or by a third party who is an accomplice, can take three forms.

It may be a *liberating death*. This is the death given to a conscious, certainly incurable patient who demands that his agony, insupportable and intractable to all physical or psychic alleviation, should be terminated by a calm and painless death.

It may be *a merciful death*. This is the death which, at the instigation of pity, is given to unconscious dying patients, in order to end their insupportable and useless sufferings and to prevent the searing sight of their awful agony.

Finally, it may be *a eugenic or economic* death. This is the suppression by euthanasia of absolutely immoral and asocial persons, monsters, the seriously insane, and in general all those who cannot lead a moral life within the framework of social life.

It has been said that the word "euthanasia" is a comparatively recent neologism, and that the phenomenon it describes is much older, being found among the practices of the earliest human groups. This is not so, because what is found among such groups is not euthanasia in the sense we give to the term, but economic euthanasia resulting from shortage of food and involving the necessary suppression of useless mouths. It is no argument to antiquity, therefore, to cite the ancient

Indian custom of carrying the incurable to the banks of the Ganges, where the patient's nose and mouth were filled with sacred mud before he was cast into the river. The same economic reason explains the ancient custom of the Isle of Cos; the old were assembled for a last banquet, in the course of which a poisoned drink—*conium maculatum*—was given to them.

We are far from the idea of sweet and easy death. All this is not euthanasia, but suicide or assassination.

*   *   *

A study of the penal codes of different countries reveals that in certain countries euthanasia is permitted, while other legislatures regard it as homicide but allow it the benefit of extenuating circumstances. Finally, other legislatures equate it, purely and simply, with murder.

The Russian penal code of 1922 completely exonerates the perpetrator of euthanasia if it is proved that he acted at the request of the deceased person. The Swiss federal penal code (Article 13) regards euthanasia as murder at the demand of the victim: "He who, at the serious and insistent demand of another person, causes the death of that person, shall be punished with imprisonment." The same code also condemns to a sentence of five years reclusion or imprisonment, any person who incites or assists another to commit suicide. Analogous clauses are found in the Italian penal code which punished with six to fifteen years of reclusion murder with the victim's consent. Similar provisions are made in the penal code of Germany, Spain, Holland, Norway, Brazil and Peru.

In Great Britain, there are no codified repressive measures, but, on its usual traditionalist basis, British law regards murder at the request of the victim as being really murder. A verdict (June 4th, 1932) of the *Chambre du Conseil de Bruxelles* leaves no doubt as to the attitude of Belgian law towards the problem of euthanasia: "Given"—reads the verdict—"that to kill or attempt to kill a person who has consented to death or who has even formally demanded that he should be killed, remains none the less murder or assassination or an attempt at these crimes. . . ."

The French penal code takes up an identical attitude, and in no way recognizes murder with the victim's consent. According to Articles 295 and 296 of the penal code, homicide with the victim's consent must be regarded, in principle and in practice, as murder. The consent of the victim cannot justify or excuse the author of this homicide, because it is contrary to the principles of Article 65 of the same code. "No crime or offence may be excused, nor may the punishment be mitigated, except in the cases and in the circumstances where the law declares the act excusable or allows a less vigorous sentence in regard to it." The old adage: *"Scienti et volenti non fit injuria,"* which some would oppose to these immutable principles, cannot therefore be invoked. Moreover, it was not the intention of its author that this adage should be applied to bodily lesions.

The intangibility of the present penal code leaves room, however, for certain decisions of jurisprudence which may, to some extent, cause surprise, but which make clear that, in the reform project, Article 518 leaves to the court the task of weighing the motives and circumstances, and of reducing by one or two degrees the penalty for homicide committed at the request of the victim.

Some people, indeed, consider that, since the right to die is something that can be exercised by the person himself, then the same right can be exercised by another person, except when such action is inspired by anti-social motives. Voluntarily perpetrated homicide is murder, but here there is question of a special type of murder which lacks the essential condition of crime—the criminal purpose, the intention to injure. This type of assassination has a right to plead extenuating circumstances, and it is analogous to therapeutic abortion which undoubtedly constitutes premeditated homicide. The majority of people, however, regard euthanasia as murder pure and simple, similar to all other types of murder. The law does not admit the consent of the victim as constituting a justifying circumstance, and this consent cannot in any way constitute an extenuating circumstance. These opposed opinions are reflected in court decisions, because, even though euthanasia has received no legal ruling, it is none the less practised for that.

From time to time, the newspapers report the murder of an incurable person by wife or husband, the murder of an infirm child by its mother, the murder of a helpless old person by his or her children. Anything is possible in this domain—for instance, murder camouflaged as prophylactic murder perpetrated by the wife of an inveterate and dangerously brutal alcoholic.

In 1925, in the *Hôpital Paul Brousse*, Mme. Unimska killed her lover, who was afflicted with cancer, had already been operated upon, and was the bearer of painful metastases. She had given her blood for a transfusion which proved useless, and she administered an unusually strong injection of morphine because she could no longer watch his already intolerable sufferings. When sleep had thus been induced, she fulfilled a wish which the patient had several times expressed. She placed the mouth of a revolver between his half-open lips and fired. During the subsequent trial, the advocate general, Donat-Guigne, warned the jury about the repercussions which would follow a complete acquittal. She was acquitted; but less than eight days later, a similar case occurred at Asnières.

In 1930, the *Tribunal de Draguignan*, amid tumultous applause from the galleries, acquitted young Richard Corbett who had killed his aged mother afflicted with a horribly painful and inoperable cancer. Corbett conducted his own defence without assistance of counsel. "I admit," he said to the jury, "that I killed my mother, knowing perfectly what I was doing. I have no regrets about that. I have exercised a human right; and I am content to accept whatever sentence you may think fit. My action would have been unnecessary if the State had promulgated a law authorizing doctors to cut short the sufferings of the incurable."

In summing up, the *Procureur Général* declared: "I do not demand an excessive punishment, but this case raises a very vital problem. If society can permit a person to take the life of another and to do so with impunity, your verdict will have repercussions all over the world. The State must maintain that there exists no right to kill." And he added: "Since we have no power to create human life, we have no right to destroy it."

On the other hand, the *Cour de Cassation*, in a verdict given on November 16th, 1927, rejected the appeal of a person condemned to death for murder with the victim's consent. It based its rejection on the fact that the consent of the victim does not constitute a valid excuse.

In a similar case, the *Cour de Cassation* quashed a decision that there was no charge to answer. It did so on the grounds that "the protection assured constitutes a public guarantee"; because Article 6 of the *Code Civil* stipulates that one may not derogate, by individual decisions, from the laws which concern public order and public conduct.

A civilized and properly conducted society cannot allow or facilitate murder; even though it must recognize, with Jimenez de Asua, "that, although justice and pity do not always coincide, justice stamped with pity is sometimes more just." This does not mean that the vagaries of sentimentality are to be erected into dogmas or into legal rulings. *Euthanasia should not and cannot enter into our medical doctrine or our medical practice.* It is not out duty, and that for the following reasons.

From the doctrinal point of view, the arguments against euthanasia are—

The fallibility of our prognosis.

The cruelty of revealing to a patient the fact that he is incurable.

It is a well known, even too well known, fact that the fallibility of our prognosis is often equalled only by the errors of our diagnosis.

We can always advance in our knowledge of our art, and what we regard as irremediable to-day may be within our medical competence to-morrow.

Montaigne writes that Pliny permitted suicide to those afflicted with vesical calculus, intense stomach pains, and cranial neuralgia. I do not think that anyone would advise suicide to-day for these diseases, since they are now curable through cystotomy, gastrectomy, or retro-gasserian neurotomy. Examples of this kind could be multiplied. It is not so long since it was the custom to smother between two mattresses those who were afflicted with hydrophobia; whereas, to-day, a few injections preserve such people from the most terrible of deaths, for which euthanasia used formerly to be demanded. The man who has been drained of his blood need no longer die; and countless unfortunate people who, but a very short time ago, would have filled our asylums and dragged out a miserable existence there, are now delivered by those wonderful therapeutic remedies known as electric-shock and neurosurgery.

The second doctrinal argument against the practice of euthanasia is the cruelty of revealing to a patient the fact that he is incurable. I may add immediately, that if the doctor makes such a revelation, he is guilty of a most serious fault.

To the very end, the doctor must sustain the hope of the incurable person. Man stands always in need of hope and he prefers, as St. Thomas Aquinas has put it, a feeling which consoles to a truth which clarifies. By his very nature, man is an uneasy being; if he is a patient, he is even more so; and if he is a man condemned, his condition must be kept hidden from him. At every moment, he manifests this need to be deceived; he keeps a vigilant eye on our diagnosis, and he uses every means in his power to prove that we are in error, through repeated checkings.

If from the doctrinal point of view euthanasia must be rejected, our duty as men, our duty as doctors, forbids us to practise it. Our rigid line of conduct is to fight indefatigably, to strive to preserve life even when there seems to be no hope.

It is no small thing to wrest from death a few precious moments which allow the patient to make his last preparations and to see once more those who are dear to him. There is no questioning this, any more than we question the assuaging of the final sufferings even at the risk of shortening them. But much more than the most modern, the least toxic sedatives which are least likely to cut short human life, there is the profound peace of conscience which gives to the end of human life its serenity and its tranquil beauty. There are the moral forces which best aid a man in "crossing the bar."

We are told that St. Francis, during his last hours, had the Canticle of the Sun chanted to him, and that he himself died intoning David's psalm: that Mistral, his eyes lifted for the last time to the horizon, murmured: *"Li Santi, Li Santi*—the Saints of Provence"; and that Goethe, on the last morning of his life, rose to open the windows to a new Spring, and collapsed murmuring: "Let there be more abundance of light."

Moral euthanasia—yes. It is the only kind that may be admitted by the doctor, who cannot, whatever the circumstances may be, allow himself to become the conscious accomplice of a voluntary death.

DOCTEUR L. DÉROBERT
Professeur agrégé de Médecine Légale à la Faculté de Paris

AMERICAN OPINIONS

In the city-states of antiquity, the rights of the human person were not clearly defined; but the influence of Christianity on western thought made great and rapid progress in this domain. However, in the XVIth–XVIIth centuries, pagan ideas began to revive, and an English Chancellor, Francis Bacon, in his "*Novum Organum*," extolled what he named "euthanasia"—the science of making death easy.

It was again in the Anglo-Saxon world that concerted efforts were made, by active minorities, some fifty years ago, to obtain legal recognition for the right to euthanasia. Frequently, English and American legislators put forward legal projects in this matter. In 1890, a Boston surgeon demanded that suffering patients who are judged to have reached their term of life should be assisted to death by analgesia. In October, 1903, more than a thousand New York doctors demanded euthanasia for cases of active, recidivous and generalized cancer. In 1906, Miss Anna Hall introduced a bill in the Ohio Parliament concerning euthanasia. It proposed that any person afflicted with an incurable disease accompanied with great pain should have the right to request an assembly of at least four persons with a view to deciding the opportuneness of ending such a painful life. It was adopted on a first reading, but was rejected by Washington. Nevertheless, euthanasia had received its first legal approval.

Less than a year later, in the neighbouring state of Iowa, Dr. Gregory proposed to the deputies that persons suffering from an incurable disease, as well as badly deformed children and idiots, should be assisted to death by analgesic means. What a deal of ground has been rapidly covered between the Anna Hall bill and that of Gregory. The first envisages only euthanasia of incurables, but the second openly proposes the extinction of children judged to be abnormal.

These two projects had great repercussions on American public opinion, and the result was a counter-proposal to the New York Assembly, declaring that any person who, by word of mouth, by written or printed circulars . . ., by publications of any kind, advocated the duty of killing, under cover of the law, those afflicted with an incurable physical or mental disease, should be declared criminally guilty.

This reaction did not discourage the advocates of euthanasia, who continued regularly to present projects in favour of their method to Congress. Furthermore, in order to give a new fillip to their propaganda, they formed an association in 1935, and its New York membership included no less than 1,200 doctors. In 1947, a legal project in favour of euthanasia was again introduced in the New York Assembly. It proposed that every person of sane mind, at least twenty-one years old, and afflicted with a very painful disease which is beyond remedy and for which the present resources of Medicine can do nothing, should be free to seek euthanasia.

This fact shows the persistence of these propagandists, and also proves the importance of the campaign begun in the United States. The clearly stated purpose of these concerted actions is to obtain *legal recognition for euthanasia*. It is therefore on the plane of law that the discussion was first of all placed. The question immediately rises: Does American law and jurisprudence favour the adoption of such a measure? Can American legislation oppose the official recognition of euthanasia, both in principle and in fact? Or does American legislation contain certain elements which could make possible, at some future date, the legal introduction of a right to easy death?

Euthanasia and American Law

As a matter of fact, no law authorizing euthanasia now exists in the United States. This resistance of legislators to a strong current of public opinion can be easily understood if one bears in mind the origins of American law. Derived from English law transmitted by the first colonists, American legislation is founded *on a common law permeated* with the Christian spirit. This source of inspiration is still recognized to-day, so that a jurist could declare, in 1933, that Christianity can be affirmed to be the authority which inspires the whole American juridical system, guiding its legislators and informing its laws.

A legal proposal in favour of euthanasia comes up, therefore, against a whole juridical system governed by a Christian conception of life. It is consequently interesting to examine some of the barriers which thus present an obstacle, on the plane of law, to the introduction into the Code of a law inspired by paganism.

With all due respect to the advocates of euthanasia, the measures which they propose immediately evoke *the problem of suicide*. Now, in the matter of suicide, American law has up to the present remained very severe. We find here the influence of English Common Law, which was particularly severe in the repression of suicide, and which provided a whole series of sanctions designed to affect the reputation of the dead person and also to serve as a public warning. The body of the person who had committed suicide was exposed in the main street of the town, with a stake thrust through him, his goods were confiscated and his memory held in dishonour.

These punishments, even though they recall an as yet barbarous code of justice, are none the less cited by commentators on American law in order to explain the rigour of American jurisprudence, not only towards the dead person, but towards his accomplices. (Cf. for example, William Blackstone: *Commentaries on the Law*, p. 830.) It is under the inspiration of this tradition that a certain number of the States have promulgated special laws. Thus, for example, Kansas has declared guilty of "homicide of the first degree" any person who has deliberately assisted another to commit suicide (*General Statute of Kansas*, section 20-408); and New York has uttered a similar law against any person who voluntarily and in any way whatever, counsels, aids or abets another to commit suicide. (Cf. McKinney's *Consolidated Laws of New York*, section 2304.)

In other States, where no special law exists against suicide, jurisprudence appeals to the Common Law in condemnation of the accomplice, as is shown by the following which came up in 1920 in the State of Michigan.

The wife of the defendant had been an incurable invalid. Having decided to commit suicide, she had asked her husband to place beside her bed a glass containing a virulent poison. The husband had done so, and the woman had poisoned herself. Counsel for the accused pleaded the husband's innocence, on the grounds that in Michigan suicide was not legally sanctioned as a crime, that therefore there had been no crime committed by the person who had committed suicide, and that consequently an accomplice could not be cited. Nevertheless, the Supreme Court of this State found the husband guilty, on the grounds that, by placing the poison near the woman in order that she might be able to take it and so end her life and her sufferings, the accused had been guilty of murder, even though he had acted at the request of his wife. (Case of People *v.* Roberts, 178 N.W. 690— Michigan 1920—13 *American Law Reports.*)

It is hard to see, therefore, how the advocates of euthanasia can succeed in having their project admitted by the jurists. Furthermore, in the text proposed to the New York Assembly in 1947, an important clause, that of *the preliminary consent of the patient*, was infected for illegality. American law in this matter is explicit in condemning the "suicide pact." The terms of this article state that if two persons decide to commit suicide together, and if the means they use succeed in the case of one alone, the survivor is to be regarded as guilty of murdering the other, the fact that the dead person consented having no effect on the premeditated nature of the action. (Cf. 26 *American Jurisprudence*, 217.)

Jurisprudence shows, moreover, that this text has not been a dead letter. A judgment given in Tennessee in 1908 clearly proves this. The accused had made a suicide pact with his mistress, but after having killed her, he himself had preferred to go on living! The verdict declared that the fact that the woman had consented and that the crime had been the outcome of a suicide pact, made no difference to its having been homicide with premeditation, since this crime comprised all the elements of malice, of coldbloodedness and of premeditation necessary to establish murder of the first degree. Though the homicide had been committed at the request of the victim, the murder was none the less murder for that. He who kills an individual at his own request, is, in the eyes of the law, a murderer, just as if he had committed this murder on his own initiative alone. (Case of Turner *v.* State, 108 S.W. 1139—Tennessee 1908—15 *Law Reports Annotated*, New Series, 988.) The question of the accomplice could not be more clearly raised, nor could it be more explicitly decided to the prejudice of the accomplice.

To meet this law about the suicide pact, the advocates of euthanasia plead the *compassion* which causes the accomplice to act. Hence the name "mercy killing" which some use to describe this type of homicide. But this piece of casuistry is not admitted by American jurisprudence, which openly declares that there is only a small number of cases of homicide where the humanitarian motives of the murderer have been thought worthy of consideration. However, in such cases, the courts have ruled that the fact that the murder had been committed for the purpose of ending present suffering or preventing future suffering, could not excuse the crime nor constitute an extenuating circumstance. The fact that the murderer had acted disinterestedly or for a motive which could be regarded as morally "good," is generally not admitted as an element of defence. (Cf. 26 *American Jurisprudence*, 228.)

However, not even in the face of such strong juridical decisiveness are the advocates of euthanasia discouraged. They hope for an alteration of the principles which at present govern American law, and indeed their hope is not without foundation. During the past thirty years, a whole current of ideas has appeared which has a tendency to transform the traditional philosophy of law. A young school of jurists is the source of this movement, and it is inspired by the philosophy of pragmatism. But what is meant by this very vague and very American-sounding term? Following Walter B. Kennedy's definition (*Pragmatism as a Philosophy of Laws*) it may be said to be a philosophy of law which seeks to adapt principles and doctrines to human circumstances which they are to direct but on which they are not to impose so-called fundamental laws.

Commenting upon and criticizing the ideas (*inspired by sociology*) of this school, two American jurists point out that it considers the attention at present given to the social aspect of the law, rather than to the analysis of rules and precepts, as a progressive advance in the philosophy of law. . . . In principle, it regards the law as a modern instrument to be used to serve the interests of humanity. The task of the legislator is, therefore, to discover the desires which society is striving to realize, and to satisfy those desires with the maximum of facility. The authors go on to point out that this sociological jurisprudence possesses no means of judging the value of the tendencies which strive to realize themselves in a law; nor does it possess any norm which enables it to decide the respective importance of opposed interests. It has no yardstick by which to measure the real importance of any human desire whatever; and, finally, it appears to be sceptical about the possibility of laying down a definitive rule to which one could appeal in estimating the value of a project of law. (Cf. *Jurisprudence*, by Francis P. Lebuffe, S.J., Ph.D., and James V. Hayes, LL.B.—1938.)

It can be seen how such ideas are a threat to the whole structure of American jurisprudence. The advocates of euthanasia discover allies here—involuntary allies, no doubt—who are preparing breaches from within the very fortification itself, through which pagan conceptions of life and death will enter and dominate. If the ideas of this school gained ascendency, *the Natural Law and the Christian Law which still inspire the legislator would be swept away, in favour of one single principle —the sovereign and fickle will of the majority.*

We may add that the sociological doctrines have already borne fruit. A precedent exists in American legislation—the sterilization of psychically deficient persons—which is quoted by the advocates of euthanasia in support of their demands. The Supreme Court of the United States has officially recognized the legality of this sterilization in a verdict which creates a law. In connection with one verdict, it has explicitly declared that the court had taken into consideration the facts reported and the fact that Mrs. X . . . could have been eventually the mother of "socially inadequate offspring," and that therefore it permitted her to be sterilized. Her health—the court declared—would be adversely affected in no way as a result, but her own happiness and the welfare of society were certain to be promoted. (Cf. Buck *v*. Bell, 274 U.S. 200, 71L—1927.)

This first important breach in the tradition of American law did not fail to disturb the jurists. One of them has recently pointed out that the sterilization of the feeble-minded is really dangerous because it equivalently accepts the principle that the State can suppress at will all mentally abnormal people.

The reason why such a measure could have been taken in spite of the opposition of a juridical tradition nourished on Christianity, is because legislators were influenced too much by medical reasons, put forward in support of sterilization. Is not eugenics, which has a great vogue in the United States, necessary to the future of the modern world? And are not—the argument goes on—the doctors essentially its high priests?

The advocates of euthanasia are alive to this lesson from a recent past. In their ceaseless campaign to win over public opinion, they make a special effort to win the adherence of the doctors, and are therefore very pleased to be able to draw on alleged medical arguments in support of their demands.

The doctors and euthanasia

For the doctors who favour this method, the point of departure for demonstrating the liceity of euthanasia has scarcely varied during the past twenty years: such recognition by the law will render legal what is in fact current practice—*the alleviating of suffering at the approach of death*. These doctors would like to see a very simple action legally sanctioned, and thus bring home to medical practitioners the seriousness of their decision.

But if the doctors are of considerable assistance by giving a semblance of scientific seriousness to the arguments in favour of euthanasia, these same doctors also serve to bring the method under suspicion by showing the logical implications of their conclusions. It is thanks to them, it must be admitted, that the hypocrisy of the advocates of euthanasia is clearly revealed; for, through naivety or as a matter of policy, these advocates wish to reserve this method to incurable dying persons only.

In an article which appeared in the *Journal of Nervous and Mental Diseases* (1944, Vol. 99, pp. 640–654), Dr. Hinman provides us with a typical example of this mentality. Therapeutic euthanasia, he says, is already a current practice in medicine; but *why not extend it to certain other categories of people?* He argues that to end a life which is both useless and hopeless is an act of pure mercy. It is desirable that an end should be put to such a life, and to do so is therefore a good, not a cruel, action—an act whose result cannot but be profitable to those who remain. A life which is "useless, helpless, and hopeless" is, he goes on, that of a person unsuited for the battle of life: the idiot, the insane person, the cretin, the psychopath—whether harmless or dangerous—the criminal, the delinquent, the monster, the abnormal person of whatever kind, the incurable, the senile—in short, all those who are no longer of any use in the world and who demand care and nursing but present no prospect of improvement.

This logical but inexorable list, which has at least the merit of showing how difficult it is to cry halt once the principle has been admitted, is one of the favourite discussion points between doctors and the advocates of euthanasia. In 1939, Dr. Wolbarst (*Medical Record*, 1939, vol. 149, p. 354) wrote that the opinions fall into three categories. In the first and definitely largest category, are those who approve of euthanasia, but only as applied to patients for whom medical science can do no more, and who have themselves requested it. In the second category are those who think that it should be extended to young people who are condemned to lead a useless life because of some deformation, defective growth or obstetrical accident. The third category comprises those who would extend euthanasia, not only to the congenitally abnormal, the senile and the incurable, but also to the incurably insane, the paralytic and the inveterate criminal.

Undoubtedly the ease with which innocent human beings are listed for death, evokes indignant protests against the doctors responsible. But their first reaction of defence is astonishment; for, as one of them said, the doctors have long since been given the right of life and of death. Others admit that such a measure would at first meet with opposition from public opinion, and that in the first years the number of people wishing to die by euthanasia would probably be very small; but they think that, in the long run, and through the example given by citizens enjoying a certain notoriety, the number of requests would rapidly increase. Dr. Milliard (*Lancet*, Vol. 2, 24th Oct., 1931) adds that it would not be the first time that an innovation was violently opposed but ultimately adopted by everyone. He instances such recent matters as the new Summer Time, the legislation concerning cremation, and the tolerance extended to birth control, which, he goes on, give every reason to hope that we shall see a healthier attitude develop towards euthanasia.

This facile optimism is not shared by all doctors who are consistent advocates of euthanasia; some are more alive to the value of the objections presented by their adversaries, and they seek to supply the answer by a severe limitation. No one, they say, will undergo euthanasia without knowing it and willing it, and without such action being legally authorized. Numerous formalities would safeguard the complete freedom of consent and the technique used.

What is the nature of these projects? The majority of them propose that, just as in certain countries the opinion of a specialist is required before proceeding with a therapeutic abortion, so too the application of euthanasia should be preceded by *a medical consultation*. As a further guarantee that the legal aspects would be respected, it has also been proposed that application should be formally made to a legally constituted Council, and that the opinion of the patient, of his doctor, of his family and of the parties financially interested, should be submitted.

In this domain, the jurists resume their right, and one of them, Kennedy, the author of *Pragmatism as a Philosophy of Laws*, proposes that, when an abnormal child reaches the age of five years, and if that child's guardians so demand, the case should be examined by a competent medical commission. The child should be examined again on two occasions with intervals of four months. If—continues Kennedy —the commission, acting at the request of the guardians and after three examinations, then decide that this abnormal child has nothing but misery in store for it, it is an act of pity to spare such a child the difficulties of life—a child who may be terribly afflicted, an idiot, a cretin, or an incapable of some kind.

As a philosophical justification for his proposition and for that of his medical friends, Kennedy points out that it is not through sluggish conservatism with regard to the law that we will be able to end social scourges. The law must measure up to our vast and new conceptions of a world which we desire to make better and wiser. The law, he says, is the garment of our social body; but it is a garment that should grow as we grow. Now, at present, our social body is growing, and it is desirable that those unfitted to live should be decently suppressed; the law, therefore, should develop to meet this need.

Thus, even for the jurist, *the final decision generally rests with the doctor.* It is the doctor who will decide whether the abnormal child will in the future be simply a burden to society, and whether the patient is absolutely incurable. This complete confidence in the doctor, however, gives food for thought to certain advocates of euthanasia. Are there never mistakes in prognosis? Do not certain unexpected cures occur, which are very often warnings to the doctor that he should act with the utmost prudence? In 1942, an advocate of euthanasia wrote an article urging its practice, in the *American Journal of Psychiatry*; but after having presented the case in its favour, the writer made the reservation that there should be no such legislation concerning persons who become ill after a long period of health, because, however seriously ill they may be, a certain number of them will perhaps be cured. Furthermore, Hinman, whose very complete list of possible candidates for euthanasia we have already cited, adds that, in his opinion, many doctors favourable to euthanasia are not wholly convinced that the suppression of those regarded as unsuited for life would be a benefit to humanity. Would not this mean, he ends somewhat cynically, the useless destruction of a necessary part of the raw material for scientific research! Finally, others point out, with Stecker, that by voting a law authorizing euthanasia, we would be thus legalizing a practice which could appear suspect to the patient, and thereby run *the risk of dangerously undermining the confidence which should exist between patient and doctor.*

The psychological situation created between the patient and the doctor by the legal recognition of euthanasia, is one of the major objections with certain doctors. In the *Journal of Nervous and Mental Diseases* (July, 1936, vol. 84, pp. 1–12) Dr. Brill sums up perfectly the uneasiness caused to men of good will. When faced with the searing question: If a patient is beyond the help of all medical resources, why not assist him to die?—he hesitates, and ends by saying that the question as thus worded is too broad. If, he argues, it is applied to the incurable patient, why not apply it to the person who finds himself in a material situation for which there is no remedy?—especially as such a person is a burden to the State. Finally, he declares himself opposed to such wholesale massacres, not for religious or sentimental reasons, but for reasons purely psychological. Mercy killing would have incalculable consequences. It would lower the moral level of doctors, because it would injure the sacred nature of human life; and in this way—he concludes—every failure in the struggle waged by men against death, finally constitutes a menace to society.

Conclusions

What emerges most strikingly from this inquiry into euthanasia in the United States, is the confusion that exists in so many minds. Dr. Milliard, president of the "Society of Medical Officers of Health," underlined, in his presidential address, that ethical objections raised against euthanasia lose their value in view of the fact that certain Protestant clergymen declare that it is impossible to discover a really decisive argument against suicide. But is not this defeatist attitude simply the logical conclusion of the attitude taken up by the Archbishop of Canterbury? In 1936, when the legal authorization of euthanasia for incurables was under discussion in the House of Lords, this prelate refused to commit himself to any position. He preferred to leave the solution of this matter to the doctors, trusting to their judgment and their professional honour!

In view of this capitulation by the spiritual authorities, what principle will guide the judgment of both the doctor and the jurist? As we have seen, the principle is that of *social efficiency*. Is this particular person capable or incapable of leading the life of the community? His right to exist depends on the answer to that question. Efficiency becomes the criterion of personal value. The modern city thus returns to the philosophy of the city of Antiquity; and this American materialism links up with Marxist materialism.

In this muddle, the doctor ends by confusing the *power* given to the doctor over the body of his patient, and the *right* to dispose freely of the life of another. Is not the same action surely involved, whether an injection is given to ease if possible the intolerable suffering of a person dying from cancer, or whether the dose is doubled in order to anticipate his death by a few hours? This over-simplified reasoning is completely wrong. It seeks to take up the material, instrumental point of view; whereas what is required, first of all, is *a judgment of intention*. The difference between the doctor who seeks only to cure and the doctor who deliberately strengthens the dose so as to make it fatal, is not therefore in the syringe but in the will. This is a difference of "nature." *The doctor does not possess rights over life or over death;* but his art may sometimes give him the illusion that he has such rights. This is a temptation to pride against which Maimonides, in the XIIth century, prayed that he might be strengthened: "O God, take far from me the thought that I can do all things."

To this temptation, two forces must be opposed: a philosophy of law and a medical deontology, both inspired by the Christian spirit.

JEAN-PAUL MENSIOR

MORAL ASPECTS OF EUTHANASIA

EUTHANASIA or "dying well" could mean "dying bravely." In the minds of the doctor and of the moralist, it formerly meant the alleviation, by means of drugs administered in therapeutic doses, of the suffering which sometimes accompanies certain deaths. Thus conceived, euthanasia is normally permissible, though in certain cases it can give rise to a moral problem.

But, in the modern sense in which we use the word here, the term "Euthanasia" has come to mean "an easy death" obtained by administering medications in fatal doses or by any other means used to hasten the last moment of a dying person. It is therefore merely euphemistic to talk about "mercy death" or "easy death"; the terms used should be suicide or murder.

The modern spirit of materialism or of agnosticism has confused the ideas of good and evil with those of pleasure and pain, and has replaced virtue by pleasure as the purpose of life. The result of this is a pagan sentimentality which finds everything good which gives pleasure, and declares that divorce, adultery, and contraception are legitimate. The desire to shorten the physical sufferings, regarded as the evil *par excellence*, has given rise to several societies in favour of euthanasia, both in the United States and in England. Legal projects have even been drawn up, with a view to legitimizing "mercy-killing." Even the medical body has allowed itself to be influenced to such an extent that the Institute of Public Opinion declared, in 1937, that 53 per cent of doctors whose opinions had been canvassed declared themselves to be in favour of euthanasia. Nay more, in New York, some years ago, a group of Protestant pastors declared that, in certain cases, voluntary euthanasia cannot be regarded as contrary to the teaching of Christ or to Christian principles. (*New York Times*, Sept. 28th, 1946.)

Voluntary euthanasia

The advocates of "mercy-killing" actually envisage only euthanasia which is voluntary—i.e. which is carried out at the request of the patient and with the proper legal safeguards. But euthanasia without the consent of the patient is the logical outcome of their erroneous idea. Furthermore, it is the purpose aimed at by the leaders of this movement, as is shown, sometimes unconsciously, by the drift of their propaganda. Before the present opposition to their ideas made them more wary in their expression, they quite readily revealed their intentions. Did not one of them, the Rev. Dr. C. F. Potter, demand the application of euthanasia to the incurably insane? (*I.N.S. Dispatch*, Feb. 4th, 1936).

Voluntary euthanasia is suicide on the part of the person who demands it, because suicide is the deliberate killing of oneself. It consists in using any freely chosen and effective means whatever to end one's life, whether by dispensing with the ordinary necessities for protecting and sustaining life, or by directly inflicting death on oneself or doing so with the aid of another. Euthanasia is therefore the formally willed suppression of oneself. It must not be confused with the death which can result from the pursuit of a legitimate good, and which is the only permissible death. Such, for instance, is the case of a soldier who through duty exposes himself to danger, or of the patient who submits to a dangerous, but necessary operation. In suicide, death is the end which is sought.

Voluntary euthanasia is not a new problem for the moral assessment of the Catholic Theologian, even though its modern methods are more refined. St. Alphonsus Liguori laid down, two centuries ago, that it is never permitted to commit suicide in order to escape a more painful death (*Theologia moralis*, III, No. 367). In doing so, he was merely echoing the constant teaching of the Church—a teaching which has not wavered when faced with the modern arguments put forward by the advocates of euthanasia.

Speaking of voluntary sterilization, Pope Pius XI, in his encyclical *Casti connubii*, recalls this traditional teaching: "It is to be observed that even the individual human being—as Christian doctrine teaches and the light of reason clearly shows—has no power over the members of his own body except so far as he uses them for their natural purpose; he cannot destroy or mutilate them, or in any other way render himself incapable of his natural functions, except when there is no other way of providing for the welfare of the body as a whole." (English translation by Canon Smith, C.T.S.)

What is true for sterilization is even more so for euthanasia. The teaching of the Church is based on the principle of the supreme dominion which the Creator exercises over the life of his creatures. This principle allows of no exception, save those of legitimate defence and of capital punishment. The right to destroy a thing belongs only to him for whom that thing has been made. God has created man for His service and His praise: therefore, it is God, and not man, who has the right to end human life. Suicide is a trespass on the Creator's rights over life.

Furthermore, is not suicide contrary to the innate tendencies of every human being? Is not self-preservation a first instinctive law in man? This natural reaction appears even in those who, theoretically, approve of euthanasia. Here, for instance, is a concrete case. A certain family caught the enthusiasm of their doctor for "mercy-killing" and became its ardent propagandists. One day, their doctor diagnosed in the wife the probable existence of a cancerous growth. Immediately, she demanded that she should be sent for treatment to a Catholic hospital because she feared the "pity" of her husband and of her doctor. (Cf. *Catholic Medical Guardian*, XV, Oct., 1937.) This anecdote is simply an echo of the frank admissions often made by advocates of euthanasia, as for instance by Dean Juge, when there is question of applying it to themselves. (Cf. Bonnar: *The Catholic Doctor*, p. 103, New York, P. J. Kennedy and Sons.)

Can the state act against the natural law?

When it is urged that man has not the right to take his own life, the advocates of euthanasia reply that the State is superior to the individual. They argue that just as it is permissible for the State to execute a criminal, so too it may eliminate any of its subjects who are useless or burdensome. Their error here lies in confusing the ideas of crime and incapacity. The death-sentence aims at punishing crime and at discouraging the potential criminal by frightening him. By the very fact of his human nature, the criminal is part of Society; but by his evil action he voluntarily separates himself from Society. He deliberately separates himself from a rational order in which he possessed the rights of a free person, and, by exceeding his rights, he merits the death-penalty. There can be no question of a similar choice or of a similar punishment in the case of an innocent person. The innocent person always keeps his rights in Society, even if he cannot exercise his reasoning powers or if, through no fault of his own, he is a burden or a threat to the community. Finally the element of preventive threat characteristic of the death-penalty, cannot be applied to euthanasia, which aims at suppressing involuntary physical or mental deficiencies.

But the advocates of euthanasia do not acknowledge defeat; they retort that the fundamental element which justifies capital punishment is the safeguarding of the common good. Now, the common good will be promoted by the suppression of those who are a burden to themselves, to their families, or to the State. This argument is based on a false conception of the common good—a totalitarian and materialistic conception which has led to those Nazi practices which were arraigned at the Nuremberg trials. This erroneous philosophy lays down as axiomatic that the whole person is subordinated to the State or the Race.

Common sense repudiates this totalitarian conception. The good of the State is not the final purpose of man; rather is the State a means given to man to help him to attain his last ends. The State was made for man, not man for the State.

Euthanasia approved by the civil authority would be a violation of the fundamental principle: "Thou shalt not kill the just and the innocent" (Exodus, xxiii, 7). The condemnation pronounced by Pius XI, in *Casti connubii*, can be applied here: "Governments and legislatures must remember that it is the duty of the public authority to protect the life of the innocent by appropriate laws and penalties, especially when those whose life is attacked and endangered are unable to protect themselves. . . . If the State authorities not only fail to protect these little ones, but by their laws and decrees suffer them to be killed, and even deliver them into the hands of doctors and others for that purpose, let them remember that God is the Judge and Avenger of the innocent blood that cries from earth to heaven." (Translation by Canon G. D. Smith, C.T.S., p. 30.)

And in connection with eugenic sterilization decreed by the State, the Pope continues as follows: "The public authorities have no direct power over the bodily members of their subjects and therefore, in the absence of any crime or other cause calling for corporal punishment, they can never directly injure or attack the integrity of the body on any ground whatever, eugenic or otherwise." (Translation by Canon G. D. Smith, C.T.S., p. 31.)

When Hitler was at the height of his power, the Holy Office was asked whether the State could put to death persons who had committed no crime, but who were useless to the nation and a burden to the public because of their physical or their mental deficiency. On December 2nd, 1940, the Holy Office issued an emphatic veto, declaring that such a procedure would be directly contrary both to the Natural Law and to the Divine Law.

By thus usurping divine rights over human life, the State would equivalently deny the existence of a higher authority. It would admit no laws except those made by itself, nor any right except those which it saw fit to allow; and this is totalitarianism.

Conclusion

If voluntary euthanasia were admitted, it would then become easy to justify the application of "mercy-killing" to persons incapable of making a rational decision—for instance, to feebleminded persons or abnormal children. From there, one would pass on to those whose care and subsistence the community could well be rid of: criminals in prison, those afflicted with contagious diseases, minorities who are

46867

174.2
C319F

1953-
v.3

Cahiers Laënnec
New problems in medical ethics, v.3.

DEMCO